THE NEW CHURCHYARD:
FROM MOORFIELDS MARSH TO BETHLEM BURIAL GROUND, BROKERS ROW AND LIVERPOOL STREET

Robert Hartle
with Niamh Carty, Michael Henderson,
Elizabeth L Knox and Don Walker

Published by MOLA [Museum of London Archaeology]

Copyright © Crossrail Limited 2017

Crossrail Archaeology Publication series designed and series-edited by Jay Carver, Marit Leenstra and Andrew Briffett

Production and design by Tracy Wellman

Design by Sue Cawood

Reprographics by Andy Chopping

Copy editing by Wendy Sherlock

General editing by Sue Hirst/Susan M Wright

Front cover: conjectural reconstruction of the burial of plague victims in the mass grave, [7482]/[8473], dug in the New Churchyard in the later 16th to early 17th century (Fig 95) (artist Faith Vardy)

Printed by Henry Ling Ltd at the Dorset Press, an ISO 14001 certified printer

MIX
Paper from
responsible sources
FSC® C013985

CONTRIBUTORS

Principal author	**Robert Hartle**
Human osteology	**Niamh Carty, Michael Henderson, Elizabeth L Knox, Don Walker**
Ceramic building materials	Ian M Betts
Clay tobacco pipes	Jacqui Pearce
Pottery	Nigel Jeffries
Glass	Jacqui Pearce
Accessioned finds	Rachel S Cubitt and Michael Marshall (site finds), Beth Richardson (burial finds), with Robert Hartle and Adrian Miles (coffin furniture)
Coins	Julian Bowsher
Leather accessioned finds	Beth Richardson
Plant remains	Karen Stewart
Animal bone	Vicki Ewens, Alan Pipe
Demographic analysis	Sharon DeWitte
Dental calculus analyses	Stephen Buckley, Jessica Hendy, Anita Radini, Camilla Speller
Ancient DNA analysis	Kirsten Bos, Elisabeth Nelson, Maria Spyrou
Isotope analysis	Janet Montgomery, with Julia Beaumont, Nidia Lisic, Ruth Morley, Geoff Nowell, Chris Ottley, Joanne Peterkin
Radiocarbon dating	Derek Hamilton, Peter Marshall
Graphics	Hannah Faux, Juan José Fuldain, Faith Vardy
Site photography	Maggie Cox, Robert Hartle
Studio photography	Edwin Baker, Andy Chopping, Maggie Cox
Project managers	Julian Hill (post-excavation), Nicholas Elsden (fieldwork)
Academic advisor	Vanessa Harding
Editor	Susan M Wright

CONTENTS

FIGURES

TABLES

SUMMARY

This book presents the results of archaeological investigations undertaken by MOLA (Museum of London Archaeology) in 2011–15 at the Crossrail Central development, in the area of the Broadgate ticket hall worksite, Liverpool Street, London. Modern Liverpool Street follows the line of a road along the south property boundary of the precinct of the priory of St Mary Bethlehem, which became 'Bethlem' or 'Bedlam' Hospital. The lands located around (and under) the west half of Liverpool Street existed for centuries as undeveloped marsh, but in 1569 were converted into the municipal, non-parochial burial ground, the 'New Churchyard'. The New Churchyard closed for burial in 1739; it remained as a ground, but unused, until 1772, when it was converted to gardens for the adjoining properties of Broad Street Buildings. Subsequently, the surrounding streetscape was transformed; Broad Street and Liverpool Street railway stations were constructed in the 1860s and '70s.

The new burial ground was founded to provide much-needed space for the dead of the City of London, following a severe outbreak of plague in 1563. Popular from the outset with Dissenters, the ground had a strong association with the Leveller movement. An annual Whit Sunday sermon was preached there. Day-to-day running of the ground was the responsibility of a keeper; four generations of the Clitherow family held this post from 1636 to 1740. A study of London's parish burial registers provides a (partial) picture of some 8000 people, their occupations and cause of death, buried at the ground, from a total of *c* 25,000 suggested by the archaeological evidence.

Many of the city's poor and those on the fringes of society would have been buried here. The majority of adults in the London population would have been born outside the city and moved there as adolescents and young adults to be apprentices or in search of work. A high proportion in this age range among the excavated burials suggests these newcomers may have been more susceptible to some of the diseases that were rife in the increasingly polluted city. Evidence of tuberculosis and syphilis, both major diseases throughout this period, was visible in the New Churchyard burials. Other infectious disease, such as typhoid, occurred on an epidemic scale, but it was plague that attracted contemporary comment. Outbreaks of plague were frequent in the city throughout the 16th and 17th centuries, and particularly severe in 1603, 1625 and 1665. In the largest of the common or mass graves excavated, the plague pathogen, *Yersinia pestis*, was identified in five individuals, but even here emergency burial practices appear orderly, not chaotic.

The excavation and analysis of the New Churchyard burial ground provided an opportunity to learn about the lives and health of a population from early modern London, bridging gaps in our knowledge between the medieval city and the 18th-century metropolis. One quarter (819) of the 3354 burials excavated from the New Churchyard went forward for full osteological analysis, providing evidence for rickets and chronic respiratory health problems, the increasing availability of potatoes and refined sugars, and the deleterious effects of smoking tobacco. Evidence of interpersonal violence and accidental injury probably reflect the crowded environment, hazardous occupations and workplace dangers; many, however, survived potentially severe injuries, reflecting a degree of medical treatment and care.

ACKNOWLEDGEMENTS

MOLA (Museum of London Archaeology) would like to thank Crossrail Limited for funding this project at Liverpool Street and Blomfield Street, and in particular Jay Carver, lead archaeologist at Crossrail. We would like to extend our thanks to a number of Crossrail staff, especially Mike Court, Marit Leenstra and Iain Williamson (archaeologists); John Doyle, Luke Mason, Visu Mathan, Victoria Richardson, Chris Sharples and James Wildgoose, as well as to the contractors: Laing O'Rourke (LOR) and their staff (in particular, Petrit Bajraktari, Brian Beatty, Vaidas Cvilikas, Valdas Dauparas, Gintaras Gelazanskas, Richard Gresham, Pat Kearney, Ross Lankshear, Martin McDonagh, Rebecca McDonough, Siu Mun Li, Kieran Murphy, Balvir Ram, Mann H Singh, Tarlochan Singh and David Sked); McNicholas (in particular, Seni Agidew, Jon Booth and Chris Murray); VCUK (Matt Hadden); Thomas Cribbs and Sons (TCS) (in particular, Mark Lund); Galldris (in particular, Lee Chapman, Tim MacKessy and Owen Sweeney); as well as JB Riney (in particular, Tom Bourke and Neil Carlsson).

For MOLA, the fieldwork was led by Alison Telfer, with fellow project officers Andy Daykin and Greg Laban, and site supervisors Portia Askew, Martin Banikov, Jessica Bryan, Bruce Ferguson, Catherine Godsiffe, Paolo Guarino, Robert Hartle, Isca Howell, Tim Johnston, Antonietta Lerz, Sam Pfizenmaier, Serena Ranieri, Jeremy Taylor, Michael Tunnicliffe, Robert Tutt and Emily Wright, and assisted by Sasathorn Charoenphan, Stephen Foster, Catherine Gibbs and Richard Ward.

MOLA staff who worked as archaeologists on the site were James Alexander, Waltraud Baier, Vesna Bandelj, Adam Barker, Silvia Barlassina, Daniel Bateman, Tony Baxter, Isa Benedetti, James Best, Charlotte Booth, Matt Bosomworth, Hannah Bosworth, Tanya Bowie, Barbora Brenderova, Andrew Brown, Ashley Bryant, Jonathan Buttery, Rose Calis, Jude Children, Harry Clarke, Umberto Crupi, Tegan Daley, Simon Davis, Jozef Doran, Brigid Geist, Chris Gerontinis, Matthew Ginnever, Emily Glass, Lara Gonzalez Carretero, Daniel Harrison, Chris Hawksworth, Sam Herbertson, William Herring, Rebecca Jones, Bonnie Knapp, Giulia Lazzeri, Rachel Legge, Paul McGarrity, Karl Macrow, Laura Malric-Smith, Ruairi Manktelow, Alice Marconi, Sinead Marshall, Roberta Marziani, Charlotte Mecklenburgh, Jacqui Mellows, Tara Mundy, Lauren Neal, Cosimo Pace, Jorge Parreira, Dave Parry, Chris Pennel, Dalia Anna Pokutta, Stefano Ricchi, Philip Roberts, David Sankey, Gideon Simons, Gavin Smith, Jack Smith, Toria Stanfield, Mick Steel, Jessica Stevens, Alexa Stevenson, Karen Stewart, Leo

Sucharyna Thomas, Mark Sycamore, Piotr Szmyd, Claudia Tommasino, Sarah Trehy, Adam Tuffey, Lorna Webb, Steve White, Tomasz Wisniewski and Nicolas Zorzin.

Simon Davis, Elaine Eastbury and Natasha Powers assisted with management of the fieldwork. The processing team included Karen Deighton, Chris Gerontinis, Sarah Matthews, Alba Moyano-Alcantara, Riley Thorne and Jessica White. Graham Spurr, Jason Stewart and Virgil Yendell carried out geoarchaeological sampling on-site; Raoul Bull, Mark Burch, Catherine Drew and Moises Hernandez-Cordero were responsible for the geomatics site work, Neville Constantine and Vicki Ewens for the digitising and 3D work, and Vicki Ewens prepared base figures for the publication; Robert Hartle and Serena Ranieri carried out the stratigraphic analysis. Catherine Gibbs and Catherine Godsiffe (osteology), and Amy Atkins (building materials), assisted with assessment and analysis. The authors would like to thank Paul Bland and Sophie Willis (Department of Radiography, City University) for facilitating radiographic work and David Allan for providing professional diagnosis of bone pathology.

The 1985–6 (LSS85) fieldwork was managed for the then Department of Urban Archaeology (DUA), Museum of London (MOL), by John Maloney. Thanks are due to Rosehaugh Stanhope Developments Plc, Arup Associates and the site management team of Bovis Construction Ltd and Griffith (McGee Demolition). The DUA excavation team was led by Dick Malt, with Portia Askew (who worked on the site in both 1985 and 2015), Julian Ayre, Chantalle Charron, Sue Cole, Jo Coomb, Lis Dyson, Dougie Killock, Tony Mackinder, Pam Mead, Wendy Murphy, Simon Nicholls, Deirdre Power, Marrieta Ryan, Craig Spence, Fiona Spence, Ken Steedman, Tracy Wellman and Aidan Woodger. Post-excavation work was managed by Frederike Hammer and the team included Julie Jones, Fiona Spence, Paul Tyres and Bill White. Jelena Bekvalac and the Centre for Human Bioarchaeology, Museum of London, facilitated access to the osteological remains from LSS85.

The authors gratefully acknowledge their debt to, and appreciation of, the work of the 17 volunteers, led by Marit Leenstra, who took part in Crossrail's volunteer programme, the 'Bedlam Burial Ground Register' project, in 2014: Sandra Claggett, Casey Clifford, Helen Clifford, Alan Cotterell, Augustin Moreno Cózar, John Foley, Daniele LaMarche, Alan Newman, Liadagh O'Shea, Steve Partridge, Andrea Schembri, Peter Shewry, Ana Silva, Adriana Solari, Val Southon, Christina White and Barbara Willis.

FOREWORD

Vanessa Harding, Professor of London History, Birkbeck, University of London

London's New Churchyard has had a strange history of being remembered and forgotten. Founded in 1569 on the periphery of the built-up area, and in constant use from the 16th to the 18th century, it was lost to sight after its closure in 1739 until the railway age brought it to light again. Successive works for Broad Street Station and the Metropolitan Railway cut through the burial ground, revealing densely packed human remains but barely breaking through to wider public awareness. The redevelopment of Broad Street Station in the 1980s once again alerted archaeologists and historians to the site's extraordinary interest, but only the major MOLA excavations entailed by the new Crossrail station at Liverpool Street have allowed a proper assessment of its historical and archaeological significance. This book traces the history and archaeology of the site, from open ground to gardens to civic burial site and back to private and commercial use, documents early modern burial practices, and examines the social and physical characteristics of a significant sample of the 25,000 people buried there.

An exceptional combination of historical reconstruction and osteological investigation offers major new insights into early modern London's population. A team of volunteers used the city's parish records to recreate a register of those buried at the New Churchyard. Brought from across the city, many of these were in some way marginal – recent migrants and strangers, servants, the poor, some of the dead from nearby Bethlem Hospital, and religious and political outsiders including the noted Leveller John Lilburne. These human stories are interwoven with the detailed analysis of over 800 skeletal remains, extensively illustrated in the volume. This analysis has provided a wealth of data on the health, nutrition, longevity, exposure to disease and trauma, and access to medical treatment, of a section of London's population about whom such detail is usually lacking.

The site's history is inseparable from the history of plague in London. The New Churchyard was founded a few years after the devastating epidemic of 1563, when the City of London feared that another such epidemic would bring a crisis of burial, and served as an additional plague burial ground for 100 years. In the great plague of 1665 it was so overused that a new burial ground, now Bunhill Fields, was founded. The recent excavations revealed varied burial patterns, including a number of pits or mass graves as well as single burials, but perhaps the most exciting discovery of the post-excavation analysis has been the identification of the plague pathogen *Yersinia pestis* in a number of bodies in one 17th-century burial pit. Assessing the implications of this finding for the longer history of plague in London is the next challenge facing historians, archaeologists and epidemiologists: the pathogen may be present, but the different characteristics of modern and historic plague remain striking. Was *Yersinia pestis* the only agent responsible for the epidemics that killed hundreds of thousands of medieval and early modern Londoners? Or do the dead of the New Churchyard have still more to tell us?

CHAPTER 1

SETTING THE SCENE

1.1   The sites in Liverpool Street and Blomfield Street

Today, Liverpool Street and Blomfield Street are located within the north-east corner of the modern City of London. Until the post-medieval period this area lay on the north margins of the city, beyond the city wall (Fig 1). The areas of archaeological investigation described here are flanked to the west by Blomfield Street, which follows the roughly north–south line of the ancient Walbrook stream (now buried in culverts and sewers), which since the medieval period has defined a parish and ward boundary. Modern Liverpool Street runs east to meet an important medieval artery into the city, Bishopsgate Street (Fig 1); the latter approximately follows Roman Ermine Street, 'Old North Road', which connected Roman London (Londinium) with Lincoln (Lindum Colonia) and York (Eboracum). In the medieval period this area east of Bishopsgate was little used and dominated by the priory and hospital of St Mary of Bethlehem.[1] Liverpool Street follows the line of a road established along the south boundary of the precinct of the hospital of St Mary Bethlem, which became known as 'Old Bethlem' before taking its later name of Bedlam (as on Fig 1). The lands located around (and under) the west half of Liverpool Street existed for centuries as undeveloped marsh, but in 1569 were converted into the non-parochial 'New Churchyard'. The site of the New Churchyard changed little until its closure in March 1738/9 and it remained as a (unused) burial ground until 1772, when it was converted to gardens for the surrounding buildings. Development in the area had intensified as the city rapidly expanded; between the mid 18th century and the 19th century the surrounding streetscape was transformed by the creation of new streets or the widening of existing ones, as well as the construction of Broad Street and Liverpool Street railway stations in the 1860s and '70s.

Between February 2011 and October 2015, as part of the Crossrail Central development, archaeological investigation took place in the area of the Broadgate ticket hall worksite, Liverpool Street, and comprised phases of evaluation, watching brief and excavation recorded under site code XSM10, hereafter known as 'the site'. The worksite covered approximately the west half of Liverpool Street between and including its north and south pavements. This book also incorporates the results of two other phases of fieldwork in the immediate area: the main archaeological excavation conducted by the Department of Urban Archaeology (DUA) at the Broadgate development site in 1985–6, which was recorded under the site code LSS85

Fig 1 Detail of the west and east sides of Bishopsgate Street from Braun and Hogenberg's map of London, published 1572, with the site superimposed (outlined in red; see Fig 2); the New Churchyard is not shown as such (arrow points to the location of the west end of modern-day Liverpool Street and the bridge and gatehouse leading from 'Bedlame' into Moorfields); the site of the former priory and hospital of St Mary Spital is top right; north is to the top

(The National Library of Israel)

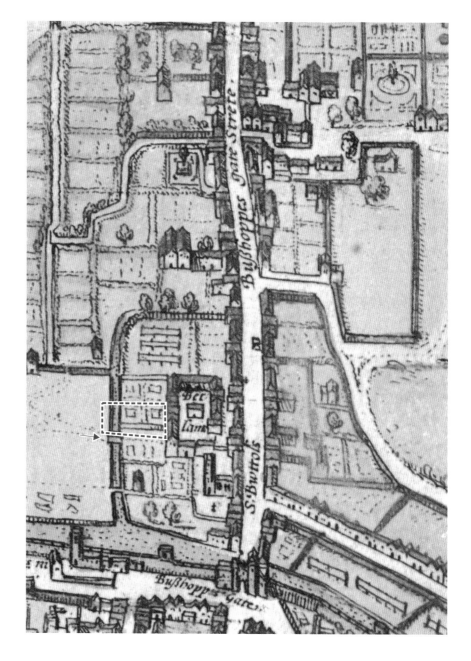

and is hereafter referred to as 'site A'; and archaeological investigations undertaken as part of the Crossrail Central development at 11–12 Blomfield Street, EC2, between May 2011 and January 2014, recorded under site codes XSL10 and XTB12 and hereafter combined as 'site B' (Fig 2).

1.2 About this book

The archaeological investigations uncovered evidence for the diverse history of this area, from the Roman period (described in a companion volume in this

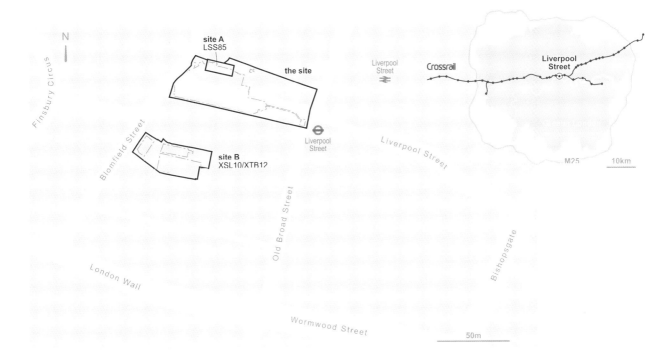

Fig 2 Map showing the location in Greater London of the site (XSM10) and sites A and B (LSS85; XSL10/XTB12) (outlined in red), together with the areas of archaeological investigation (outlined in grey; see Fig 67 a), superimposed on the modern street plan (scale 1:2500; inset 1:1,250,000)

series)[2] through to the early 20th century. This book presents a chronological account of the later evidence from the excavations, beginning with the medieval marsh, including its management and final reclamation in the early post-medieval period (Chapter 2), and ending with urban development – from the 18th- and 19th-century occupants of no. 1 Brokers Row to the 21st century (Chapter 13). The focus of this book, however, is very much on the 'New Churchyard', established as a burial ground in 1569 and in operation to March 1738/9 (Chapters 3–12, 14); this heavily used ground was also known, somewhat confusingly, as the 'Bethlem' or 'Bedlam' burial ground from its location on land adjacent to, and that had once belonged to, the hospital of St Mary Bethlem for the insane (Chapter 3.1).

The results of the analysis of the stratigraphic sequence and of the artefactual, faunal, floral and human remains evidence for the burial ground are incorporated, together with pictorial and documentary sources, into thematic chapters: the foundation and running of the burial ground (Chapters 3, 14.1); funerary choices and burial practice, from funeral rites to monuments (Chapters 4, 5, 14.2, 14.3); comparing what burial registers and the excavated sample tell us about the people buried here (Chapter 6); living and working in the city (Chapter 7); plague – as experienced by Londoners and specifically plague victims buried in the New Churchyard (Chapter 8); and, finally, the health and lifestyle of these people, including disease and trauma, and their life stories as revealed by osteological analysis and related studies (Chapters 9–12).

The evidence and conclusions presented here will be supported and amplified by an online resource,[3] which will include detailed osteological and related scientific analyses, including full reports on isotopic analysis and the metagenomic and microscopic analyses of dental calculus, together with parish register data derived from Crossrail's Bedlam Burial Ground Register project (Chapter 6.1) and referred to as the 'Bedlam Register' here.[4]

More detailed accounts are given elsewhere of selected important aspects of the site: the pre-burial ground, 16th-century, Moorfields ditches and their rich finds assemblages; the turner's workshop operated by two keepers of the New Churchyard; late 17th-/early 18th-century glass-working waste, possibly deriving from the closest contemporary glasshouse at 'Old Bedlam'; and the household goods discarded by the 18th-century occupants and middlemen of no. 1 Brokers Row.[5]

Site archives and recording conventions used

The paper and digital archives, together with the finds from the site, are publicly accessible in the Museum of London (MOL) Archaeological Archive, at Mortimer Wheeler House, 46 Eagle Wharf Road, London N1 7ED, where they are held under their site codes and can be consulted by prior arrangement; the digital archive will also be deposited with the Archaeology Data Service (ADS).[6]

The basic unit of cross-reference throughout the archive that supports this book is the context number. This is a unique number given to each archaeological stratum or event representing a single action (such as a layer, pit, ditch, etc) on site. Context numbers appear in the text in square brackets, for example [10]. The archaeological investigations reported here were principally recorded under four site codes (above). Context numbers from the site, XSM10, appear with no letter prefix, for example, [10]. Contexts from site A and site B appear prefixed, respectively, as follows: A[10] and B[10]. Contexts are grouped into the land-use entities referred to here as Open Areas (OA). Environmental data are referred to by context number (not sample number).

Accession numbers given to significant artefacts from the site are shown in angled brackets thus: <1>. Artefacts from sites A and B were recorded separately, resulting here in two additional accession number sequences: A<1>– and B<1>–.

Pottery and ceramic building materials were recorded using codes, and expansions of the codes are given at the first mention in a text section. Detailed descriptions of building material fabrics and complete lists of pottery codes, their expansions and date ranges are available at the MOLA (Museum of London Archaeology) website.[7] Pottery is quantified by sherd count (SC), by estimated number of vessels (ENV) and by weight (g/kg).

The clay tobacco pipes were recorded in line with current MOLA practice;[8] the bowls were classified and dated according to the chronology of London bowl types,[9] with further refinement of 18th-century types according to Oswald's simplified general typology of 1975,[10] indicated respectively by the prefixes AO and OS. Accessioned finds and jettons were also recorded on the MOLA Oracle database.

For the osteological data, crude prevalence is the prevalence per individual; true prevalence is the prevalence per bone.

Details of the calibration and modelling of radiocarbon dates are given in Chapter 8.2 and Tables 16 and 17.

Site codes in the text refer to MOLA/DUA excavations. County names refer to historic counties. Weights and measures quoted in the text are, where appropriate, in the units used before metrication. The documentary evidence is reported with imperial measurements (feet, abbreviated to ft) as originally used, along with conversions when appropriate (1ft equals 0.305m). An acre is 0.4 hectare, or alternatively a hectare equals about 2.5 acres. Sums of money are quoted in the text as cited in £, s and d, where 12 pence (d) made one shilling (s) and 20 shillings (or 240d) a pound (£), and one guinea equals £1 1s, since modern equivalents would be misleading.

Dates from sources contemporary with the New Churchyard (eg wills, burial registers, including the Bedlam Register) are cited 'Old Style' (specified in text and captions for clarity on occasion), whereby according to the Julian calendar adhered to in England before 1752 the year begins on 25 March (eg 1 February 1654/5); from 1752, dates are 'New Style' and the year begins on 1 January.

Notes to Chapter 1

1   Andrews et al 1997; Barron and Davies 2007, 113–15

2   Ranieri and Telfer 2017

3   ADS https://archaeologydataservice.ac.uk/

4   Bedlam Register http://www.crossrail.co.uk/sustainability/archaeology/liverpool-street/bedlam-burial-ground-register; ADS https://archaeologydataservice.ac.uk/

5   Cubitt et al in prep b; Cubitt et al in prep a; Brain and Pearce in prep; Hartle et al in prep

6   ADS n 3

7   MOLA http://www.museumoflondonarchaeology.org.uk/Publications/Online-Resources/MOLA-ceramic-codes.htm

8   Quantification and recording follow Higgins and Davey 1994

9   Atkinson and Oswald 1969

10 Oswald 1975

CHAPTER 2

THE EARLIER HISTORY OF THE AREA, FROM THE 11TH CENTURY TO *c* 1600

During the medieval period, the sites (including sites A and B) were located north of the city, on the east edge of the 'Moor' (later 'Moorfields') and the east bank of the Walbrook stream – a watercourse formed of several tributaries, which originated in springs in modern-day Islington and Shoreditch, and flowed south into the River Thames. Nothing remains of this landscape today; the marsh has been built over as part of urban expansion, while the Walbrook only exists underground. By the late medieval period, drainage of the Moorfields marsh was considerably hindered by the dumping of waste in the stream and ditches; by the early 17th century those sections of the Walbrook which flowed through extra- and intramural London had been covered or diverted into culverts and sewers.

2.1 Medieval Walbrook and the Moorfields marsh

Documentary evidence

The Walbrook stream was incorporated into the city's medieval defensive ditch system when the latter was built in 1211–13.[1] The sections of the Walbrook and the city ditch immediately to the north of the city wall became known as the 'Deep Ditch' and 'Moorditch', respectively; however, by the mid 16th century the two had become so inextricably linked in the minds of Londoners that the former was often synonymous with the latter.[2] This network of watercourses facilitated the free flow of water southward from Moorfields to the Thames, but the City of London faced a running battle with its citizens, who became increasingly determined to use them for both rubbish disposal and as open sewers.[3] Moorfields remained largely unexploited and marshy, despite some efforts to 'cleanse' and 'free' the watercourses during the late 13th and 14th centuries from 'dung', 'rotton matter' and 'nuisances'.[4] The marsh may have persisted for as long as it did in part due to its defensive value; in the early 15th century it was still considered the 'strongest and most impregnable part of the city'.[5]

Stow, writing at the end of the 16th century, described Moorfields as a 'Fen or More field stretching from the wall of the City betwixt Bishopsgate and the posterne called Cripples gate to Fensbery, and Holy well, [which] continued a wast and vnprofitable ground a long time'.[6] FitzStephen, writing in the 12th century, noted that Moorfields was so prone to flooding during winters that 'great throngs of youths' used bone skates on the 'vast spread of ice'.[7] The marsh of Moorfields was home to industrial activities which were unacceptable within the walls and/or could take advantage of the large open spaces and ready supply of water. In 1374 the 'moor' and the Walbrook were leased without rent to Thomas atte Ram, a 'brewere',[8] and the presence of tanners and leather-workers in Moorfields in the 14th century is well documented.[9]

In 1247 Simon Fitz Mary, sheriff of London, granted lands in lower Moorfields for the foundation of the priory of St Mary of Bethlehem.[10] The area which would become the New Churchyard was located within approximately the south-west quarter of these lands, which were described as bounded to the west by the 'depediche' and to the south by the lands of the church of 'S. Botulphi'. The grant described the features of these lands as houses, gardens, orchards, fishponds, dikes (ditches) and marshes, although the precise location of each was not specified.[11] Mid 16th-century maps indicate that development was concentrated to the east, near to Bishopsgate, which suggests that the fishponds, dikes and marshes are likely to have been concentrated in the marshy lands to the west (Figs 1, 3).[12]

The drainage and reclamation of the marsh lands of lower Moorfields began in the first half of the 15th century. The first significant drainage works occurred in 1415 and Stow tells us that they included the 'Deepditch by Bethlehem'.[13] An entry in the letter books of the City of London, dated 2 July 1415, notes in greater detail how the 'fossam de Walbrooke' (from Latin 'fossa', meaning ditch/trench) was choked by latrines, laystalls and 'other kinds of filth', and describes orders for its revetment and cleansing so that 'the flow of the waters from the Fosses without the walls of the City, which discharge into the Foss of Walbrooke aforesaid, be carried off and got rid of.'[14] These works were prompted by the needs of a growing population. They resulted in 'greatly drained and dried' lands which were 'allotted and divided' and let for the 'common advantage', with paths provided to allow the citizens of London to pass 'into the field for their recreation'.[15] Further drainage and ground-raising efforts in the 15th and early 16th century completed the reclamation and 'by these degrees was this Fenne or More at length made main and hard ground' (below, 2.2).[16]

Archaeological evidence

The area remained undeveloped and little used until the early 15th century as shown by excavation at sites A and B. The build-up of peaty humic

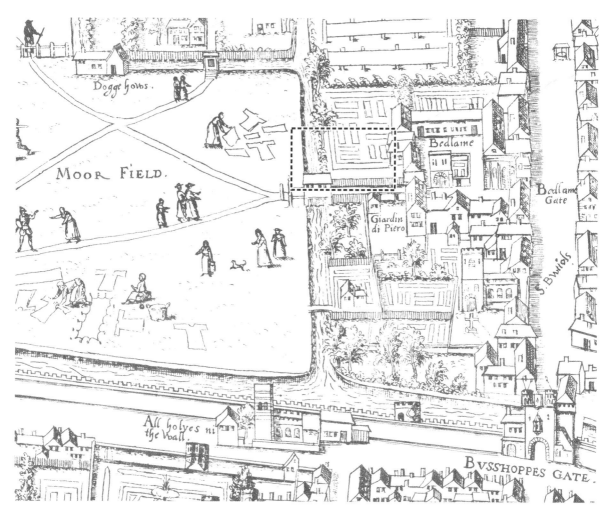

Labels visible on map: Dogge houss. — MOOR FIELD. — Bedlame — Bedlam Gate — Giardin di Piero — S. Butiols. — All holyes ni the Wall. — BVSSHOPPES GATE.

Fig 3 Detail of the copperplate map of London, *c* 1553–9, with the site (outlined in red) superimposed on the garden as it then was; note the deep ditch with its bridge and gatehouse, giving access from the west via an alley to the Bedlam Hospital, and to the west (left) Moorfields; north is to the top (Margary 1981)

deposits seen at the base of the medieval sequence clearly shows the continuation of the marshy conditions which had begun in the late Roman period.[17] Palaeoenvironmental remains suggest that water pooling or flooding was short-lived and did not allow aquatic vegetation to take hold. The area of flood would have been suitable for seasonal pasture, at least during the summer months, and activities associated with this use are indicated by byre waste material found within the sediments. Evidence for skating on the marsh during winters in the medieval period was provided by the discovery of bone skates within these deposits (Fig 4).

Two parallel series of large linear pits were found at the site (Fig 5 a). Pottery from the fills provided a *terminus post quem* (TPQ) of *c* 1080, although the precise date of these features is unclear. It is possible they were dug in an attempt to quarry brickearth, but it is clear that they had been left open for a considerable amount of time and contained water. Fish scales and eel (*Anguilla anguilla*) bone remains were found within the fills, suggesting that they may have been used as waterholes and/or fishponds, perhaps belonging to the priory of St Mary Bethlehem.

Excavation indicated that the medieval deep ditch was below and aligned with what is now Blomfield Street and followed the approximate course of the natural stream (the Walbrook). A timber structure found to the north-west of the site (land tie assembly [1293]–[1295]) was probably part of the rear bracing of a revetment built on its east bank (Fig 5 a). This revetment may

Fig 4 Cattle bone skates <70> and <71> (scale *c* 1:4)

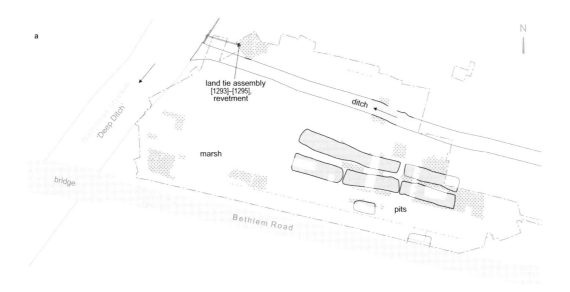

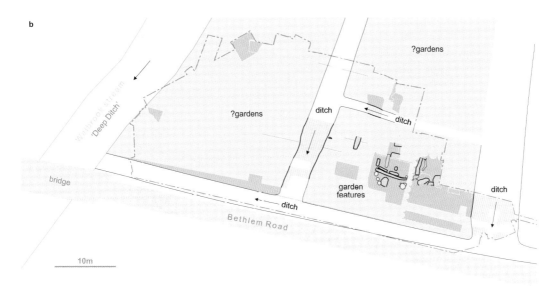

Fig 5 Plan showing medieval features: a – *c* 1400–50; b – *c* 1450–*c* 1500 (scale 1:600)

have been part of the revetment works in 1414–15 or could represent a later 15th-century modification or repair. Construction techniques suggest a date no earlier than *c* 1400.

2.2 Moorfields and the 'Deep Ditch' in the 16th century

Documentary evidence

Mid 16th-century maps (Figs 1, 3) show an extensive garden on the site bounded by Old Bethlem (the road) to the south, the 'Deep Ditch' to the west, 'Bedlam' Hospital to the east and tenter grounds to the north.[18] By 1561 this plot was known as the 'greate gardens' to the 'west parte of Bethlem'.[19]

The ditches of Moorfields continued to be hindered by industrial dumping into the 16th century. On 6 June 1532, for example, the Curriers' Company (of leather-workers) were strictly prohibited from discarding their waste into the ditches of Moorfields.[20] However, the local area was being increasingly developed and dumped domestic rubbish also began to threaten the free flow of drainage.

The course of the medieval deep ditch appears to have become unsustainable during the 15th century. Re-establishing or 'cleansing' the channel in its original location must have become unviable because it was entirely recut as a ditch *c* 7m east of and parallel to its former course (below). The precise date at which this happened is uncertain but stratigraphy indicates the late 15th or early 16th century. It is possible that it was one of the ditches dug as part of major drainage works in 1512: 'Roger Acheley Mayor caused diuers dikes to be cast, and made to drein the waters of the sayde More fields, with bridges arched ouer them, and the groundes about to bee leuelled, whereby the sayd fielde was made somewhat more commodious.'[21]

Archaeological evidence

The change from little-used marshland to gardens in the late 15th–16th century was seen archaeologically in dumping as consolidation and the deliberate infilling of the ponds. The gardens were evidenced by a cluster of bedding trenches, pits and possible tree-planting holes (Fig 5 b). These features produced a number of peg roofing tiles, most of late 15th-century date and of typical London type with two round nail holes located near the top edge, and a worn brown-glazed floor tile, a Low Countries (also known as 'Flemish') import dating to the 14th to late 15th century.

The deep ditch artificial channel was by far the largest ditch in a new drainage network and would have been the principal drainage feature of Moorfields during the 16th century (Fig 6). It is drawn as a major north–south watercourse on mid 16th-century maps (eg Figs 1, 3).[22] It extended beyond the excavated

N

Moorfields

'Deep Ditch'

garden/tenter ground

paths

bridge

pit

ditch

Bethlem Road

10m

Fig 6 Plan of early modern features, *c* 1500–69, showing recut 'Deep Ditch', refuse pit and associated drainage ditch (scale 1:600)

areas of the site, was truncated on site B but was found on the same alignment and course to the south at 42–46 New Broad Street in 1906.[23]

The 16th-century ditch measured 12m wide and was up to 2.5m deep; there was no archaeological evidence that it had ever been recut. The lower fills were predominantly firm black silts and clays, up to 1.2m thick, which were formed in flowing water and represent a gradual silting up over many decades. Its upper fills, dated approximately to the mid to later 16th century, provide clear archaeological evidence of deliberate dumping – fly-tipping – when, as documentary evidence attests, the local population used the watercourses of Moorfields for general rubbish and waste disposal, and as open sewers.

Selected 16th-century finds from ditches and pits

Hundreds of artefacts were recovered from the deep ditch fills, as well as from another, west–east, ditch and adjacent pit sealed by the dumping to create the New Churchyard (below, Chapter 3.1; Fig 6). These finds included building materials and pottery, metalwork, and organic materials such as leather items and fragments of willow or poplar basketry; a selection of these finds are described and illustrated here.[24]

A rich and diverse assemblage of waterlogged plant and insect remains were recovered from the deep ditch lower fills, [1036] and [6640]; these included food plants, mostly fruits, plants that are likely to have been growing in or on the edges of the ditch, such as pondweeds (*Potamogeton* sp) and crowfoots (*Ranunculus sceleratus*), and plants suggestive of disturbed or waste ground nearby. Garden plants were also present, in particular seeds of pot marigold (*Calendula officinalis*) and hemp (*Cannabis sativa*), and leaves of box (*Buxus sempervirens*). The first two of these may be evidence of local textile manufacture, with hemp grown for its fibres and pot marigold as a dye plant. Samples taken from the upper fills of the deep ditch ([1034], [1066], [6639]) were dominated by what might be 'stabling waste', including abundant cereal bran fragments, grass seeds, stems, corncockle (*Agrostemma githago*) fragments and many 'hay meadow' taxa. The upper fills also included hemp and abundant teasel (*Dipsacus* spp) seeds. Teasel has been used in the wool textile industry during the finishing stage for cleaning and raising the nap on fabrics;[25] cultivation of teasel locally is evidenced nearby at the 'teasel' field in Spitalfields, which went out of use in 1538.[26] Further evidence of garden activity within the upper fills was an unusual item of historic woodwork: a group of interlaced laths that were part of a fallen or dumped trellis, [6761]. Evidence for diet comes from the upper fills where a large collection of animal bone was predominantly from cattle, pig and sheep/goat, but also included poultry and a sparse but diverse assemblage of wild game and freshwater, migratory and marine fish.

The deep ditch upper fills contained an impressive range of dumped items, among which was a large assemblage of waste fragments and tools associated with both leather and textile working (Fig 7), including two iron tenter hooks, which provide a link to the site's use as a tenter ground by a clothier immediately prior to the establishment of the New Churchyard (below, Chapter 3.1). In addition, the overall finds indicate that other local industries included both ferrous and non-ferrous metalworking, and carpentry.

Nearly 200 mid 16th-century leather shoes and clothing accessories were also recovered from the upper fills, as well as in the other ditch and pit sealed by the burial ground's horizon of dumped soil (Fig 8). The shoes reflect changing fashions between the 1530s and 1550s, with low open shoes fastened with straps over the instep giving way in the upper fills to the plainer high latchet-fastening and slip-on styles of the mid and later 16th century. Several of the more

Fig 7 Selected leather- and textile-working tools: leather-working stiletto <2519> and knife <2917> with a fleur-de-lys cutler's mark; iron tenter hook <1051> and copper-alloy thimble <1294> with maker's stamp indicating it was imported from Nuremberg, Germany (scale *c* 1:1; except knife <2917>, *c* 1:2, with detail of cutler's mark *c* 2:1; detail stiletto <2519>, *c* 2:1; detail thimble <1294> maker's stamp 4:1)

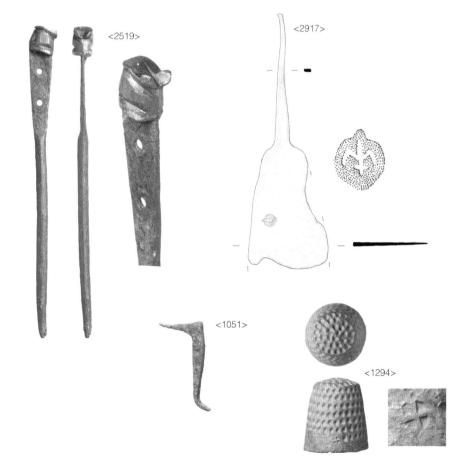

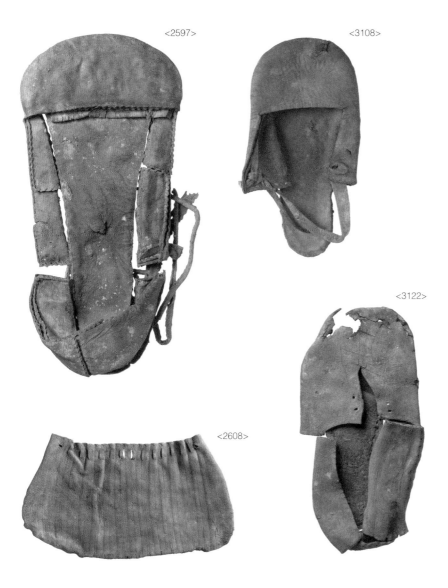

<2597>

<3108>

<3122>

<2608>

Fig 8 Examples of leather items from the ditches and pits: shoe fashions dating from the 1530s to 1550s – adult shoe <2597> and children's shoes <3108> (missing its back), <3122>; and small drawstring pouch <2608> (scale *c* 1:3)

complete shoes are children's, sometimes more sturdily constructed but otherwise identical to adult footwear. The assemblage also contains large pieces from at least five drawstring pouches which would have been used for money and other items, and worn on belts at the waist (Fig 8).

The same features also produced a quantity of metal, bone and wooden objects that illustrate the full breadth of 16th-century life. Dress accessories, including a large number of copper-alloy pins, provide further evidence for clothing and appearance in this period. Efforts made to maintain appearance are hinted at by wooden combs and a bone toilet set. Despite, or perhaps because of the religious changes taking place in this period, a number of discarded pilgrim badges were found, including several from the same shrine, thought to be in Willesden, Middlesex (Fig 9).[27]

While the groups of finds recovered were dominated by deliberately discarded objects and materials, some items were clearly accidental losses. Several silver coins, copper-alloy tokens and jettons were found in the upper fills, issued in or current at dates ranging from the later 15th century to the first half of the 16th century.

Fig 9 Lead-alloy pilgrim badges depicting Our Lady from the shrine at Willesden <2076>; the Annunciation of Our Lady from the shrine at Walsingham <1453>; and St George <1454> (scale *c* 1:1)

The half-ducat, <328>, of Leonardo Loredan, Doge of Venice, came from an upper fill, [1034], of the deep ditch (Fig 10). It has been pierced for suspension, so may no longer have been used as currency but perhaps as a necklace or as a 'sequin' sewn on to clothing. The ducat, later called the zecchino, and its 'half' were gold coins minted in Venice from the late 13th to the late 18th century. The obverse legend is an abbreviation of 'Leonardo Lauredano, Dux, sacra moneta Venetiae' (Leonardo Loredan, Doge, Sacred Money of Venice); St Mark is the patron saint of Venice and he is shown passing the flag of office to the Doge. The reverse legend 'ego sum lux mundi' (I am the light of the world) is from Jesus' discourse with the Pharisees (John 8:12). Leonardo Loredan (1436–1521) was elected Doge in 1501, the same year his famous portrait (in the National Gallery, London) was painted by Bellini. Conversely, his silver coins (soldini) are extremely common in Britain, brought here by Venetian sailors, where they were known as 'galley ha'pennies'.

Fig 10 Gold half-ducat <328> of Leonardo Loredan, dated 1501–21 (obverse, left, and reverse) (scale *c* 2:1)

That valuables could and were being lost in the ditches of Moorfields was recognised as early as the late 14th century, when Thomas atte Ram was made responsible for 'cleansing' the ditches and watercourse of Moorfields. The City decreed that: 'if in so cleansing it … he shall find aught therein, he shall have for his own all that he shall so find in the dung and filth thereof'.[28]

Notes to Chapter 2

1 Stow 1603, i, 19

2 LMA, COL/CA/01/01/018 (Rep 16), 476v; Lambert 1921, 83, n 1

3 Rawcliffe 2013, 23, 143–4, 205–6

4 *Cal L Books A*, 212, 217, *E*, 147, *F*, 120, *H*, 216, 247; *Cal Plea and Mem R*, 278

5 *Cal L Book I*, 101

6 Stow 1603, ii, 76

7 Ibid; Levy 1990, 79

8 *Cal L Book G*, 324

9 Memorials: 1415 in Riley 1868, 614–16; *Cal E Mayor R*, 161

10 Barron and Davies 2007, 113

11 *Mon Angl*, 622

12 The copperplate map, *c* 1553–9: Margary 1981; 'Civitas Londinum' or the Agas, *c* 1562; Braun and Hogenberg's map, 1572

13 Stow 1603, ii, 76

14 LMA, COL/AD/01/009 (I), 152; translated from Latin in Memorials: 1415 in Riley 1868, 614–15

15 Memorials: 1415 in Riley 1868, 614–15; Stow 1603, i, 32–3, ii, 76–7

16 Stow 1603, i, 32–3, ii, 77

17 Ranieri and Telfer 2017

18 The copperplate map, *c* 1553–9: Margary 1981; 'Civitas Londinum' or the Agas, *c* 1562; Braun and Hogenberg's map, 1572

19 Andrews et al 1997, 42

20 LMA, COL/CA/01/01/008 (Rep 8), 230v

21 Stow 1603, ii, 77

22 The copperplate map, *c* 1553–9: Margary 1981; Agas *c* 1562; Braun and Hogenberg 1572

23 Norman and Reader 1906, 206–7

24 Full discussion of finds from the ditch and contemporary features in Cubitt et al in prep b

25 Hall 1992

26 Harward et al 2015, 71

27 Egan 2005, 205

28 *Cal L Book G*, 324

CHAPTER 3

THE NEW CHURCHYARD BURIAL GROUND, 1569–1739

3.1 Foundation

Documentary evidence

The Corporation proposed a new burial ground for the use of the City of London on 9 June 1569. High mortality during the influenza epidemic of 1557–9[1] was closely followed by a severe outbreak of plague in 1563, testing the capacity of existing parish churchyards to breaking point:

> … this honourable City of London hath many times heretofore bin visited by hand of almighty God with sickness whereof many people have died of late years with plague … experience then did teach that the common churchyards of the City being very small for the most part, were so pestered dead bodies that there was no room left for any further burial if the same [plague] should have any longer endured. And forasmuch as it is thought common and good policy to provide for remedy for such a lack before the time of necessity requireth, that great care and diligence hath been used in searching out and finding some apt and fit piece of ground of the City's for that purpose.[2]

In July 1569 the Lord Mayor Sir Thomas Rowe issued orders to convert an extramural plot of land between the 'backside of Bedlem' and the 'banke of deepe ditch' (Figs 1, 3).[3] The land was part of the 'greate gardens', which had once belonged to Bethlem Hospital but were available in 1569 because the possession and administration of the hospital and its lands had passed to the Crown and the City Corporation following the Dissolution.[4] Nevertheless, obstacles had to be overcome before it was ready. Firstly, the plot had been recently let to John May, a 'clother', who was using it as a tenter ground and who thus had to be compensated for loss of the remaining part of his lease.[5] Secondly, it was recognised that the land was prone to flooding due to its location adjoining the deep ditch. To reduce this risk the City ordered that the ground was to be raised over a period of six weeks by dumping soil and rubbish brought out from the city. This included all the earth from cellar and well diggings but strictly excluded 'soilage of the street or dung'. The work was encouraged by the promise of 2d per cartload. Lastly, the nearby doghouse (shown on Fig 3) of the City's common hunt was also to be moved, presumably due to its potential to cause a nuisance.[6]

The City intended that the New Churchyard would act as an overflow ground to which the parishes of London could send burials they could not accommodate. John Sherbrooke, who was buried at the New Churchyard sometime between 19 January and 19 February 1569/70, was recorded as the 'first that was buried there'.[7]

Naming the burial ground

For the first *c* 100 years of its use the burial ground was known by Londoners as the 'New Churchyard' (despite it not being attached to or associated with a church). Parishes also occasionally referred to the ground's location, for example 'in Moorfields' or 'in Bethlem'. However, some neighbouring extramural parishes began calling the ground simply 'Bethlem' or 'Bedlam' (spelt variously) as early as 1635.[8] More parishes began using this name in the mid to late 17th century, to avoid confusion with other 'new' grounds, in particular, Bunhill Fields established in 1665.[9] The change is reflected in City of London parish burial registers. In the parish of St Margaret Moses, the ground was the 'new church-yard' until April 1666, when it was first referenced as 'Beddlem'.[10] However, the change took decades to be universally adopted. The parish of All Hallows Bread Street, for example, did not start using the name 'Bedlam' in preference to the 'new church yeard' until August 1692.[11]

Fig 11 London-area post-medieval slipped red ware flared dish fragment <3259>, with sgraffito decoration of a cockerel, and Raeren stoneware mug fragment <3260>, with face mask (not shown), both from [507] (scale *c* 1:4)

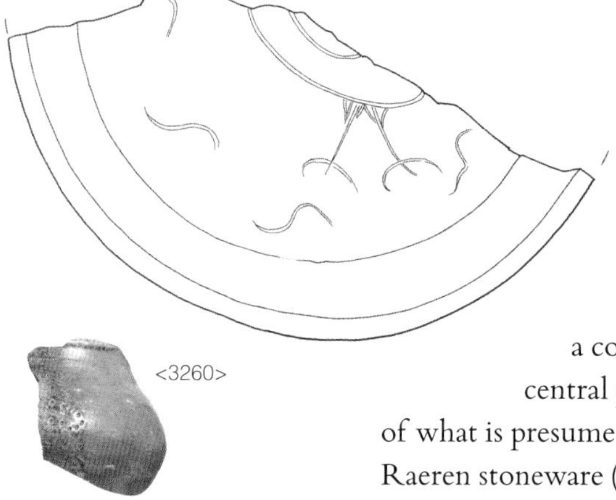

<3259>

<3260>

Archaeological evidence

The six-week period of dumping, as described in documentary sources, was seen as a distinct *c* 0.3–0.5m thick site-wide soil horizon, truncated and sealed by burials. This consisted of building rubble and silt dumps, characterised by crushed brick and mortar. The dumps contained large amounts of residual Roman pottery, brick and tile, suggesting that the material had been sourced from diggings in the City as documented. However, the horizon also included occasional dumps of cessy silt and animal bones, which suggests that some of the dumping may have been in contravention of orders to exclude 'soilage of the street or dung'.

The composition of fragmented pottery groups from this horizon reflects well the range of pottery used in London when the New Churchyard was founded in 1569. Pottery vessels of note include the profile of a London-area post-medieval slipped red ware (fabric code PMSRY) flared dish with sgraffito decoration (<3259> Fig 11); sooted from use, this was recovered from a consolidation dump/make-up layer, [507]. The surviving central portion of the dish has two clawed feet and the lower body of what is presumed to have been a cockerel. Also in the same context is a Raeren stoneware (RAER) mug with a face mask (<3260> Fig 11).

3.2 The pulpit and Whit Sunday sermon

Documentary evidence

Its foundation orders stipulated that the New Churchyard was to have an outdoor preaching pulpit, that an annual Whit Sunday sermon was to be endowed and that the preacher was to be paid 13s 4d.[12] Churchyard sermons were popular events and important locations for public pronouncements from the late 15th to the 17th century. Religious significance was matched by secular status: the sermon was also an opportunity for a display of civil cohesion and prestige.[13] The New Churchyard Whit Sunday sermon, on the seventh Sunday after Easter (commemorating for Christians the descent of the Holy Spirit at Pentecost), became part of a series of annual City sermons, alongside those already established at St Paul's Cathedral (Fig 12) within the walls and in the cemetery of the medieval hospital and priory of St Mary Spital on the north-east side of Bishopsgate (Fig 1).

The sermon was a prominent feature of the ground for 72 years.[14] During this period, crowds gathered annually at 9am on Whit Sunday and listened to the sermon alongside the mayor, two sheriffs and aldermen, all of whom were expected to attend dressed in their finery and lined scarlet gowns.[15] The preachers were appointed by the Court of Aldermen[16] and many of their payments are recorded in the surviving City accounts.[17] The first Whit Sunday sermon was given on 14 May 1570 by 'Mr Palmer of St. Lawrence'.[18]

Fig 12 A diptych of 1616 showing a sermon being preached in St Paul's churchyard; the New Churchyard pulpit may have looked broadly similar
(Society of Antiquaries of London/Bridgeman Images)

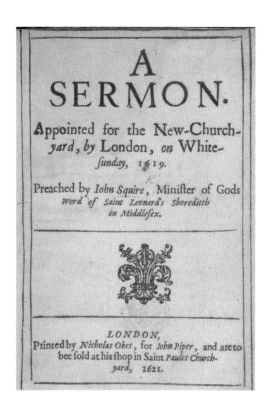

Fig 13 Title page of John Squire's 'A Sermon appointed for the New-Church-yard, by London, on White-Sunday, 1619', published 1621

(The British Library Board, 4479.aaa.35)

In a letter to the Lord Treasurer, dated 18 June 1584, William Fleetwood, City Recorder, made reference to a 'very good sermon preached at the new churchyard near Bethlehem' and how 'all the City was quiet' since no plays had been permitted that day.[19] The ground's only surviving pulpit sermon is one of several printed sermons given by John Squire (c 1587–c 1653), a fellow of Jesus College, Cambridge, and the vicar of the church of St Leonard Shoreditch (Middlesex), 1612–43 (Fig 13). It was preached on 16 May 1619 on the theme of the Pentecost, including a discussion of the etymology of 'Whit Sunday', and was probably given before the Lord Mayor Sir Sebastian Hervey.[20]

The New Churchyard pulpit benefited from at least two charitable endowments. In 1585, Thomas Randall, first keeper of the New Churchyard, left an annuity of 20s for two additional sermons to be preached annually during Easter week. Furthermore, he left funds for a tent so that, in the event of unsuitable weather, those attending 'maie sitt drye and out of the sonne' and requested that the Mercers' chapel might be considered the official alternative venue if the New Churchyard was unavailable.[21] The will of Peter Symonds, Mercer of London, proved September 1587, left an endowment so that 60 loaves could in perpetuity be carried annually to the ground on Whit Sunday and delivered to 60 poor people after the sermon.[22]

By the 1630s the preacher's payment had risen to 60s. This was a considerable increase above inflation and may reflect a rise in the perceived significance of the event by the early 17th century.[23] The last recorded Whit Sunday sermon preached at the New Churchyard was on 24 May 1642.[24] However, the New Churchyard continued to be considered the correct venue until 1657, despite the sermon being preached during the intervening years at the Mercers' chapel or St Paul's church Covent Garden.[25] Why the New Churchyard was not used as a venue between 1643 and 1657 is not recorded. The absence of the sermon may have been associated with the turmoil of the Civil War; the churchyard of St Giles Cripplegate, for example, was used for military training between c 1647 and 1659.[26] Alternatively, the absence was perhaps due to the unavailability of the pulpit, which does not appear on Faithorne and Newcourt's map, surveyed in c 1643–7 and published in 1658 (Fig 16). It may simply have become too dilapidated for use after 1643 or, if decorated with religious imagery, may have become a target for Puritan iconoclasm and been defaced and/or demolished.[27] Whatever the case, St Paul's church, Covent Garden, became the permanent home of the City's Whit Sunday sermon from 1657.[28]

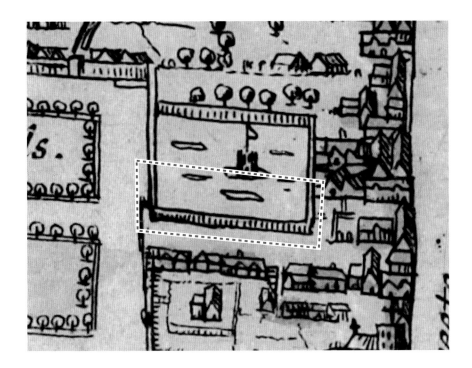

Fig 14 The New Churchyard pulpit depicted on Ryther's map, 'Cittie of London', published *c* 1633, with the site superimposed (outlined in red); north is to the top
(The British Library Board, Crace Collection, 1.31)

The only known images of the New Churchyard pulpit are indistinct drawings seen on maps published in *c* 1633 (Fig 14) and *c* 1654.[29] These depict it as a small roofed structure, perhaps set on a platform, topped with a flag or cross. Although lacking in detail, both depictions of the pulpit resemble the St Paul's and St Mary Spital pulpits, as seen on the copperplate map of the 1550s.[30] The 15th-century St Paul's pulpit cross was recorded in detail in early 17th-century images as an octagonal booth, with a timbered lower elevation, built on a stone platform (Fig 12).[31] At St Paul's and at St Mary Spital, galleries and/or timber stands provided separate cover for dignitaries in the 16th and 17th centuries.[32]

Archaeological evidence

No archaeological remains of the pulpit were found. The mid 17th-century maps (eg Fig 14) show it at the centre of the ground, which places it outside excavated areas and within those truncated in the 19th century by Broad Street Station.

Archaeological evidence for the St Mary Spital pulpit from the Spitalfields Market excavations suggested a timber pulpit reached by about nine or ten steps, with the base of the pulpit perhaps 1.5m or 2m above ground level on a stone platform built from faced flint and chalk blocks. The main body of the structure was built on a rectangular chalk foundation, 1.3m in depth and 3.4m by 1.7m in plan.[33]

3.3 Enclosing the burial ground and westward expansion

Documentary evidence

Sir Thomas Rowe funded the construction of the ground's boundary walls 'in the name of a frende', who, according to Stow, was his wife, Mary Rowe.[34] Norden's map of 1593 is the first known map to depict the burial ground. Boundary walls are shown on the east, north and south sides of the ground (Fig 15).[35] The deep ditch, as previously seen on maps published *c* 1553–72 (above, eg Figs 1, 3), is shown circumscribing the ground's west boundary.

By the end of the 16th century the ditches of Moorfields were in a deplorable state, something familiar enough to Elizabethan Londoners to allow Shakespeare to use 'the melancholy of Moorditch' as a proverbial expression.[36] Stow gives us the following description of the city ditch (Moorditch), which adjoined Petty France to the south of the New Churchyard:

a causeye [a paved way] leading to a quadrant, called Petty Fraunce, of Frenchmen dwelling there, and to other dwelling houses, lately built on the banke of the saide ditch by some Cittizens of London, that more regarded their owne priuate gaine, then the common good of the Cittie; for by meanes of this causeye raysed on the banke, and soylage of houses, with other filthines cast into the ditch, the same is now forced to a narrow

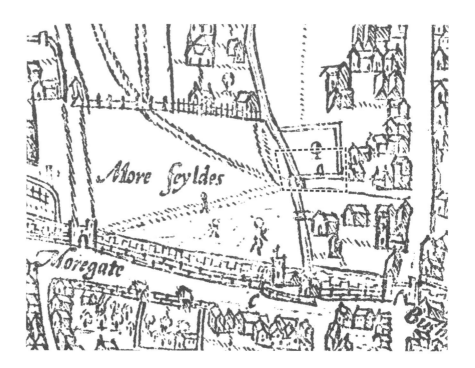

Fig 15 Detail of Norden's map of London and Westminster, 1593, showing the burial ground, walled on three sides with a gate in the south wall and a tree in the centre, with the site superimposed (outlined in red); north is to the top

channell, and almost filled vp by vnsauorie things, to the danger of impoysoning the whole Cittie.[37]

Although Stow refers here to the 'Town Ditch', the 'deepe ditch' seems to have been similarly affected. The deep ditch must have been a very unpleasant nuisance for the adjoining New Churchyard for perhaps decades prior to its infilling; the stench of the ditch may have deterred people from burying at the ground or at least from visiting their departed loved ones. Excavation showed that by the late 16th century the deep ditch was only shallow and, like the city ditch, was 'forced to a narrow channel' as a result of extensive silting and dumping.[38] This would have significantly reduced the ditch's capacity, which is likely to have resulted in at least occasional flooding at the New Churchyard.

During the first decade of the 17th century, however, lower Moorfields was transformed into a landscaped public space.[39] In May 1604, as part of this process, the City of London ordered that the deep ditch should be 'wholly filled up, for avoyding of the noysome and unwholesome smells and savours arising from the same ditch very dangerous for infection'. Again, in June 1604, the City appointed representatives to 'consider of some meanes for remedyeing & avoyding of the annoyances of the sewers and ditches in and nere Morefields'.[40] However, these remediation works did not happen immediately. On 14 May 1605 the City ordered that the Whit Sunday sermon was to be preached at the Mercers' chapel because the New Churchyard was still 'very much annoyed by the smelles and savors comming from the ditch nere adioning'.[41]

Once the deep ditch had been filled in, the New Churchyard expanded westward by incorporating the reclaimed land (Fig 17). Augustine Ryther's map of 1633 is the first to show these changes (Fig 14).[42] Both the burial ground and Moorfields are drawn fully walled, with the latter now shown divided into quarters by fences and pathways. The new west gate to Bedlam (the neighbourhood), built in 1614, is depicted immediately outside the south-west corner of the burial ground.[43] Crucially, the map shows that the east wall of lower Moorfields also served as the New Churchyard's west boundary. The Court of Aldermen issued an order on 4 August 1607 that the construction of the east wall of Moorfields was to be delayed until the following year.[44] Based on these various documented events, it seems that the deep ditch was filled in sometime between 1605 and 1607, but most probably in late 1607.

Filling in this ditch in the burial ground would have exacerbated existing problems in the Moorfields area. On 30 June 1607, the Governors of Bethlem Hospital were informed of a ditch adjoining the 'garden plott' at the back (north) of the hospital that stood 'full of filth and stincking water', which was 'very noisome to the prisoners [inmates] of the said house [Bethlem Hospital]'.[45] This garden can be seen on Ryther's map of 1633 (Fig 14) and would previously have been bounded to the west by the deep ditch (Fig 15). A 'vault' or sewer was built across lower Moorfields in 1610/11. This sewer, and the successive sewers which replaced it, have provided the drainage for the area up to the present day.[46] The expansion of the New Churchyard may have inspired their neighbours, the church of St Botolph without Bishopsgate (hereafter St Botolph Bishopsgate), who in 1615–17 infilled part of the city ditch in order to extend their churchyard.[47]

The earliest known engravings of the site are dated to the early 19th century (Chapter 13.3).[48] However, a picture of the New Churchyard can be formed from contemporary cartographic and documentary sources. The maps of Ryther and Porter are notable as the only known images depicting the interior of the ground and show the pulpit at the centre surrounded by graves or burial monuments (Fig 14).[49] Descriptions of wall repairs in the records of the Court of Aldermen and City Lands Committee indicate that they would have originally been substantial and impressive.[50]

The ground was initially accessed by a folding gate in the south wall over which was an inscribed memorial stone, which read:

THOMAS ROE miles, cum Prætor esset LONDINENSIS, hunc locum Reipublicæ, in usum publicæ Sepulturæ communem, suo sumptu dedicavit, Anno Dom. 1569
(Thomas Roe Knight, when he was mayor of London, at his own expense dedicated this place [ground] belonging to the City for common use as a public burial ground, in the year of our Lord 1569)[51]

The location of this gate at the approximate centre of the south wall is shown on maps published in 1593 and in 1658 (Figs 15, 16).[52] The south gate opened on to the alley that led east to Bedlam (the alley roughly equates with the south pavement of modern Liverpool Street). However, the south gate was at some point replaced by one in the west wall, the location of which is recorded on plans dated to the 1760s.[53] The last known map to show the main gate located on the south wall is Doornick's *Map of burnt London*, dated 1666.[54]

Archaeological evidence shows that the west wall was rebuilt (below). The location of the later wall as excavated aligns with the west boundary as drawn on maps and plans dated 1676–1858. It is possible it was part of works to relandscape Moorfields associated with the construction of 'New Bethlem' in 1675–6.

While the burial ground's south gate had been rather hidden at the midpoint

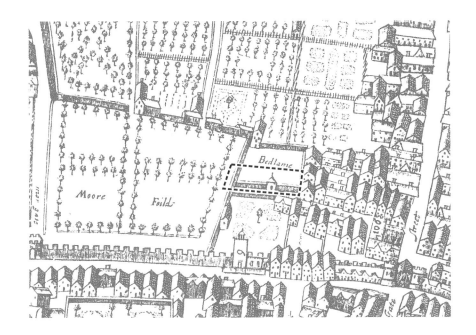

Fig 16 Detail of Faithorne and Newcourt's map of London, surveyed *c* 1643–7 and published 1658, which shows an entrance into the alley leading east to Bedlam and a gate in the middle of the south wall of the burial ground on the north side of this alley, with the site superimposed (outlined in red); north is to the top (Margary 1981)

of a narrow alley, its new west gate would have been in a prominent position, visible from across Moorfields. Designed to impress, it was flanked by two brick piers each 'surmounted by sepulchral urns' and 'a stone shield of the City arms'.[55] The relocation of the ground's gate appears to have influenced a change in the layout of the burial ground in the late 17th century (below; Chapter 5.1). Fig 17, showing the development of the burial ground from its foundation to *c* 1676, is informed by the plan evidence for Brokers Row (Chapter 13) and the earlier maps detailed above.[56]

Archaeological evidence

The location and dimensions of the deep ditch at the time of its infilling, as well as the infilling itself, were not clear archaeologically due to extensive truncation of this area by both modern activity and grave cuts. However, several dumps discovered in the west end of site A may have been part of infilling and levelling associated with the event. These deposits were of similar character to the burial ground consolidation dumping of *c* 1569–70 but overlay early burials and were given a *terminus post quem* (TPQ) of *c* 1580 by pottery and clay tobacco pipes (A[1214], A[1238], A[1243], A[1258] and A[1315]).

The south boundary wall was heavily truncated by late 19th- to 20th-century construction and survived only as elm piles in the south-west corner of the site (Fig 17 c). Remains belonging to two phases of west boundary wall were found on the west edge of the site. The original west wall, dated *c* 1607,

Fig 17 The development of the burial ground, 1569–c 1666–76: a – 1569–c 1607, bounded on the west by the narrowed 'Deep Ditch'; b and c – extended and walled on the west, c 1607; d and e – west wall rebuilt c 1666–76 and west gate added (scale 1:1000; details c and e, 1:300)

THE NEW CHURCHYARD

survived as a 0.5m-wide foundation of 16th-century bricks, constructed on large elm piles in order to prevent the wall subsiding into the (until recently) wet and marshy ground. Surviving fragments of this structure showed that it had indeed suffered from subsidence despite its extensive pile footing. The wall was then reconstructed *c* 1m to the west of the original, using the same building techniques; bricks from the wall were broadly dated, *c* 1550–*c* 1666/ 1700.

No contemporary burial ground surface survived but the general pattern of burial levels suggests that the contemporary surfaces would have sloped down *c* 0.6m north–south across the burial ground and a similar depth east–west.

3.4 Administration: the City and the keepers of the burial ground

Documentary sources

As a municipal non-parochial ground the management of the New Churchyard was overseen by the City. Some administrative information therefore survives in the records of the Corporation, principally the surviving Court of Aldermen repertories, City account books and journals of the City Lands Committee. However, the day-to-day running of the ground was the responsibility of 'keepers' appointed by the Court of Aldermen (Chapter 14.1). The first keepers appointed in 1569 were Thomas and Mary Randall, the son-in-law and daughter of Sir Thomas Rowe. Between 1636 and 1740 the keepership was held by the Clitherow (spelt variously) family and passed from father to son for four generations. The first Clitherow appointed, Benjamin Clitherow I, was the 'kinsman' (probably cousin) of Sir Christopher Clitherow (below; Fig 19).[57]

The position of keeper was desirable, a 'gift', since keepers were allowed all the 'fees, profits and commodities' of the ground. The keepers' income would have mainly come from charges associated with grave digging and perhaps bearers, since they were not permitted to charge fees themselves (Chapter 4.1), but the occasional provision and construction of burial monuments for the wealthy may have been the most lucrative source of profits. There is some evidence to show an increased commercialisation of the ground in the 18th century (below, 3.5; 3.6).

While keepers were appointed for life, they could lose their position if they did not 'well and honestly use and behave' themselves; none were dismissed but several were criticised (Chapter 6.1).[58] In *c* 1638–9, Benjamin Clitherow I was accused of 'profanely' keeping and using the ground; allowing a local resident to tenter cloth in the ground; and occasionally allowing the dead to 'lie all night unburied'.[59] Benjamin Clitherow III built a house for himself early in his keepership without authorisation from the City. The building does not appear on Doornick's *Map of burnt London*, dated 1666, and is first shown on Ogilby and Morgan's map, published in 1676, as a rectangular building in the south-west corner of the ground (Figs 18, 29).[60] The keeper's house was either constructed simultaneously with or shortly after the west boundary wall (before 1676, possibly *c* 1675–6; above, 3.3), since the west side of the house was formed by the rebuilt boundary wall. The location of the house was probably influenced by the proximity of the new west gate, for reasons of convenience.

The City only became aware of the building in 1703–4 after Benjamin Clitherow III requested permission to modify the burial ground wall in order to convert the ground floor into a shop.[61] Despite at first objecting to it, the City allowed the house and its herbage to stand and become the official residence of the keepers. The freehold became part of the City's estates and 'Benjamin Clitherow' is recorded as the lessee in surviving land tax records dated 1692–1739.[62] Notably, all appointments to the keepership after 1705 included the strict proviso that no one could build on any part of the burial ground without the prior consent of the Corporation. Despite this, Benjamin Clitherow IV violated these terms by building stables and a chaise (ie carriage) house without permission. He also gained another source of income by building an unauthorised extension to the keeper's house and subletting this to a series of tenants between 1718 and 1739.[63]

Archaeological evidence

The foundations of the keeper's house were found in the south-west corner of the site, formerly the south-west corner of the burial ground. The original building was constructed of post-1666 London-made brick and reused pre-1666 brick. Evidence was also found of rebuilds, dated *c* 1707, 1718 and *c* 1737, as well as possible outbuildings or yard structures (Fig 18). These features were constructed of post-1666 dark red bricks, with a scatter of reused pre-1666 brickwork, and and also incorporated reused stone, including fragments of millstones (<197> and <202>), possible burial monument slabs/covers (<199> and <200>) and gravestones (Figs 45–7). All phases of the property overlay and truncated the burial ground.

3.5   A dynasty of keepers: the Clitherows

It seems likely that the majority of the Clitherow family were buried at the ground during their time as keepers. However, although most of the burial records associated with the family are found in the parish of St Botolph Bishopsgate few mention a specific burial ground. Only two members of the family are recorded as buried at the New Churchyard: Christopher Clitherow, son of Benjamin Clitherow I, and Mary Clitherow, daughter of Benjamin

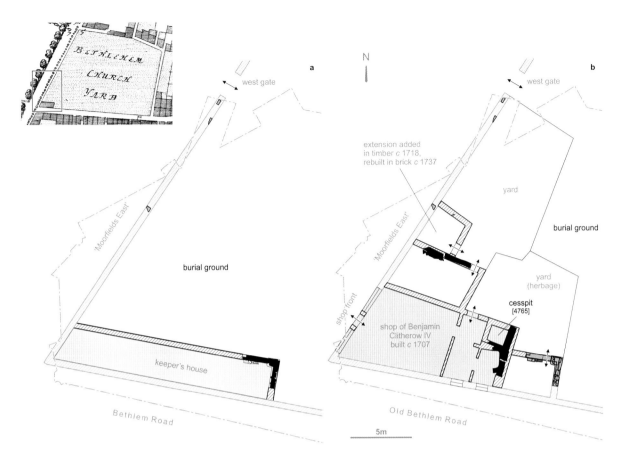

Fig 18 Phased plans showing the development of the keeper's house c 1666–76 to 1761: a – as built in c 1666–76; b – rebuilds/ extensions c 1707 to 1761; (inset) the area on Ogilby and Morgan's 'Map of the City of London', 1676 (Fig 29) (scale 1:300; inset not to scale)

Clitherow III.[64] The last keeper, Benjamin Clitherow IV, died aged 58 of 'consumption' on 24 November 1740 and was buried in St Giles Cripplegate (Fig 19).[65]

The four Clitherow keepers would have received income from the position (above, 3.4; Chapter 14.1), but they could also have continued to trade in their respective professions. Benjamin Clitherow I and II were freemen of the Worshipful Company of Vintners and the Worshipful Company of Drapers, respectively, but their trade is not confirmed.[66] However, both Benjamin Clitherow III and IV were freemen of the Worshipful Company of Drapers and are known to have traded as turners.[67]

Benjamin Clitherow IV converted part of the keeper's house into a shop sometime after 1707.[68] The alley to the south of the ground was, by the late 18th century, famous for its turners' shops and was known as 'Spinning Wheel Alley' (Chapter 13); the name perhaps came from the wheel lathes of the workshops and/or the spinning wheels which they produced.[69] The shops would have worked wood as well as ivory and bone, and stocked a large selection of items, including a 'vast variety of necessary household-stuff'.[70]

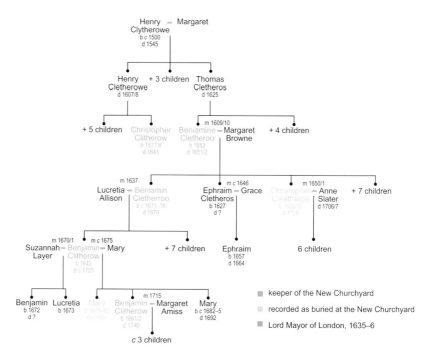

Fig 19 The Clitherow family tree (with original variant spellings)

3.6 Industrial waste and other material disposed of in the burial ground

The sheer volume of worked animal bone and glass waste recovered from the New Churchyard may suggest that the Clitherows in particular were not only burying their own waste in the ground but also offering a waste disposal service for their neighbours. Other material may represent the loss or deliberate discarding of objects by mourners, visitors and attendees of the Whit Sunday sermons.

Waste from the bone and ivory workshops of keepers Benjamin Clitherow III and IV

An extraordinary assemblage of worked animal bone and ivory waste was found among the soils and charnel pits of the burial ground. It can be dated by form to the late 17th to first half of the 18th century and came from the turning workshops of Benjamin Clitherow III and IV.[71] As keepers, both were able to instruct gravediggers to dispose of their waste in the burial ground. The waste represents all stages of production from the subdivision of raw material to the final stages of finishing. It reflects a diverse industry in which bone and ivory were worked on the lathe and with a variety of hand tools, demonstrating real skill in using the raw materials to their best advantage to produce a wide range of products, from needle cases made from elephant ivory to bone telescopes (Fig 20).

HOW TO MAKE A BONE TELESCOPE (Fig 20)

The (unusable) ends of cattle foot bones (metapodials) were sawn off, leaving the hollow shaft;

the shaft was worked with a file and a blade to strip off the surface and create a sub-circular section ready for turning;

the shaft was turned to produce an even cylinder, to add decorative grooves and ribs and to produce threaded ends so the pieces could be joined together;

a circular eyepiece and a lens cap were turned from solid slabs of metapodial shaft wall;

glass lenses were added (probably made by a specialist lens grinder);

result – telescope!

Glasshouse waste

A large quantity of glass was recovered from the burial ground (221 fragments, weighing 6158g). More than half of this consists of glass-working waste (123 fragments, 4144g), most of which comes from soil in two contexts dated at the latest to the early to mid 18th century.[72] The glass is chiefly green or natural green in colour, and includes a wide range of waste from production processes, including pot metal, slag, pulls, drops, gathers and 'knock-offs' (Fig 21).[73]

One of the two glasshouses run in London by Sir Robert Mansell, was in Austin Friars, Broad Street, relatively close by; it was set up to make 'crystal' or clear, good-quality drinking glasses (in soda glass), was staffed by Venetians and operated from 1616 up to the 1650s.[74] The finds from the New Churchyard, however, largely appear to represent a different type of glass manufacture, with only limited evidence for the manufacture of fine table glass. The predominantly green glass represented in the waste would most probably have been used to make bottles and possibly phials, neither of which is usually associated with the Austin Friars glasshouse. There are also fragments from a finished squat beaker and a tankard with *vetro a fili* decoration in *façon de Venise* style, dating between the early/mid 16th and late 17th century (Fig 21).[75] The discovery of part of a waster from a tankard in opaque white glass, and part of a cane with two thin opaque white trails in the waste from site A, as well as a few lumps of clear glass waste from this and the main site, suggests that some fine glass working was also taking place alongside the production of green glass bottles.

One other glasshouse is recorded at Old Bedlam, north of New Broad Street (shown on Fig 24) and to the immediate south of the site, and is first mentioned in 1696. It is possible that the finds from the New Churchyard may represent a clearing-out of accumulated glass waste from this glasshouse, conveniently dumped on the site of the burial ground in the late 17th/early 18th century. The fine glass, however, is somewhat earlier (possibly 1670s), and this may indicate either that production started at Old Bedlam before the first surviving record or that the glass came from a different glasshouse. The only other known candidate would be the glasshouse at Goodmans Yard, Minories, which started in the 1670s, and from which glass-working waste comparable to these finds has been found over a relatively wide area (including Aldgate High Street and Crosswall).[76]

Fig 20 Bone waste from making a telescope: whittled cattle metapodial shaft section <911>; partially lathe-turned shaft section with decorative grooves <1739>; part-finished eyepiece <1706> and lens cap <846> (scale *c* 1:2)

Fig 21 Glass waste <3228> and base fragment from glass tankard <2160> with *vetro a fili* decoration in *façon de Venise* style (scale *c* 1:2)

<3336>

<3337>

<3338>

Fig 22 Three glass phials <3336>–<3338> from the burial ground (scale *c* 1:2)

Finds from the burial ground

As well as the glass waste incorporated in the burial ground deposits, there are fragments from a number of vessels, including at least 40 phials in colourless or natural green glass, of the kind used for medicinal preparations (Fig 22). There are also fragments from wine bottles of various shapes in green glass, including three onion bottles, six onion/mallet bottles and one mallet bottle datable to the late 17th/early 18th century.

A single example of an armorial wine bottle seal (Fig 23) is indicative of ownership at a time when bottles were delivered to a vintner for filling, making it necessary for individuals to personalise their stock of glass containers. In addition to the fine drinking vessels described above, there are also fragments from a possible rummer with short quatrefoil stem in blue glass and two stoppers in colourless glass, one spherical with multiple small tiers and one double-tiered with vertical ribbing. These items were all found mixed in with the soils of the burial ground or scattered within a number of inhumations; they were most probably utilised within the general area of the site over the period that the burial ground was active.

There may be, however, some connection with the Clitherows. As already noted, the keeper Benjamin Clitherow I was a freeman of the Worshipful Company of Vintners (above, 3.5). A trading token, <1206>, in poor condition but identifiable as belonging to Ephraim Clitherow, another son of Benjamin Clitherow I, was discovered residually within the burial ground soil. Ephraim Clitherow was a vintner and the innkeeper of the 'Sun Alehouse', which was located to the north of the site on the corner of Sun Street and Lamb Alley.[77] There were a range of finds, in addition, that may represent domestic rubbish, material dumped by the Clitherows or gravediggers, or that may be casual losses of everyday items, perhaps lost by people visiting graves or attending sermons (Fig 23).

A large number of clay tobacco pipes (445 bowls and 37 stem fragments) were also found mixed in with the soils of the burial ground,[78] while a few pipe fragments were associated with individual interments or found in the fill of charnel pit [4203]. Only 18 examples pre-date *c* 1660; the earliest example dates to the earliest period of tobacco use (*c* 1580–*c* 1610).[79] A total of 186 pipe bowls were made in forms introduced *c* 1700 or later (41.8% of all pipes from the burial ground), with 173 bowls made *c* 1680–*c* 1710 (38.9%). A number of coins were found residually with the burial ground soils, including Nuremberg jettons and English coins of Charles II and William III, as well as Roman coins. Only two coins and one jetton appear to have been deliberately deposited with burials (Chapter 5.3).

Fig 23 A selection of finds from the burial ground: armorial wine bottle seal <2156>; bone toothbrush <1697>; bone brush head <1731>; ivory fish-shaped counter <1850> (scale *c* 1:2)

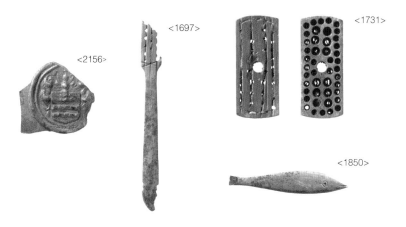

<2156>

<1697>

<1731>

<1850>

3.7 'now full of corps' – the closure of the New Churchyard

The neighbourhood surrounding the ground saw sweeping changes in 1737. While Moorfields remained a public park, Petty France to the south was rebuilt as 'New Broad Street'[80] and Old Broad Street was extended northward across the city wall as 'Broad Street Buildings' (Fig 24). The latter was a street of terraced houses, 'very hand-some … regularly built, leading from Moorfields to Broad street' inhabited by 'people of fortune and distinction'. *Kent's directory* of 1740 lists merchants and a surgeon as residents. The houses of Broad Street Buildings did not encroach into the burial ground but adjoined its north and east walls.[81]

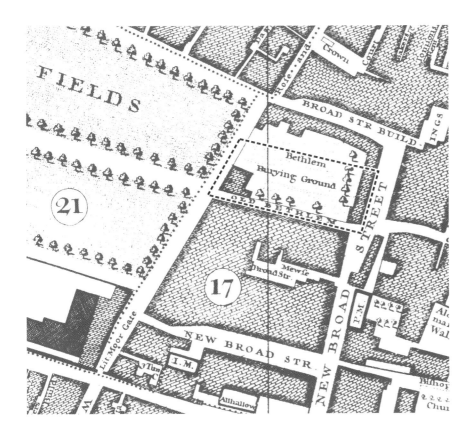

Fig 24 Detail of Rocque's map of London and Westminster, 1746, showing New Broad Street, Broad Street Buildings north of the burial ground and Moorfields to the west (left), with the site superimposed (outlined in red); north is to the top (Margary 1971)

By the late 1730s, the burial ground was densely filled; every new interment would have disturbed earlier burials, but burials continued despite the presence of new neighbours overlooking the ground. The last known burial was Mary Burt who died aged 105 on 9 April 1738.[82] The full details of the unpleasant situation were brought to the attention of the City on 19 February 1738/9 by a petition of the residents of Broad Street Buildings. They not only complained of the 'very great nuisance occasioned by the great numbers of corps brought from all parts and buryed' but also of the 'manner of filling':

> … they are brought are put into a great Hole or Pitt made for that purpose and are left open till the place is filled with coffins which usually contain from sixteen to twenty without any earth between them, and only covered over with a little porous earth, from whence intolerable steams and vapours of a most noxious and pestilential quality are always ascending so that the inhabitants are obliged to shut their doors and windows to keep out the same.[83]

A decision to cease burial was reached on 1 March 1738/9:

> … it appeared to this Court that the said Burying Ground is now full of corps, and that it will be inconvenient, and dangerous to bury any more corps there till those that remain are sufficiently covered and decayed to prevent the noisome steam and stench which proceeds from such a multitude of dead corps being buryed, and not sufficiently covered, which if not prevented may be dangerous and infectious … the said Burying Ground shall be shut up and that there shall be no more corps buryed therein, until the end of seven years from this time …[84]

Notes to Chapter 3

1   Harding 2002, 66

2   LMA, COL/AD/01/020 (V), 245

3   LMA, COL/CA/01/01/ 018 (Rep 16), 476v; COL/AD/01/020 (V), 237; Harding 1989, 119; 2002, 95; LMA, COL/ CA/01/018 (Rep 16), 492; COL/AD/01/020 (V), 245; Stow 1603, i, 165

4   Andrews et al 1997, 17, 42, 60

5   LMA, COL/CA/01/01/ 018 (Rep 16), 491v; COL/AD/01/020 (V), 245

6   LMA, COL/CA/01/01/ 018 (Rep 16), 492; COL/CC/01/01/019 (JORS/19), 180; COL/AD/01/020 (V), 245

7   LMA, P69/BAT1/A/ 001/MS04374/001

8   LMA, P69/BOT2/A/ 015/MS09222, Henry Reynolds buried 4 Apr 1635

9   Harding 2002, 99

10 Bannerman 1912, 93–4

11 Bannerman 1913, 210–13

12 LMA, COL/CA/01/01/ 018 (Rep 16), 492

13 Hill 2010, 50 and n 183

14 De Laune 1681, 258–9; Harward et al 2015, 56–8, 60–8; Stow 1603, i, 167–8; LMA, COL/CA/ 01/01/057 (Rep 53), 186; /065 (Rep 61), 110, 205; /066 (Rep 62), 284v; /067 (Rep 63), 65, 85; /068 (Rep 64), 129v; /069 (Rep 65), 77v; /073 (Rep 69), 84v

15 De Laune 1681, 258–9; LMA, COL/CA/01/01/ 019 (Rep 17), 10v–11

16 LMA, COL/CA/01/01/ 019 (Rep 17), 10v–11; /022 (Rep 20); 65; /023 (Rep 21), 552; /030 (Rep 27), 14v; /031 (Rep 28), 13; /036 (Rep 32), 102, 272v; /037 (Rep 33), 97v; /038 (Rep 34), 106v, 426; /043 (Rep 39), 213; /044 (Rep 40), 203v; /057 (Rep 53), 186

17 Masters 1984, 97, 237; LMA, COL/CHD/CT/ 01/001, 59v, 241v; /002, 50v, 140, 217; /003, 53v, 147v; /004, 50v, 146v, 215v; /005, 55v, 255v; /006, 46v, 152v, 258v; /007, 58v, 145v; /008, 139; /009, 57v, 136v, 214v; /010, 61v, 133v

18 LMA, COL/CA/01/01/ 019 (Rep 17), 10v–11; William Palmer (c 1539– c 1605), vicar of the church of St Lawrence Jewry 1566–70: *Cambridge alumni*

19 Wilson 1926, 91

20 Squire 1621; Browne et al 1843, 527

21 TNA, PROB 11/68/494

22 TNA, PROB 11/71/136

23 The sermon is mentioned in Thomas Powell's *The mystery and misery of lending and borrowing*, dated 1636, cited in Scott 1812, 222

24 LMA, COL/CHD/CT/ 01/004, 146v

25 LMA, COL/CHD/CT/ 01/004, 215v; /005, 55v, 255v; /006, 46v, 152v, 258v; /007, 58v, 145v; /008, 139; /009, 57v, 136v

26 Baddeley 1888, 16, 194

27 Firth and Rait 1911, 265–6; Spraggon 2003

28 LMA, COL/CHD/CT/ 01/009, 214v; /010, 61v, 133v

29 BL, 1.31; 1.34

30 The copper plate map, c 1553–9: Margary 1981

31 Morrissey 2011, 223

32 Harward et al 2015, 56– 7, 60–6

33 Harward et al in prep

34 LMA, COL/CA/01/01/ 018 (Rep 16), 492; Stow 1603, i, 165

35 Norden 1593

36 Shakespeare 1992, *Henry IV Part I*, 1.2

37 Stow 1603, i, 164

38 Ibid, 165

39 Lambert 1921, 81–4

40 LMA, COL/CA/01/01/ 029 (Rep 26/2), 377v, 403v

41 LMA, COL/CA/01/01/ 030 (Rep 27), 14v

42 BL, 1.31

43 LMA, COL/CA/01/01/ 036 (Rep 32), 21v

44 LMA, COL/CA/01/01/ 031 (Rep 28), 71

45 BRH, BCB-05, 198

46 LMA, COL/CA/01/01/ 033 (Rep 30), 88; CLA/006/AD/10/022, 142–8; /PL/01/013, 2, 26, 42

47 Harding 1989, 117

48 LMA, q8020108; q8019625

49 BL, 1.31; 1.34

50 LMA, COL/CA/01/01/ 103 (Rep 99), 57; COL/CC/CLC/01/076 (J 84), 75, 83–v, 106–7, 115, 125v–6, 174, 178

51 Strype 1720, i(2), 96; Faithorne and Newcourt 1658

52 Norden 1593; Faithorne and Newcourt 1658

53 LMA, COL/CCS/PL/ 02/149; /142

54 LMA, SC/GL/STP/ 006/004/016

55 Brayley 1828, 9

56 Norden 1593; BL, 1.31; Faithorne and Newcourt 1658; Ogilby and Morgan 1676

57 LMA, COL/CA/01/01/ 054 (Rep 50), 168v

58 LMA, COL/CA/01/01/ 023 (Rep 21), 228; /051 (Rep 47), 381; /054 (Rep 50), 168v; /065 (Rep 61), 61; /114 (Rep 110), 102v–3; /149 (Rep 145), 43–4, 48

59 Cal S P Dom 1638, vol 409, undated 1638, pp 217–18; 1639, vol 427, 1–31 Aug 1639, pp 466– 7

60 LMA, SC/GL/STP/006/ 004/016; Faithorne and Newcourt 1658

61 LMA, COL/CC/CLC/ 01/002 (J 10), 77v and 99v–100; COL/CA/01/01/112 (Rep 108), 654–6

62 LMA, COL/CA/01/01/ 149 (Rep 145), 74–6; CLC/525/MS11316/001 –120

63 LMA, COL/CA/01/01/ 147 (Rep 143), 347–8; COL/CC/CLC/01/023 (J 31), 25v–6v, 37v–8; CLC/525/MS11316/001, 18–19; /066, 17; /078, 17; /099, 20; /120, 14– 15; COL/CA/01/01/147 (Rep 143), 359–60

64 LMA, P69/BOT4/A/ 002/MS04516/002, 147; /001/MS04516/001, 128

65 LMA, P69/GIS/A/002/ MS06419/017

66 Webb 2006, 305; Dale 1931, 225–9; Boyd 1934, 41

67 Boyd 1934, 41; Webb 2014, 27, 53; ROLLCO; LMA, COL/CHD/FR/ 02/0641-0-648; Four shillings in the pound aid assessment of 1693– 4, taxation district Bishopsgate Ward (Without), the first division, Moorfields to the right hand in Keene et al 1992; Flying Post, 11–14 July 1702, 2 col B

68 LMA, COL/CC/CLC/ 01/002 (J 10), 77v and 99v–100; /003 (J 11), 197–v

69 Smith 1829, 221; Morning Chron, 19 Nov 1806, 4 col C

70 Waller 1747, 211

71 Cubitt et al in prep a

72 [3010]: 57 fragments, 2976g, dated c 1700–60; [1521]: 39 fragments, 805g, dated c 1730– c 1800

73 Brain and Pearce in prep

74 Willmott 2005, 95, 107

75 Willmott 2002, 10.3, 3.3 and 9.2

76 C Brain (Ass Hist Glass), pers comm; Buckley 1915, 24; Powell 2014, 91

77 LMA, P69/BOT4/A/ 001/MS04515/001; /003; Webb 2006, 44, 149, 253; LHT, Bishopsgate Ward, first precinct west

78 All from OA105A, OA105F and OA106

79 [3010] (phase 2, OA106): AO type 3 pipe bowl; 293 bowls, eight stems

80 Wheatley and Cunningham 1891, 277

81 MOL, Social Hist Collect, obj no. 7192; Dodsley and Dodsley 1761, 33; LMA, COL/ CC/CLC/01/046 (J 54), 129v–130; GL, Kent's 1740; Rocque 1746; LMA, COL/CC/CLC/ 01/046 (J 54), 213–17v

82 Common Sense, 15 Apr 1738, 2 col B

83 LMA COL/CA/01/01/ 147 (Rep 143), 158–9, 167–8

84 LMA COL/CA/01/01/ 147 (Rep 143), 182–3

CHAPTER 4

FUNERARY CHOICES, COSTS AND CONNECTIONS

4.1 Fees and charges

The New Churchyard had been established in 1569 to be 'free for the whole Citie to burye in without payinge anything'; the only permissible charge was for grave digging which was set at 6d per burial.[1] Nevertheless, the deceased's parish of origin normally took a fee for his or her burial there, and the family would also have paid for a minister's attendance and any funeral costs such as bearers, bells, or hearsecloth.[2] The minister's fees are mostly not known, but at St Mary Colechurch he took only 1s for accompanying a corpse to the ground compared with 4s for burial in the church.[3]

Some parishes noted fees in their burial registers, either by acknowledging payment (eg 'all duties paid here') or recording the amount paid.[4] Parish fees for the ground often reflected the status of the deceased or those responsible for their burial. While fees for the wealthy were roughly equivalent to parish burial, some parishes offered reduced fees for the poor or bore the expense of burying the very poorest themselves (as they were required to do). Between 1600 and 1614, All Hallows Honey Lane sent 19 parishioners to the New Churchyard: ten were charged 3s for an adult and 20d for a child, compared with 6s 4d for burial in the parish churchyard. In the case of four burials, which represented the poorest of the parish, there was no payment. Among the latter was Edmond Harrice, son of William Harrice, who was buried on 9 November 1611. William Harrice had been able to afford the 20d to bury his son Joseph at the ground on 25 October 1606 but appears to have been too poor to afford the fees for his son Edmund five years later. The parish clerk noted regretfully against the burial 'he is a poore man & ye duties wch is 20d is loste'. The remaining five burials represented wealthier parishioners, including two members of the respectable Norrington family (below, 4.4, 'Burial location'), who were each charged either 5s or 6s for burial at the ground.[5]

Between 1620 and 1651, All Hallows Bread Street sent 33 parishioners to the New Churchyard: seven were charged between 8d and 2s, compared with the 4s the parish charged for their cheapest parish burial, and 23 appear to have been too poor to pay fees. One unnamed man was buried on 28 May 1645: 'a parish man in the new churchyard but [paid] nothing he was soe poore'. The remaining three burials were all plague victims recorded as 'not paid' (Chapter 8.2, 'Documentary evidence').[6]

The burial of the poor at the New Churchyard at the cost of the parish appears to have been a long-standing practice. When John Price was 'killed in affray' in St James Garlickhithe on 8 November 1672 he was 'buried in Bethlehem Churchyard at a parish charge'.[7] William Barwick from St Michael Paternoster (Royal) was buried without fees on 5 March 1696/7, when the usual fee for burial in the parish churchyard was 6s 4d.[8]

The keeper of the New Churchyard appears to have begun charging fees by the beginning of the 18th century, or at least increasing the charge for grave digging. In February 1702/3 the City intervened on behalf of London's poor and ordered that 'all Persons dying under the care of the President and Governors of the Corporation for the Poor of this City' should be buried at New Churchyard 'upon the payment of two shillings and no more for each person so interred for breaking up the ground'. The City's insistence that paupers should continue to be buried at a low rate was not well received by the keepers and they responded by overcharging or denying service to the poor. In 1704, the Court of Aldermen sternly reminded Benjamin Clitherow III that the poor should be buried 'gratis', including 'so many of the children or vagrants belonging to the workhouse in Bishopsgate Street as shall hereafter happen to dye in the said workhouse'. Similarly, following complaints in 1710 that the keeper had 'sometimes refused to permit such persons [paupers] to be there buryed, unless he be paid more than the said two shillings', the court ordered that Benjamin Clitherow IV was not to 'take or demand any greater fee … as he will answer for so doing at his peril'. Nevertheless, he was again accused of 'irregular practices' in 1720/1 and was instructed that the charge for grave digging for 'poor persons' should be limited to 'twelve pence and no more for each'.[9] The enforcing of price restrictions for pauper burials in February 1702/3 appears to have prompted several parishes to begin sending significant numbers of paupers to the ground. St Bartholomew the Great, for example, rarely used the ground before 1703 but registered 71 'Bedlam/Bethlem' burials between June 1703 and January 1710/11. Accompanying notes suggest that these burials were perhaps exclusively parish children (foundlings) and that all were buried at the expense of the parish.[10]

Interestingly, some parishes took steps to limit the number of their parishioners choosing the New Churchyard in order to protect parish profits. The majority of the parish churchyards of St Giles Cripplegate were closed between 1667 and 1674[11] so that they could recover from the plague. During this period, burials for the poor could be free or charged at a reduced fee at the discretion of the churchwardens.[12] In this same period, New Churchyard burials increased steadily before rising dramatically: from 32 in 1667, to 154 in

1673 and 145 in 1674 (Fig 25).[13] This situation represented a considerable financial loss to the parish and the vestry took action. On 3 February 1674/5 they ordered that no certificates for burial 'at Mr. Tindall's ground or at Bethlem' were to be issued without payment of 6s 6d.[14] Although it is unclear how much the parish charged for the New Churchyard prior to this, it was probably in line with the parish's cheapest parish burial location, which in 1664 was the upper churchyard at 2s 6d. Burial in the church was also raised in 1674 to 25s and the authority to charge reduced fees was greatly restricted in 1675.[15] These measures, together with the reopening of the parish churchyards, had an immediate effect: New Churchyard burials fell to just 23 in 1675 and by 1691, the year the measure appears to have been rescinded, there were only 18 burials (Fig 25).[16]

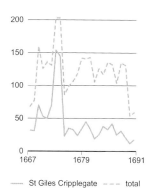

Fig 25 Number of burials recorded as sent from St Giles Cripplegate to the New Churchyard compared with total burials recorded at the New Churchyard, 1667 to 1691 (Old Style)

4.2 Dissenters at the ground

The New Churchyard was from the outset attractive to those not part of the Established Church because its non-parochial status meant burial did not have to conform to the Book of Common Prayer. Moreover, there is no record that the New Churchyard was ever consecrated by Church of England officials. The use of the New Churchyard by irregular or dissenting congregations and individuals continued into the 17th century despite an attempt in 1590 by the ecclesiastical Court of High Commission to curb the ground's use by such groups.[17] However, by the late 17th century, religious belief and practice in London was diversifying and, as nonconformity increased, a measure of tolerance was granted. From the mid 17th century Nonconformists were increasingly drawn away from the New Churchyard to new burial grounds and churchyards, notably Bunhill Fields which became the burial ground of choice for Dissenters after it opened in 1665. Religious minorities, such as Quakers, French Huguenots and Jews, had established their own London burial grounds by the late 17th century.[18] By the 1680s and 1690s the City parish of St Dionis Backchurch was recording burials in its own church and yard and also at 'Bethlem', 'the Quakers' ground', the 'Swedes church', the 'Jewes burial place' and 'Tindalls ground by Bunhill fields'.[19]

Some Nonconformist funerals at the ground are recorded in historical sources. Perhaps the earliest was the funeral of James Lawson, the radical Scottish minister, who was buried at the ground on 13 October 1584. His large funeral procession was headed by pastors of the Reformed faith, including 12 Scottish, eight English and three French. Behind them walked 500 people; amongst them were 'gentlemen, honest burgess[es], famous and godlie matrons' and 'godly brethren, ministers and citicens'. The ground's location outside parochial limits allowed the Reformed order of burial service to be used.[20]

Samuel Eaton, the semi-separatist and Baptist pioneer, was buried 'in the new Church yard neere Bethelem' by a gathering of over 200 Brownists and Anabaptists in August 1639. A button-maker from St Giles Cripplegate, he was marked by the authorities as a 'Schismattical and dangerous fellowe' and he died in Newgate prison.[21] If a contemporary (Anglican) account of Eaton's burial is to be believed, the New Churchyard had by 1639 become 'a comon receptacle for schismatique sectaries, sometimes excommunicate persons to bury yr dead in what forme or fashion they will.' Eaton's burial is described as a funeral without services or any ecclesiastical paraphernalia, much in keeping with the traditional separatist view that such features had no scriptural foundation:

> … they, like so many Bedlams cast the corpse in; & with their feet, in stead of spades cast & thrust in the mould till the grave was allmost full: then they paid the grave maker for his paines, who told them he must fetch a minister, but they said, he might spare his labour.[22]

John Biddle, the repeatedly imprisoned theologian and 'father of English Unitarianism', and Anthony Palmer, the Congregationalist, were buried at the New Churchyard in 1662 and 1679, respectively.[23]

The burial of Henry Jessey, Nonconformist minister and founding member of the Puritan religious sect, the Jacobites, was recorded (without a location) in the parish of St Stephen Coleman Street, on 8 September 1663. His funeral on 7 September at Woodmongers' hall in Duke's Place, London, was attended by some 4000 or 5000 people.[24] A critical Anglican account of his burial noted that he was 'laid to sleep with his fathers, in a hole made in the yard joining Old Bethlam, Moorfields, in the suburbs of London [New Churchyard], attended with a strange medley of fanatics, mostly Anabaptists, that met upon the very point of time, all at the same instant, to do honour to their departed brother'.[25] Jessey left instructions that his burial was to be without ceremony: 'Nor any mourning worn for me, or given, or complemental in any pompous way.'[26]

Ann Overton, wife of Major General Robert Overton and a devoted follower of Jessey, may have attended the funeral. She herself was buried in the New Churchyard in 1665 (below, 4.4). Robert Overton was a prominent English soldier and scholar whose strong republican views saw him imprisoned a number of times during the Protectorate (1653–60) and after, following the Restoration of Charles II.

Alexander Delamaine and his wife Anne were buried in their own vault at the New Churchyard, on 23 December 1685 and on 26 December 1688, respectively (below, 4.4; Chapter 5.5).[27] Alexander Delamaine was a wealthy tobacconist and the son of Richard Delamaine, maths tutor to Charles I; Alexander devoted himself to Muggletonianism in 1671.[28] An Alexander Delemaine who was buried at the New Churchyard on 26 March 1684 was probably his son.[29]

Lodowicke Muggleton, the religious thinker and self-proclaimed prophet who gave his name to Muggletonianism, died on 14 March 1697/8, aged 88 (Fig 26). His body lay in state at Loriners' hall before being buried 'without noise, or without tumult' on 17 March in a tomb at the New Churchyard near fellow 'prophet' John Reeve, who had been buried there in 1658. Muggleton's funeral was attended, according to his wishes, by a group of 248 friends and followers and was witnessed by thousands of spectators.[30]

Fig 26 Lodowicke Muggleton, died 14 March 1697/8 and buried in the New Churchyard: (above) shown in a portrait by or after William Wood, painted *c* 1674 and (below) his death mask, by an unknown artist
(National Portrait Gallery, 4939)

4.3 Levellers at the ground

The New Churchyard had a strong association with the Leveller political movement, which perhaps began with the burial of Robert Lockyer, the Baptist and Leveller martyr. Lockyer was a young private trooper in Oliver Cromwell's New Model Army who led a revolt over unpaid wages. On 27 April 1649 he was executed by firing squad at St Paul's churchyard and his funeral proved to be a dramatic reminder of the strength of the Leveller organisation in London.[31] He was buried in the New Churchyard with 'funeral pomp, answerable to his worth' on Sunday 29 April 1649. Starting from Smithfield in the afternoon, his funeral procession wound slowly through the heart of the city and then back through Moorfields.

… six trumpeters went foremost, giving many a mournfull Blast: After them marched many hundreds of Troopers, and other Souldiers on Foot, all with mourning Ribbons, and on each a green Ribbon tyed next the heart [to show their Leveller allegiance]. Next followed Lockiers own Charging horse, all in Black, being led by two Gentle-men in mourning suites and cloaks. In the same habit came six moe, and after them the corpse with a naked Sword upon the herse, carried by six Souldiers in mourning. The rear was brought up with Lockier's kindred, and many hundreds of Citizens and others with mourning ribbons, to let Cromwell and Fairfax both know that Blood requires Blood, and that this is not the way to crush the Free people of this nation.[32]

John Lilburne, the much-imprisoned Leveller leader 'Freeborn John', died at Eltham on 29 August 1657. His corpse was placed in a plain coffin 'without any Pall or other Covering' and brought to the Bull and Mouth inn, a venue for Quaker meetings off St Martin's-le-Grand. As a Quaker he did not follow the practices of the Church of England and could not be buried in a parochial ground. On 31 August his body was carried 'in Contradiction to ancient Custom, with the Head foremost, to the New Church-Yard at Bethelem, where it was interred, without Christian Burial, or any Ceremony, but the Signs of the Brethren'. His funeral was attended by c 4000 London citizens but was not without trouble; scuffles took place both before and during his funeral over whether a velvet pall should be put over his coffin.

Lilburne himself was notoriously quarrelsome and a contemporary epigrammatic epitaph suggested that alone in the grave he would find quarrel with himself:

> Is John departed, and is Lilburne gone?
> Farewell to both, to Lilburne and to John.
> Yet, being dead, take this advice from me,
> Let them not both in one grave buried be:
> But lay John here, lay Lilburne thereabout,
> For, if they both should ever meet, they should fall out.[33]

Fig 27 Engraving of William Walwyn (buried in the New Churchyard 16 January 1680/1) by Robert White, late 17th century
(National Portrait Gallery, D30093)

Further burials associated with the Levellers followed in the late 17th century. William Walwyn, another founding Leveller leader, was buried at 'Bethlem' on 16 January 1680/1 (Fig 27).[34] Born in 1600, Walwyn was a London silk merchant, a member of the Merchant Adventurers' Company, a pamphleteer and activist. On 17 April 1627 he married Ann, daughter of William Gundell, a chandler, in the parish of St James Garlickhithe. The couple had some 20 children between 1628/9 and 1650 (although most died in childhood).[35] In 1643 the Walwyns moved to Moorfields, where he retreated from politics and became a medical practitioner, maintaining his family 'in a middle and moderate but contentful condition'.[36] He died wealthy with an estate worth £5000. He outlived his wife and all but two of his children, Ann Halford and Sarah Jenkes.[37] His wife, Ann, was buried at 'Bethlem' on 1 July 1676; Ann Halford and Sarah Jenkes were buried in a vault at the ground alongside several of William's grandchildren and in-laws (Chapter 5.6).[38]

Dorothy Tulidah, wife of Major Alexander Tulidah, a Leveller sympathiser, was buried at the New Churchyard on 15 August 1678.[39] Alexander Tulidah was named as a witness in the will of William Walwyn's son-in-law, Richard Halford.[40]

4.4 Wills and funerals

There are 26 testators currently known to have either requested burial at the New Churchyard or to have been buried there. Of these, 13 left instructions for their burial and/or funeral beyond simply requesting to be buried 'decently' or in the 'Christian' manner.

Funeral directions through time

The English Reformation challenged the rationale for church burial and many aspects of medieval funeral custom. The reigns of Henry VIII (1509–47) and Edward VI (1547–53) brought Protestant reforms which would affect burial practice, including regulating those aspects of the traditional funeral which were found to be 'superstitious'.[41]

In her will, proved 18 January 1582/3, Mary Rowe, the wife of Sir Thomas Rowe, made funeral requests in keeping with pre-Reformation tradition. She asked that 'some godly learned man make a sermon at my burial for the instruction of those who shall be present', that her funeral be attended by the poor, that friends and family be given rings and that black clothing, including mourning gowns and coats, be provided to family, friends and servants.[42]

The funeral directions within the will of Thomas Randall, mercer and first keeper of the New Churchyard, proved 16 August 1585, are a mix of old and new. In keeping with pre-Reformation traditions he left instructions for an extensive funeral procession and a sermon to be preached at his burial. The procession was to be formed of his friends and neighbours plus the 'whole Company of the Lyvery of the mercers and the parishioners of the parish where I dwell'. However, he also instructed that mourners were not to wear black but were to dress in 'such other seemly apparel as they shall think best'.[43] This reflected the beliefs of many Protestants who rejected the wearing of black to denote mourning on the grounds that grief for the dead showed a lack of faith in the Resurrection. His last funeral request, that there was to be no ringing of bells except for one knell, reflects the restrictions placed on funeral services by the first Book of Common Prayer of 1549.[44]

Robert Greene, the English dramatist and critic of Shakespeare, died on 3 September 1592. His body, according to his wishes, was crowned with a garland of bays, and buried on the following day in the New Churchyard.

An image of him writing in his funeral shroud was published in 1598 (Fig 28).

William Walwyn left instructions in his will, proved 14 January 1680/1, that he was to be buried 'according to the discretion of my executors provided that no mourning be worne for me'.[45]

In 1688 Anne Delamaine requested that she be buried 'in Bethlehem burying place in Moorfields from Larrimers [Loriners'] Hall and rings worth tenn shillings a peece I order to bee given at my funerall to what persons my executors hereafter named shall thinke fit'.[46] The will of Anne Delamaine is also notable in that she requested to be 'decently buried in linen'[47] at a time when this would have been unlawful. The Burial in Woollen Acts of 1666–80 were designed to bolster the English wool industry by the exclusion of imported foreign textiles. Items associated with burial – such as clothing, sheets, shrouds, as well as coffin linings and upholstery – had to be made with English wool. Proof of burial in wool had to be provided with an affidavit and non-compliance resulted in a fine of £5. The only exceptions to this were plague victims and the destitute.[48] It is not known how long these statutes were fully enforced but between 1682 and 1690 the parish of St Nicholas Abbey Cole recorded numerous burials 'in woollin' at 'Bethlem Churchyard', including that of Alexander Delamaine on 26 March 1684,[49] and the parish of St Michael Queenhithe recorded 'affid [avit] made' beside 'Bethlehem' burials between 1687 and 1706.[50]

Fig 28 Woodcut of Robert Greene (buried in the New Churchyard 4 September 1592) 'suted in deaths livery', from John Dickenson's *Greene in conceipt* (1598)
(The British Library Board, 2326.g.6.(2.)

Funeral costs

In the early modern period funeral charges could include a wide variety of items and services depending on the wealth, taste or religious preference of the individual or family – for example, the coffin; a vault; the ringing of bells; bearers; a hearse; a preacher to perform a sermon; the provision of mourning clothes and rings.

Mary Rowe's executors were under strict instructions not to spend more than £73 6s 8d on her funeral, but this was a very significant sum for the time.[51] The prestigious funeral of Francis Jenkes was even more expensive, at £87 19s (Chapter 5.6).

In contrast, other funerals were deliberately modest. The will of Mary Randall, wife of Thomas and joint first keeper of the New Churchyard, proved 28 February 1599/1600, left instructions that her funeral costs should not exceed £20.[52] Mary Rowe and Thomas Randall both left 10s for a preacher to perform sermons at their funerals, while Lawrence Anthony, haberdasher of St Mildred Poultry, left 5s as payment for a preacher in 1627.[53]

In her will, proved 21 February 1708/9, Sarah Williams (née Jenkes) requested to be 'privately buryed with very moderate expense', but that 57 mourning rings, valued at 15s each, should be given in remembrance of her (Chapter 5.6).[54] The will of Jacob Hubbard, butcher of St Botolph Bishopsgate, proved 22 October 1719, noted that his burial should be made with 'as little charge as may be as my executors shall order'.[55]

Burial location

It is clear that familial ties influenced the choice of burial in the New Churchyard. Once a family precedent had been established the desire to be buried near kin clearly operated, perhaps regardless of whether later members of the family shared the original motives behind the choice of location. Of those burial register entries compiled as part of the Bedlam Register project (Chapters 1.2, 6.1), 19 included notes indicating that the burial had been 'together' or 'with' a parent, sibling, child or spouse. Many family groups are discernible in the burial registers; for example, at least four members of the respectable Norrington family of All Hallows Honey Lane were buried at the New Churchyard between 1587 and 1615.[56] These familial ties were seen archaeologically in mother and child burials, and in family vaults, notably the eight individuals identified from coffin plates in the vault, A[556], belonging to an extended family group (Walwyn/Jenkes/Halford/Farrington/Williams) (Chapter 5.5, 5.6).

Six testators buried at the ground either did not mention their choice of burial location in their wills or left it to the discretion of their executors,[57] but eight requested burial near or with a predeceased friend or relative.[58] While Sir Thomas Rowe chose to be buried in Hackney in 1570, his wife, daughter and son-in-law all chose to be buried in the burial ground he founded.[59] As a devotee of Henry Jessey, Ann Overton requested to be 'as neare ye olde prophet Mr Jesse, as could be', thus making her burial into a public statement of loyalty through proximity.[60] Her husband, Major General Robert Overton, was buried in Seaton, Rutland, but had requested in his will, proved 29 January 1678/9, to be buried at the New Churchyard 'neare the body of my dearest deceased wife'.[61] 'Monsieur Norrington', an 'ancient and grave citizen' from All Hallows Honey Lane, is known to have been buried near Mary Rowe, although it is not known if this was by request.[62]

Only two testators requested a location which can now be recognised. Thomas Randall wished his grave be 'made right afore the pulpitt there thirtie foote [c 9m] distant from the sayde pulpit'. Peter Simmonds also instructed that his vault should be 'righte before the pullpitt'.[63] The pulpit was the only ecclesiastical feature of the ground and therefore, while extant, was probably considered the most prestigious place to be buried (Chapter 3.2). Its central location made it the physical as well as spiritual focal point of the ground. Thus, a burial located near the pulpit gave visual expression to the deceased's social status and position within the community.

Notes to Chapter 4

1 LMA, COL/CA/01/01/018 (Rep 16), 492

2 Harding 2002, 97; Bannerman 1914, 264–8

3 Harding 2002, 97

4 LMA, P69/KAT2/A/001/MS07889/001, 1668–9

5 Harding 2002, 97; Bannerman 1914, 264–8

6 LMA, P69/ALH2/A/002/MS05032

7 LMA, P69/JS2/A/002/MS09140

8 Harding 2002, 97; LMA, P69/MIC5/A/003/MS05144

9 LMA, COL/CA/01/01/111 (Rep 107), 135; /118 (Rep 114), 252–3; /129 (Rep 125), 119, 135, 197

10 LMA, P69/BAT3/A/010/MS06780 (parish not checked by Bedlam Register)

11 Old Style years

12 Baddeley 1888, 192–3

13 Bedlam Register (Old Style years); Chapter 1.2, n 4

14 LMA, P69/GIS/B/001/MS06048/001, 143

15 Baddeley 1888, 193, 199; Harding 2002, 61

16 Bedlam Register (Old Style years); Chapter 1.2, n 4; LMA, P69/ GIS/B/001/MS06048/001, 224

17 Harding 2002, 98

18 Achinstein 2003, 43–4

19 Harding 2002, 100

20 Collinson 1983, 245

21 Burrage 1912, 329–30

22 *Cal S P Dom 1639*, vol 427, 1–31 Aug 1639, pp 466–7

23 *EB*; Neal 1837, 649; Pike 1770, 64

24 LMA, P69/STE1/A/002/MS04449/002; Gordon 1892, 371, portrait of Henry Jessey by an unknown artist; NPG, D26853

25 Ivimey 1814, 426

26 Achinstein 2003, 31

27 TNA, PROB 11/381/636; LMA, P69/NIC2/A/002/MS05686; TNA, PROB 11/393/401; LMA, P69/GIS/A/002/MS06419/011

28 Gordon 1888, 301; Lamont 2004

29 LMA, P69/NIC2/A/002/MS05686

30 Underwood 1999, 10–11, 28, 77; Williamson 1919, 45–6

31 Gentles 2004

32 *Mercurius Pragmaticus*, 24 Apr–1 May 1649, 7 col A

33 Salmon 1735, 249; Rushworth 1680, 468; Peacock 1851, 134; Sharp 2006; Smith 1867, 110–23

34 LMA, P69/GIS/A/002/MS06419/010; TNA, PROB 11/365/71

35 LMA, P69/JS2/A/003/MS09139: first child, William Walwyn, baptised 27 Feb 1628/9; LMA, P91/LEN/A/001/MS07493: last child, Margaret Walwyn, baptised 23 Aug 1650

36 Firth 1899, 284–5; Taft 2008

37 LMA, COL/CCS/SO/01/04/016

38 LMA, P69/GIS/A/002/MS06419/008: the entry records 'Ann Wallwin' as the daughter of William. This must be an error. His wife, Ann, was already deceased at the time of his death in 1680 and his daughter, Ann Halford (née Walwyn), died in 1712 (Chapter 5.6).

39 LMA, P69/GIS/A/002/MS06419/008

40 TNA, PROB 11/369/460

41 Miles and White 2008, 39

42 TNA, PROB 11/65/13

43 TNA, PROB 11/68/494

44 Miles and White 2008, 39

45 TNA, PROB 11/365/71

46 TNA, PROB 11/393/401

47 Ibid

48 Raithby 1819, 598, 885–6 and 940

49 LMA, P69/NIC2/A/002/MS05686

50 LMA, P69/MIC6/A/001/MS09147

51 TNA, PROB 11/65/13

52 TNA, PROB 11/95/133

53 TNA, PROB 11/65/13; 11/68/494; 11/152/739

54 TNA, PROB 11/506/349

55 TNA, PROB 11/570/451

56 Bannerman 1914, 262, 266–8; LMA, P69/ALH3/A/001/MS05022, 40–53; Harding 2002, 98

57 TNA, PROB 11/369/460; 11/365/71; 11/423/122; 11/447/393; 11/506/349; 11/541/129

58 TNA, PROB 11/95/24; 11/109/212; 11/260/370; 11/301/450; 11/359/132; 11/365/319; 11/393/401; LMA, MS 9052/5/50

59 TNA, PROB 11/52/418; 11/65/13; Stow 1603, i, 165

60 Achinstein 2003, 44

61 West 1997; TNA, PROB 11/359/132

62 Bannerman 1914, 292

63 TNA, PROB 11/68/494; 11/71/136

CHAPTER 5

BURIAL PRACTICE

5.1 Layout and operation of the burial ground over time

The New Churchyard covered an area c 2420m² (0.60 acre) when opened in 1569 and c 3350m² (0.83 acre) after it was extended in c 1607. Excavated burials (c 3700) covered an area of c 500m², which represents c 15% of the total burial ground post-1607 (Fig 29). Excavation showed that, by the time the ground closed, burials were on average c 1.4m thick but up to 2m thick in places; each cubic metre of the ground was filled by 6–8 individuals (Fig 30). If this burial density is typical of the entire New Churchyard, then it can be estimated that at least 25,000 burials took place between 1569 and 1739.

Phasing the excavated burials

The sequence of burials at the New Churchyard could be determined stratigraphically. However, close phasing was impossible due to the unusually high density of burials and frequency of intercutting graves. Such conditions meant that the soils of the burial horizon were heavily reworked and redeposited over time. Close relative dating of individual burials was therefore extremely rare (below, 5.3), since grave fills were almost always contaminated and grave cuts were largely undefinable.

Nonetheless, two phases of use could be broadly defined. Phase 1 (OA105), use of the burial ground prior to c 1670, was characterised by burials almost always set parallel with the south boundary wall, on a roughly east–west alignment (Figs 30, 31). The south wall was likely the prime determinant of grave alignment during this period not only because it was parallel with traditional east–west burial alignment but because it also included the ground's main gate, and was thus the 'façade' of the burial ground.

Phase 1 includes all burials within the original extent of the burial ground (OA105A), at least one burial structure (below, 5.5) and the burial ground's only distinct 'event boundary' – the infilling of the deep ditch in c 1607 (above, 3.3). It can be safely assumed that any burials in the area of the deep ditch or to its west (OA105C) cannot pre-date the infilling of the ditch, the associated land reclamation or the extension of the west boundary which followed. Phase 1 also includes two mass or common burial 'events': mass burial pit [7482]/[8173] (in OA105A) and a group of burial pits (distinguished as OA105E) (Fig 31; below; Chapter 8.2). Burials either stratigraphically

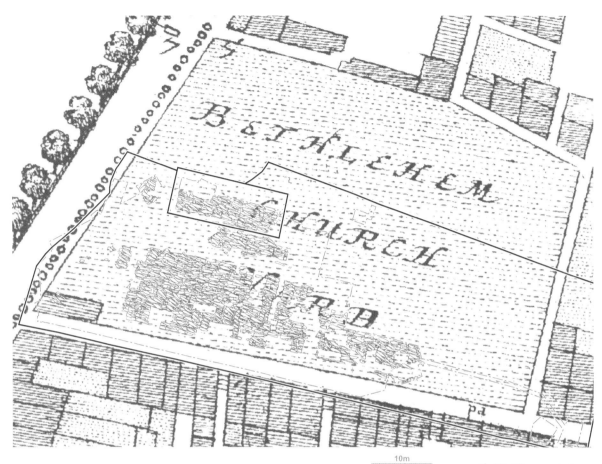

Fig 29 All excavated single burials (phases 1 and 2) overlain on Ogilby and Morgan's 'Map of the City of London', 1676, which shows the New Churchyard, labelled 'Bethlehem Church Yard', and the keeper's house in its south-west corner, with the site and areas of archaeological investigation superimposed (outlined in red and grey; see Figs 2, 67 a); note the alley still running along the south side of the burial ground, but the Bedlam Hospital was relocated in 1676; north is to the top (Margary 1976) (scale 1:600)

earlier (OA105B and OA105D) or stratigraphically later (OA105F) than the pits were distinguished at analysis.

Approximately 60% of phase 1 burials were coffined, with the majority of uncoffined burials occurring at the base of the archaeological sequence (eg Fig 32). No textile survived with uncoffined burials, but burial shrouds were occasionally indicated by the presence of copper-alloy pins or of green staining on bone suggesting pins.

Within the various grave cuts and soils identified as phase 1 were small-sized pottery sherds and a large quantity of building material, with a few of these deposits also containing some glass and clay tobacco pipes. The dating framework this material provided implies most phase 1 interments are dated 1569–c 1670. Residual material includes floor tiles dating from the 13th/14th to the 16th century, types used extensively in London's monastic buildings and parish churches, which is probably the origin of the tiles dumped in phase 1.

Fig 30 Three-dimensional view of burials in the central, main areas of excavation, with phase 1 burials shown in dark pink and phase 2 in blue, looking north-east (scale 1:200)

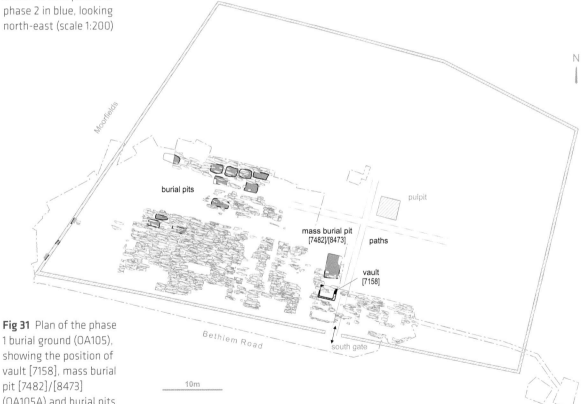

burial pits

pulpit

mass burial pit [7482]/[8473]

paths

vault [7158]

Moorfields

Bethlem Road

south gate

N

Fig 31 Plan of the phase 1 burial ground (OA105), showing the position of vault [7158], mass burial pit [7482]/[8473] (OA105A) and burial pits (OA105E), with conjectured locations of the burial ground gate, pulpit and footpaths (scale 1:600)

10m

Phase 2 (OA106) includes burials dated *c* 1670 to 1739, of which approximately 78% were coffined. This phase was characterised by a marked change in burial alignment, which occurred during the *c* 1670s (Fig 33). This change was almost certainly prompted by the rebuilding of the west boundary wall and the relocation of the main gate to the west (Chapter 3.3; Fig 17), which occurred sometime between 1666 and 1676.

These features became the new 'façade' of the burial ground and thus replaced the south wall as the prime determinant of grave alignment. Although many burials located close to the south boundary wall continued to reflect its alignment, phase 2 burials were predominantly aligned north-west to south-east and set at right angles to the west wall (Figs 17, 33). It seems that most exceptions to this alignment occurred in order to make the best use of all the available space: for example, smaller child burials which could be positioned where convenient between adult burials.

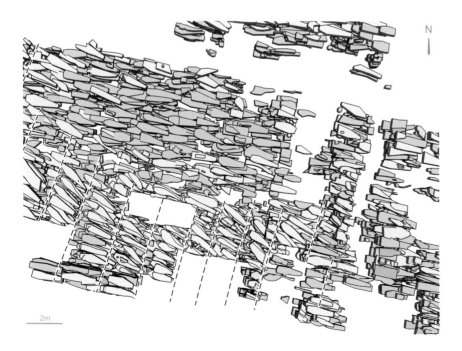

2m

Fig 33 Two-dimensional detail of the burials in the central, main areas of excavation, with phase 1 burials (dark pink) and phase 2 (blue) highlighted to show the shift in burial alignment after *c* 1670, with the possible row system indicated for the latest, 18th-century, phase 2 burials orientated north-west to south-east (scale 1:200)

Phase 2 burials included 72% of decorated coffins (those with studs and/or breastplates) recovered from the site, and perhaps all the remaining burial structures (below, 5.5). This reflects the proliferation of coffin decoration and rise in popularity of burial monuments during the late 17th to mid 18th centuries. This phase also included seven coffins with biographic lid motifs dated 1674 to 1721 (below, 5.2).

Within the redeposited, disturbed and imported soils that characterise phase 2, the level of artefact contamination was high; much of the pottery (1471 SC, 1263 ENV, 47.6kg), clay tobacco pipe, building material and glass recovered was intrusive from later periods, together with some residual, medieval, material. Nevertheless, overall, the chronologies applied to the majority of the artefact types found in phase 2 give a consistent date range of the third quarter of the 17th century to the mid 18th century. Residual building materials included medieval and 16th-century floor tiles, similar to those in phase 1. Two decorated tin-glazed floor tiles are both probably from a London pothouse: one (<2485> [3010]) has an early–mid 17th-century polychrome design (Fig 34); the other has the popular 'Tudor rose' design in blue on white and is unusually thin (10–11mm), suggesting a mid 17th-century date.[1] One London-made tin-glazed ('delftware') wall tile, dating to c 1740–60, shows part of a blue-on-white landscape scene set in an octagonal, powdered purple border with carnation head corners (Fig 34).[2]

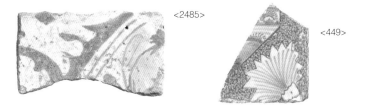

<2485>

<449>

Fig 34 Tin-glazed tiles from phase 2: floor tile <2485> with polychrome design from [3010]; wall tile <449> with landscape scene from [1156] (scale c 1:2)

Burial modes and layout

Excavation indicated earth-cut graves in a variety of forms – single, double and stacked burials, as well as mass or common graves (or pits) containing multiple individuals (Chapter 8.2). In addition, coffins occasionally contained two individuals (Chapter 12.3; Fig 157). The large number of family groups evident in the burial registers, as well as documented requests for burial with family members already interred at the ground (Chapter 4.4, 'Burial location'), indicate that at least some familial plots were established and in some way marked. However, the unusually high density of burials and frequency of intercutting, affecting even stacks, made the identification of such features difficult and largely impossible to define with any degree of confidence.

There is no documentary or archaeological evidence to suggest that burials were zoned according to religious, or indeed political, affiliation. The spatial distribution of burials does not indicate any zoning according to age or gender (Chapter 6.2; Fig 68).

Archaeological excavations have shown that row systems were a common feature of London burial grounds throughout the post-medieval period, but that rows were not always consistent and that considerable divergence occurred when, or even before, burial space became limited.[3] It is clear some attempt was made to bury in rows throughout the use of the burial ground. The ground's last row system can be tentatively seen in the distribution of the stratigraphically latest phase 2 burials (Fig 33). It is clear, however, that the position and alignment of a 'row' changed considerably over time; this and pressure on space led to severe intercutting and truncation of earlier graves. Thus, even when row systems were established it is clear that they were not strictly adhered to. A large number of burials, both phase 1 and 2, do not appear to conform to any kind of row system. These were perhaps located randomly, but it is also possible that they were located in the most convenient place at the time of interment, as indicated by burials marked on the surface.[4] Such irregularities and anomalies meant it was impossible to demonstrate the earlier, and earliest, row systems spatially. The issue is further confused by considerable variation in the depth of burials.

Certain other aspects of the internal arrangement of the burial ground can be suggested. Documentary evidence indicates that burial close to the pulpit was deemed desirable by some, at least during the late 16th century (Chapter 4.4; below, 5.5). Archaeological evidence indicates that other elements of the built environment began to influence the choice of burial location following the demolition of the pulpit in c 1643–57. High-quality coffins (those decorated with breastplates and/or studs; Fig 35) appear to cluster towards the main gate on the west boundary wall or are located close to possible pathways (below). Burial in such locations would have best displayed the deceased's wealth, social status and position within the community (Chapter 4.4, 'Burial location'; below, 5.5). Coffins with biographic stud motifs (all phase 2, dated 1674–1721; below, 5.2) in particular show a linear distribution, suggesting proximity to the ground's pathways was favoured by the wealthy as a burial location during the late 17th to early 18th century.

Burial vaults of both phases appear to have been deliberately located near the main gates and possible pathways. Two groups of charnel pits had been dug (in phase 2) in two lines aligned north-west to south-east; they were probably dug beside footpaths and Fig 36 conjectures footpaths using this evidence in combination with the location of gates, vaults and coffins with biographic lid motifs in phase 2.

N

stud-decorated coffin with breastplate

coffin with breastplate

stud-decorated coffin

plain coffin

10m

Fig 35 The spatial distribution of phase 2 high-status burials, as indicated by coffins with stud decoration, coffin lid breastplates, and coffins with stud decoration and breastplates (scale 1:400)

Grave alignment and burial orientation

Analysis of excavated burials suggests that elements of the built environment (specifically boundary walls) were the prime determinants of grave alignment, as seen in the shifts between phase 1 and phase 2 (above).

Burial orientation, however, largely conformed to Christian practice: 95% of New Churchyard burials were orientated with the head of the deceased to the west. In just under 5% of cases the head lay to the east. There is no indication that irregular orientation was Nonconformist; rather, it is likely such burials were for pragmatic reasons. Irregular orientated burials were generally located near or at the top of the burial sequence in phase 2, representing a period near or at the end of the ground's use. Head-to-the-east burials were more often set in rows alternating with head-to-the-west burials – a way of maximising use of available space. Individuals were buried with head to the north or south in 11 and six cases, respectively. These burials were all located either against walls or within mass graves. Two coffined, prone (ie lying on their front) burials were found at the site; there is no evidence, however, to suggest that these were anything more than a gravedigger's error with unmarked coffins.

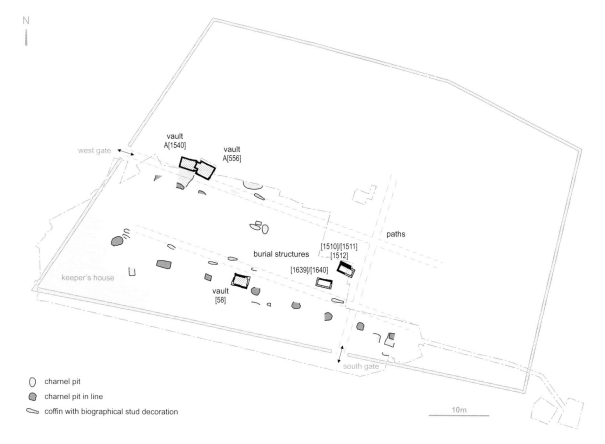

N

vault
A[1540]

vault
A[556]

west gate

paths

[1510]/[1511]
[1512]

burial structures

[1639]/[1640]

keeper's house

vault
[58]

south gate

○ charnel pit

● charnel pit in line

▱ coffin with biographical stud decoration

10m

Charnel

Disturbance of existing burials inevitably was a growing problem as the burial ground filled up. For most of the time the New Churchyard was in use, the favoured method of dealing with disarticulated bone was *ad hoc* redeposition within new graves. All charnel pits (located on Fig 36) were near, or at the top of, the burial sequence and are probably associated with the last decades of the ground's use, when any new interment would have almost certainly disturbed earlier burials (Fig 37).

One New Churchyard burial, consisting of an empty coffin, [4747], filled with charnel [4746], is potentially evidence of clearance of a family plot, tomb or vault and reburial.

5.2 Coffins

Coffin manufacture, furniture and fittings

The use of private coffins in England was largely limited to higher-status individuals until the early 16th century,[5] and there are few references to coffin burial in London churchyards before the late 16th century. By the early to

Fig 36 Plan of the phase 2 burial ground, showing the location of the burial ground gates and conjectured footpaths, and the position of vaults, coffins with biographical stud decoration, charnel pits and suggested lines of charnel pits (scale 1:600)

Fig 37 Charnel pit
[4203], looking south
(0.5m scale)

mid 17th century the majority of burials would have been coffined,[6] even during time of plague (Chapter 8.2). Until the late 17th century, poorer Londoners could make use of the 'parish coffin', which was used to transport shrouded corpses to the grave, but, rather than being buried with the individual, was returned to the parish for reuse.[7] The undertaking trade, as it is known today, first took shape in the 17th century and was firmly established by the early 18th century.[8] During these years the furnishing of funerals would have often been performed by furniture-makers and traders, including the manufacture and sale of coffins. It is likely that some of the late 17th- to mid 18th-century coffins found at the New Churchyard were bought from the shops of Brokers Row (Chapter 13.1).

Since the level of coffin decoration was directly proportionate to the cost, the post-medieval coffin quickly became a status symbol, indicating the wealth and social standing of the individual, or at least of the person paying for the funeral. The late 17th to mid 18th centuries saw the proliferation of a variety of coffin fittings and decorations which could be purchased according to developing fashions.[9] Unfortunately for modern researchers, the earliest surviving undertaker's trade catalogue dates to 1783.[10] Evidence of coffin decoration contemporary with the New Churchyard is therefore reliant on excavated archaeological examples, supported by the limited surviving contemporary trade card illustrations (Figs 41, 58). Additionally, coffins sometimes feature in late 17th- to 18th-century depictions of funerals, illustrating the form and decoration (Fig 38).[11]

The total number of excavated coffined burials was just over 2500 or 67% of

THE NEW CHURCHYARD

Fig 38 A flat-lidded, shouldered coffin with stud decoration and coffin grips in an engraving by William Hogarth, showing Moll's funeral (published in 1733 in his *A harlot's progress*, pl 6)
(The British Library Board, Tab.583)

the total number excavated. Although coffin wood occasionally survived as decayed fibrous fragments, most coffins were represented only by dark brown organic staining and their method of construction was not usually discernible beyond the presence of decayed iron nails. All coffins were to some degree distorted by collapse and/or slumping. It must be noted that due to poor preservation, together with high burial density and levels of truncation, the number of recorded coffins is a minimum and not an accurate representation of coffin use.

Where discernable, coffins were almost exclusively of the flat-lidded 'single break' or shouldered form (Figs 38, 41, 55, 58). This form, recognisable to modern eyes, first emerged in the last quarter of the 16th century, became the most popular form from *c* 1660 onwards and was ubiquitous by the early 18th century.[12]

The typical coffin was constructed with six pieces of wood – two sides, two ends, a base and a lid – and the pieces were fixed with nails or panel pins. Coffin shoulders were achieved by cutting a series of lateral grooves (called kerfs) with a saw on the inside of the side pieces. Rare exceptions to this form were rectangular or trapezoidal (the latter being wider at the head than the foot). Although there were rare examples made of conifer and oak, the majority of the coffins at the New Churchyard were made of thin and inexpensive pine (*Pinus* sp) boards. Elm (*Ulmus* sp) was the second most commonly used wood and has a long history of being used for coffins because it is less prone to splitting and offers water-resistance.[13]

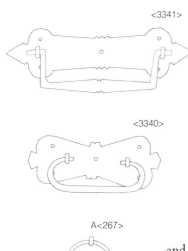

Fig 39 Examples of the three iron coffin grip types found at the New Churchyard, with two examples of grip plates: upper – right-angled grip <3341> from [8084]; centre – curved grip <3340> from [3010]; lower – ring grip A<267> from A[682] (scale 1:4)

Coffins were usually simple and plain, but there were occasional well-made and highly decorated examples. Iron grips (handles) were the most common form of coffin decoration and were noted on 10% of the excavated coffins, generally with decorative plates (grip plates). Only a limited number survived well enough to be retained and recorded; most examples were too severely fragmented and corroded to allow analysis. Of those recorded almost all grips were of a right-angled type (Figs 38, 39 upper). Litten suggests that this type of grip is confined to the period *c* 1650–*c* 1750.[14] Securely dated examples of this form found at the New Churchyard provide a date range of between 1674 and 1721 (coffins [5587] and A[677] respectively).[15] Rare exceptions to the right-angled type were plain rounded handles and simple oval or circular rings (Fig 39 middle and lower). Dating of these types is less clear but the similarity of the grip plates of the former with those of the right-angled type may suggest they are roughly contemporary, while the ring type is perhaps of a slightly earlier 17th-century date.[16]

Copper-alloy upholstery stud decoration was found on 4% of excavated coffins (Figs 35, 50). These studs were used on the more elaborate coffins to create panelling effects or motifs on the sides and/or lids, arranged in single, double or triple rows. Although decorative in themselves, studs would have been used to hold exterior fabric coverings in place. No identifiable pieces of these fabric coverings were found, but a few traces seen in the corrosion products of the studs and coffin plates indicated a fairly coarse cloth (eg [1557]/ [1558]). The fabric covering of the inner wooden coffin [1466] in vault A[556], belonging to Frances Williams, was identified as red velvet (below, 5.6).

Organic material originally present within the coffins – whether hair or fabric (including burial clothing, coverings or linings) – rarely survived. One exception was coffin [7692] which was partially lined with sawdust; this would have acted as an absorbent for body fluids and is a common find on post-medieval burial grounds.[17]

Due to the poor preservation, it was possible to draw only limited statistical conclusions about construction and decorative styles in relation to status, distribution in the burial ground or date.

Coffin plates and biographic lid motifs

Biographical details were recorded in initials and numbers formed by studs on the lids of 11 coffins or *c* 0.5% of the total excavated. This was the most common form of coffin marking during the late 17th century (Figs 40, 41).[18] The practice continued in the early to mid 18th century,[19] but during this period it was also common to indicate the age of the deceased as a number or

Fig 40 Excavation of a burial with stud-decorated coffin [5194], inscribed 'PW 1676', looking west

Fig 41 A studded coffin with initials and lid motifs shown on a trade card of William Boyce, undertaker, c 1680 (Trustees of the British Museum, Heal 124.6)

by including the year of birth.[20] All 11 coffins have been assigned to phase 2; seven coffins had legible years of death/burial, the earliest of which was 1674 ([5587], Fig 57) and the latest 1721 (A[677], Fig 55). The latter is the ground's latest archaeologically datable burial and the only named burial not found within a vault (below, 5.6).

The practice of displaying biographical data on coffin lids with either studs or metal lettering became increasingly rare during the 18th century as improvements in manufacturing methods reduced the costs of the alternative – breastplates.[21] Breastplates were more impressive and could provide information more efficiently and cost-effectively.

The presence of inscription and/or decorative plates was indicated on 3.5% of the New Churchyard coffins. The plates were made of either die-stamped iron or inscribed lead. Unfortunately, poor preservation meant that designs were largely indeterminate and inscriptions were almost all corroded beyond legibility. The five lead plates found with coffins in vault A[556] were the only readable examples (below, 5.6).

5.3 Grave goods

In the early modern period it was not common practice to bury items of personal, religious or other significance as grave goods. However, recent archaeological evidence has shown that 'irregular' burial traditions and superstitions persisted well into the 18th and 19th centuries and that personal or family possessions were also occasionally buried with the dead.[22] Burial finds from the New Churchyard can be assigned to two categories: items worn by the deceased and items deliberately placed in the coffin.

The deliberate depositions comprised six items: a necklace, two plates, two coins and a jetton. The necklace (<171> [349], phase 2) was made of 20 beads of amber, white amber, carnelian, glass and bone, which were found scattered around the neck of a one year old child who may have been suffering from rickets at the time of his/her death (Fig 42).[23] Although the necklace was presumably not worn in everyday life, it may have been worn in sickness. The amber and carnelian beads are of particular significance as amuletic stones with traditional properties of healing and protection, but white and blue spherical objects and gemstones were also placed in medieval and earlier graves as amulets thought to have transformative or healing powers.[24]

Two plates were found deposited with burials, one made from thin pewter, <2085> [5265], the other ceramic, <3170> [5613]. Such plates are thought to have held salt, which, as a preservative, symbolised eternal life and was thought to provide protection from the devil and delay decomposition.[25] They are unusual finds, although recently a small number of other plates, dishes and saucers have been recorded in graves dating from the late 17th to early 19th centuries from London and elsewhere.[26] Both are burials which probably took place at the end of phase 1, or perhaps the beginning of phase 2. The ceramic plate is a London-made tin-glazed ware product decorated in a distinctive style known as 'Chinaman among grasses', closely dated to *c* 1670–90 (Fig 43). It is extremely similar

Fig 42 Necklace <171> (reconstructed) made from 20 amber, carnelian, glass and bone beads found scattered beside the neck of one year old child [349] (scale *c* 1:1)

<171>

<3170>

Fig 43 Coffined burial of female [5613], aged over 46 years, with, on her stomach, late 17th-century tin-glazed ware plate <3170> with 'Chinaman among grasses' motif, looking north (detail, scale *c* 1:4)

to a 'Chinaman and rocks' plate found with a burial in St Martin Vintry churchyard, City of London, previously the earliest known plate from a London burial.[27] The pewter plate (Fig 44) cannot be closely dated, but the stratigraphic location of the burial suggests it is of a similar period. Two thin plain pewter plates were recently found in London with 18th- and early 19th-century burials.[28]

Coins, tokens and jettons – usually of low value or of none as currency because foreign or obsolete – are occasional finds with post-medieval burials, placed on the eyes or in the hands or mouths of the dead, an ancient custom thought to further passage into the afterlife. Two coins and a jetton were all found with adult burials: the corroded copper-alloy jetton, <407> (probably Nuremberg, *c* 1550–*c* 1630), with a woman with an unborn child ([1121], phase 1); a low denomination Dutch provincial coin dated 1636 (<1225> [5373], phase 1); and a George I farthing dated 1719–24 (<1213> [3148], phase 2).

The dress accessories consisted of a copper-alloy finger ring, <1525>, found on the central finger of the left hand of probable female adult burial [3180], and a row of eight paired copper-alloy buttons, <1613>, found on the chest of probable female adult burial [3417]. An internally sprung object in a copper-alloy casing with a looped terminal, <427>, found with a male adult, may also

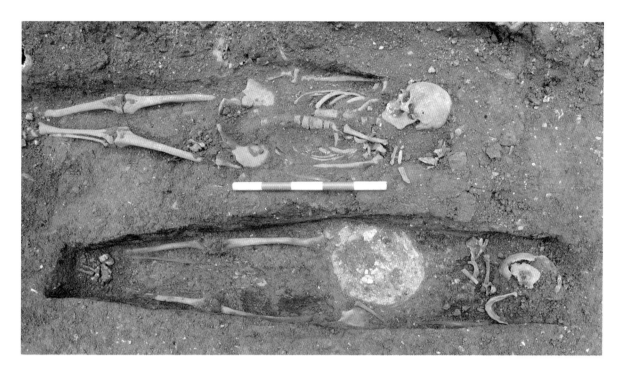

Fig 44 Coffined burial of probable female [5265], aged 36–45 years, found with pewter plate <2085> on her stomach, looking south (0.5m scale)

be a dress accessory. It is very similar to a fastening from a possible hair band or choker found in a grave excavated at St Marylebone's Paddington Street north burial ground, which took burials between 1772 and 1853.[29]

5.4 Gravestones

Before the English Reformation, most churchyards would have contained few gravestones and, although some graves may have been accompanied by wooden markers, most would have been unmarked. Headstones, as we recognise them today, started to appear in the early 17th century and small numbers were widely erected across the English-speaking world by the mid 17th century. Between the mid 17th and the 18th century, although still only for the relatively well-to-do, headstone and other stone grave markers slowly became more common and developed a wide variety of forms. Decoration often included architectural or furniture elements and sometimes included designs symbolic of mortality.[30]

It is rare for gravestones of the 16th to 18th centuries to have survived *in situ* in London churchyards and burial grounds; they were mostly cleared in the 18th or 19th centuries or supplanted by features of the same periods. A small number from archaeological excavations in London have been found *ex situ*, broken and redeposited within rubble/debris and foundations or laid flat as paving for footpaths, and the epigraphic information they provide is therefore very limited.[31]

All standing New Churchyard gravestones were taken down by order of the City in 1762.[32] If any wooden markers had existed at the ground, they left no discernible trace in the archaeological record. However, the site did produce 11 (incomplete) gravestones, dated 1653–1726, comprising fragments of seven headstones and four ledger slabs (Figs 45–7, 96). They had remained on the site because they had been reused in the foundations of later structures.

Although none of the gravestones were found *in situ*, and therefore could not be used to identify burials, the inscriptions of seven (<198>/<201>; <522> Fig 45; <664> Fig 96; <2267> Fig 46; <2543>; <3052>; <3053> Fig 47) contained enough biographical detail to match with burial registers (Chapter 14.2). Only two of the associated register entries noted that the burial had been at the New Churchyard ('Sarah wife of Sefton Long stopped stomach Bethlem' (<522> Fig 45) and

<522>

Fig 45 Portland stone headstone <522> of Sarah Long (d 1672) (scale *c* 1:6)

<2267>

Fig 46 Purbeck limestone headstone <2267> of Jane Atterbury (d 1686) (scale *c* 1:6)

<3053>

Fig 47 Blue Lias ledger slab <3053> of Katherine Wykes (d 7 January 1653/4) (scale *c* 1:6)

'Anne Cock at Bedlam' (<2543>)). The burial location of Katherine Wykes (or Wikes) (Fig 47) was not noted in her burial registration, dated 7 January 1653/4.[33] However, she had requested burial at the 'New Churchyard neare Bethlem otherwise Bedlam' in her will, dated 20 December 1653 and proved 4 February 1653/4.[34]

London and south-east England have no local stone suitable for accurate inscription and embellishment as vertical gravestones and horizontal ledger stones. The New Churchyard stones comprised a number of rock types, including dark blue-black, Blue Lias (limestone or wackestone) (<2537/8>; <3053> Fig 47), white-grey Portland stone (oolitic grainstone) (<522> Fig 45; <2543>), cream-grey Purbeck limestone (shelly limestone) (<198>/<201>; <2267> Fig 46; <2542>)[35] and a cream fossiliferous limestone similar to Corallian limestone (<664> Fig 96; <3052>);[36] all of these would have been transported by sea, probably as ballast, from the Dorset/Somerset region.

5.5 Monuments and tombs

Documentary evidence

Burial vaults and tombs were physical statements of an individual's or family's wealth and standing in society. These were less expensive options in an open burial ground than within a parish church, but they were still a considerable investment.[37] The construction of a vault or tomb took up a significantly greater area than a standard grave and the potential loss of income to the parish or, in this case, the keeper of the churchyard in terms of grave digging charges needed to be overcome; not only was space required for the structure but, in the case of vaults, sufficient ground also had to be set out for a passage or entrance.

Some documentary evidence survives for the presence of vaults at the New Churchyard. The will of Anne Delamaine, proved 22 December 1688, indicates her family owned a vault in the ground. It is likely to have also contained the body of her husband, Alexander Delamaine (Chapter 4.2).[38] Similarly, the will of John Quince, Barber-Surgeon of St Botolph Bishopsgate, proved 5 December 1656, indicates that he wished for a vault to be built in the New Churchyard for himself and his wife.[39]

The will of Peter Simmonds, mercer, proved 9 September 1587, included instructions for his burial structure near the pulpit: 'a valte of bricke for my bodie and coffin to lie in and so the same to be raised with bricke a yearde above the grounde with a faire great stone upon it with suche graven matter uppon latten the same stone as my executors and overseers shall think convenient'.[40] For an uncertain number of years, bread given to the poor after the annual Whit Sunday sermon was distributed from the slab of his tomb.[41]

Documentary sources recorded that Lodowicke Muggleton was buried in a 'tomb' at the ground on 17 March 1697/8, and the tomb was inscribed with the following:

> While Mausoleums and large inscriptions give,
> Might, splendour, and past deaths make potents live,
> It is enough to briefly write thy name,
> Succeeding times by that will read thy fame,
> Thy deeds, thy acts, around the globe resound,
> No foreign soil where Muggleton's not found.[42]

Archaeological evidence

Tombs

Three structures ([1510]/[1511], [1512] and [1639]/[1640]) may represent the remains of brick-built burial structures intended for single interments – perhaps brick-lined graves, or chest or table tombs. Structures [1510]/[1511] and [1512] were dated by brick type as post-1666. Structure [1639]/[1640] was provided a *terminus post quem* (TPQ) of 2 September 1665 by a gravestone reused within its walls. All of these structures may therefore belong to phase 2 of the burial ground or perhaps the final years of phase 1.

Vaults

All upstanding monuments at the ground were taken down, with gravestones, in 1762.[43] No plans or engravings exist which show the layout of the burial ground or location of burial monuments, but the remains of four brick burial vaults were excavated (located on Fig 31, one from phase 1, and Fig 36, phase 2). All were similarly constructed, with floors and walls made of red brick.

Vault [7158] did not contain *in situ* burials and the owner of the vault is unknown. It was 2.9m long externally and was probably square or rectangular in plan before truncation; the vault was constructed with brick dated *c* 1500–1666 and was at the base of the burial ground stratigraphic sequence. The location of vault [7158] would probably have placed it between the pulpit and the south gate, and adjacent to any pathway between the two (Fig 31; Chapter 4.4, 'Burial location'), reinforcing the suggestion that this vault belonged to a high-status individual, buried in the late 16th century (phase 1). The vault appears to have been cleared in order to make space for further single interments. It had been demolished, largely robbed out and then sealed by late 17th- to early 18th-century burials.

Vault [58] was roughly square in plan (Figs 36, 48), with an external measurement of 2.6m by 2.1m, and sufficient internal space for two coffins side by side and a second layer placed above. However, it contained only one

Fig 48 The remains of brick burial vault [58], looking north; it contained one disturbed *in situ* coffined burial [3000]/[3001] and was truncated to the north by the 1824 garden boundary wall [1642]/ [1648] (0.5m scale)

in situ coffined burial (skeleton [3000]/coffin [3001]), which, like the vault itself, had been badly disturbed and truncated by later construction activity (Chapter 13.3; Fig 177). This individual could not be identified but the coffin furniture indicated a date after the mid 17th century; bricks used in the construction of the vault were dated post-1666. Vault [58] was aligned parallel to the south wall and may be associated with phase 2 of the burial ground or perhaps the final years of phase 1.

Vaults A[1540] and A[556] probably both belonged to the same extended family group (Walwyn/Jenkes/Halford/Farrington/Williams) and represent three phases of vault burial dated late 17th to early 18th century (Fig 36): first, burial in vault A[1540]; second, burial in vault A[556]; and third, lead coffin burial in vault A[556], with probable reinterment of burials from the first two phases.

The main structure of vault A[1540] was rectangular and measured 2.0m long by 1.2m wide internally. Putlog holes in the walls indicated that a second layer of burials would have been carried on cross-beams above those on the floor. There was space for at least four adult-sized coffins, but more could have been accommodated if some were smaller, child-sized, coffins.

Vault A[556] was built as a replacement for vault A[1540], presumably because the earlier vault was too small to accommodate further burials. It was larger and roughly square in plan with an external measurement of 3.0m by 2.8m. The roof had collapsed and was mixed with the destruction debris, [1341], but was apparently a vaulted structure with the ceiling starting at 1.2m from the floor. Vault A[1540] was emptied when vault A[556] was built and incorporated in the latter's brick-stepped entrance passage. The original brick floor of vault A[556] was covered with coffin fragments which indicated the vault was initially used to store burials in wooden coffins. A second brick floor was built over the original, on which six lead coffins were stacked, arranged as two layers of three (Fig 49). The entrance was sealed with bricks following the last lead coffin burial.

Fig 49 Bottom (lower) layer of lead coffins in vault A[556] (left to right, A[1465], A[1468] and A[1471]), looking west (0.5m scale)

The inner wooden coffins contained within the lead coffins of vault A[556] were particularly prestigious and finely finished (Fig 50). Coffin decoration included breast and decorative escutcheon plates, grips, grip plates, fabric coverings, decorative panelling and motifs formed of studs on the sides and/or lids.

Coffin plates attached to the *in situ* lead coffins provided dating and biographical information (below, 5.6). Five of the lead coffins in vault A[556] contained single individuals. However, the sixth coffin (coffin A[1468]/[1469]) contained multiple individuals (A[1470]). Its breastplate (A<283> Fig 52) recorded the names of four individuals who died in 1686, 1694, 1696 and

Fig 50 Wooden inner coffins of top layer of coffins in vault A[556] (left to right, A[1373], A[1360] and A[1354]), looking west (0.5m scale)

1698, but it contained the charnel remains of at least 12 individuals. The inscriptions with the remaining five burials in vault A[556] recorded that they were interred in or after 1708. The sequence in which the lead coffins were stacked suggests a deliberate positioning of the coffins according to family relationships (below, 5.6).

This information indicates a chronology for three phases of vault burial, with vault A[556] built in c 1686 and vault A[1540] built sometime prior to 1686. The construction of the second floor of vault A[556], representing its change from a repository for wooden coffins to one for lead coffins, must have taken place before 1708 (the date of the inscription on the first, single, lead coffin interment). Deposit [1526] associated with the construction of the second floor included pottery and clay tobacco pipes, as well as two Low Countries tin-glazed wall tiles, dated c 1670–c 1700 and c 1700–50, giving a date of after c 1700 for the final phase of vault A[556].

It seems probable that A[1540] was built in the 1670s as a family vault either by William Walwyn or Francis Jenkes. The four named individuals in coffin A[1468]/[1469] (Francis Jenkes (d 1686), Harbert Jenkes (d 1696), Elizabeth Jenkes (d 1694), Sarah Jenkes (d 1698)) were most likely originally interred within wooden coffins belonging to the first phase of vault A[556]. The unnamed charnel remains within coffin A[1468]/[1469] may represent the reinterment of burials from the first phase of vault A[556] or from vault A[1540]. Burials in vault A[1540] may have included: Francis Jenkes Jr (d 1673), Walwyn Jenkes (d c 1675), Frances Halford (d 1676), Ann Walwyn (d 1676), William Walwyn (d 1680/1) and Richard Halford (d 1681) (below, 5.6).

Both vaults, A[1540] and A[556], would have occupied a prime location immediately opposite the ground's west gate, possibly north of and adjacent to a path leading from the gate into the ground (above, 5.1; Fig 36).

The types of family burial vaults discovered at the New Churchyard, together with other possible smaller burial structures, were common in the churches and churchyards of England from the late 17th century.[44] Numerous comparable examples have been archaeologically recorded in London burial grounds.[45]

5.6 The named burials

Only ten individuals could be identified from the total of over 3700 articulated human burials excavated from the site as a whole, including site A. This was achieved by linking archaeological evidence, principally biographic coffin decorations and osteological data, with a variety of contemporary documentary sources, although in two of the ten cases evidence was insufficient to support more than a tentative identification.

Vault A[556]

FRANCIS JENKES (d 1686, aged 46)

Skeleton A[1470]
Lead coffin A[1468]
Inner wooden coffin A[1469]
Coffin plate A<283> (Fig 52)
Osteology: assemblage of disarticulated adult bones from multiple individuals

Francis Jenkes was baptised at Eaton under Heywood, Shropshire, on 5 November 1640, and was one of the four children of Herbert Jenkes, Esquire, of New Hall, Shropshire, and his wife, Elizabeth. The wealthy Jenkes family held substantial lands in Shropshire (Fig 51). Herbert Jenkes, an Oxford-educated barrister,[46] committed suicide following a period of financial 'delinquincy'.[47] His burial was registered in St Andrew Holborn on 15 March 1651/2.[48]

Francis Jenkes was apprenticed in 1658 to a member of the London Fishmongers' Company, and married Sarah Walwyn (below), daughter of the Leveller William Walwyn, in 1666. He became a merchant (linen draper), Whig activist and a political agitator. As a member of Common Council and the Green Ribbon Club, he was closely involved in the political turmoil and crises of the 1670s and '80s, a period which saw him occasionally imprisoned.[49] Francis and Sarah Jenkes had six children. Three of them, Elizabeth, Francis and Walwyn Jenkes, did not live beyond infancy. Francis Jenkes Jr died at the age of 3 and was buried on 11 February 1673/4 'in the new ground in Bethlehem by Dr John Merriton Rector of this parish [St Michael Cornhill]'.[50]

Francis Jenkes died at the age of 46 and his burial at 'Bethlehem' on 30 November 1686 was registered in the parish of St Leonard Shoreditch.[51] Coffin plate A<283> recorded that he died 5 December 1686 (Fig 52). Alternatively, it is possible that his coffin plate records the date of his funeral, while the burial register recorded his date of death. His cause of death was not recorded but was probably unexpected, perhaps sudden illness or accident, since he died intestate and with business dealings very much unresolved. His largest business venture had been made in the year before his death. On 23 March 1685/6 he took possession of lands adjoining Wallingford House at Buckingham Court, Westminster, from the Duke of

Fig 51 The family tree of the extended family group – Jenkes, Walwyn, Halford, Williams and Farrington – associated with vaults A[1540] and A[556] in the later 17th to early 18th century

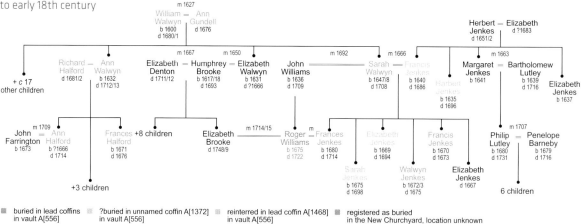

◼ buried in lead coffins in vault A[556]　◻ ?buried in unnamed coffin A[1372] in vault A[556]　◼ reinterred in lead coffin A[1468] in vault A[556]　◼ registered as buried in the New Churchyard, location unknown

Buckingham and began renting them out. At the time of his death he owned two houses (one in Hoxton, Middlesex) and a draper's shop. An inventory and appraisal of his estate in February 1686/7, including property, goods and chattels (furniture, fittings, furnishings, and household goods and equipment), valued his wealth at some £11,500. However, he was a debtor with over 100 outstanding debts, and settling these reduced his estate to some £5000.[52]

The appraisal recorded the total cost of his funeral as £87 19s. Although black mourning apparel was noted, the costs were not itemised and it is not known how much was spent on individual items, for example, his coffin.

ELIZABETH JENKES (d 1694, aged 25)

Skeleton A[1470]
Lead coffin A[1468]
Inner wooden coffin A[1469]
Coffin plate A<283> (Fig 52)
Osteology: assemblage of disarticulated adult bones from multiple individuals

Elizabeth Jenkes was the oldest daughter of Francis and Sarah Jenkes. She was christened 20 July 1669, died a spinster in Hoxton aged 25 and was buried 'at Bethlem' on 9 November 1694.[53] Cause of death was not recorded. Her will, proved 10 November 1694, indicates she died wealthy. She held part or all of her father's lands in Buckingham Court, which she left in trust for her sister Sarah, who at the time of writing was still under 21. Her sisters Sarah and Frances were also left £50 each, as well as valuables, including her camblet (an expensive woven fabric, also known as camelot or camlet), curtains, beds, bedding and 'mothare of pearle'. Her remaining 'goods, Chattels and Estate' were left to her mother Sarah Williams.[54]

A<283>

Fig 52 Detail of coffin plate A<283> recording the deaths of Francis, Elizabeth, Harbert and Sarah Jenkes (scale c 1:5)

HARBERT (HERBERT) JENKES (d 1696, aged c 61)

Skeleton A[1470]
Lead coffin A[1468]
Inner wooden coffin A[1469]
Coffin plate A<283> (Fig 52)
Osteology: assemblage of disarticulated adult bones from multiple individuals

Coffin plate A<283> recorded that Harbert Jenkes was the elder brother of Francis Jenkes and that he died in 1696. Harbert was born in New Hall, Shropshire, in c 1635. An inquisition into his sanity was undertaken in 1660 and he died a 'lunatic' in 1696, sometime after 28 May. In the year of his death his care and his affairs were the responsibility of his sister-in-law, Sarah Williams (formerly Jenkes, née Walwyn), her husband, John Williams, and their lawyer, John Freke. Although there is no record that he was ever a patient at an asylum during his life, the relocation of the Jenkes family from the parish of St Michael Cornhill to Hoxton in St Leonard Shoreditch, sometime in the late 1670s, may point to this, since the first of the famous private asylums or 'madhouses' of Hoxton were established in the late 17th century.[55]

SARAH JENKES (d 1698, aged 23)

Skeleton A[1470]
Lead coffin A[1468]
Inner wooden coffin A[1469]
Coffin plate A<283> (Fig 52)
Osteology: assemblage of disarticulated adult bones from multiple individuals

Sarah Jenkes was the second daughter of Francis and Sarah Jenkes. Coffin plate A<283> recorded she died aged 23 on 7 September 1698. Her will, proved 5 October 1698, describes her as a spinster of St Andrew Holborn and reveals she held land in Shropshire and Herefordshire. These lands, together with the majority of her personal goods and estate, were placed in trust for the use of her mother Sarah. She bequeathed any remaining lands and goods to her sister Frances Jenkes, and four others received gifts of 20 guineas (£21).[56]

SARAH WILLIAMS (FORMERLY JENKES, NÉE WALWYN) (d 1708, aged 60)

Skeleton A[1361]
Lead coffin A[1359]
Inner wooden coffin A[1360]
Coffin plate (damaged) A<219>
Osteology: female aged ≥46 years at death; possible bathrocephaly; possible pipe facet or notch; possible hip dysplasia; dental caries and periapical lesions; vertebral osteophytes

Sarah Williams (formerly Jenkes) was christened Sarah Walwyn on 29 February 1647/8 and was the penultimate child of William and Ann Walwyn.[57] Following the death of Francis Jenkes, she married Dr John Williams on 16 April 1692, who was appointed bishop of Chichester in 1696. The couple did not have any children. Williams died at Gray's Inn on 24 April 1709 and was buried in the chancel vault at the church of St Mildred Poultry on 28 April 1709 alongside his first wife, Margaret, and first son, John.[58]

Sarah Williams's coffin plate recorded she died on '[2]9th Sept 1708' at the age of 60. Her coffin was placed on the coffin of her first husband and children (burial A[1470]/[1469]/[1468]). Her will, dated 4 August 1708 and proved 21 February 1708/9, left the majority of her estate to her surviving daughter, Frances Williams, her son-in-law and stepson, Roger Williams, and her husband John Williams. Her remaining bequests included sums of between 20 guineas (£21) and £10 to various cousins, £5 to her maid servant and 20 guineas to her nurse. She did not mention a choice of burial location. One of the executors of her will was John Freke (1652–1717), the lawyer and Whig conspirator. He was also named a trustee in the wills of her daughters Sarah Jenkes and Frances Williams, and helped the family manage the affairs of Harbert Jenkes.[59]

ANN HALFORD (NÉE WALWYN) (d 1712, aged 81)

Burial A[1471] (skeleton, inner wooden coffin and lead coffin)
Coffin plate not retained but inscription recorded
Osteology: skeleton not recorded

Ann Halford (née Walwyn) was christened on 4 August 1632. She was the fourth child of William and Ann Walwyn and the older sister of Sarah Williams (formerly Jenkes and née Walwyn).[60] Ann's husband, Richard Halford, was a physician in the parish of St Giles Cripplegate and an associate of her father.[61] He died of 'feaver' and was buried at 'Bethlem' on 17 March 1681/2.[62] Their daughter, Frances Halford, died of 'flox' at the age of five years and was buried at 'Bethlem' on 20 December 1676.[63]

Ann Halford's coffin plate recorded her death on 16 March 1712 at the age of 81. The date of her death was recorded in the rough death register of St Stephen Coleman Street and that she 'dyed of age'.[64] Her burial 'at Bethlem' on 20 March 1712/13 was recorded in the parish's burial register.[65] In 1681 Ann Halford and her husband, Richard, were involved in a legal dispute with her sister, Sarah Jenkes, and her husband, Francis, over the division of their father's estate.[66] However, since ultimately Ann was buried in the same vault as Sarah and Francis Jenkes, we can presume 'family' overcame any previous difficulties.

A<284>

FRANCES WILLIAMS (NÉE JENKES) (d 1714, aged 34)

Skeleton A[1467]
Lead coffin A[1465]
Outer wooden coffin A[1464]
Inner wooden coffin A[1466]
Coffin plate A<284> (Fig 53)
Osteology: sealed coffin sent for reburial; skeleton not recorded

Frances Williams (née Jenkes) was the youngest daughter of Francis and Sarah Jenkes. Her coffin plate records she died aged 34 on 10 June 1714 (Fig 53). Her will, dated 29 September 1712 and proved 19 July 1714, describes her as the wife of Roger Williams, Esquire, of Gray's Inn (below). Her husband was the son of her stepfather John Williams, Bishop of Chichester (above).[67] Her will describes considerable wealth and reveals that she had inherited her family's estate in Eaton-Under-Heywood, Shropshire. She and Roger Williams were childless, and on her death the manor of Eaton passed to her cousin Philip Lutley, the son of Bartholomew and Margaret Lutley (née Jenkes), her paternal aunt.[68]

Fig 53 Detail of Frances Williams's coffin plate A<284> (d 1714) (scale *c* 1:5)

ANN FARRINGTON (NÉE HALFORD) (d 1714, aged *c* 48)

Skeleton A[1355]
Lead coffin A[1353]
Inner wooden coffin A[1354]
Coffin plate A<220> (Fig 54)
Osteology: skeleton not recorded

Ann Farrington (née Halford), the daughter of Richard and Ann Halford and the granddaughter of William and Ann Walwyn, was born *c* 1666. Her husband, John Farrington, was born in the parish of St George the Martyr Southwark, on 8 December 1673.[69] They married in the parish of St Michael Cornhill on 28 November 1709[70] and she died of 'convolsions in more fels [Moorfields]' on 22 August 1714 and was buried on 27 August at 'Bethlem ground'.[71] Coffin plate A<220> recorded her as 'Mr[s] Ann Farrington' who died at the age of 48 (Fig 54). Her coffin was placed on the coffin of her mother, Ann Halford (burial A[1471]).

A<220>

Fig 54 Detail of Ann Farrington's coffin plate A<220> (d 1714) (scale *c* 1:5)

Fig 55 Reconstruction of coffin lid A[677] inscription (Robert Hartle) (scale *c* 1:10; length 1.84m)

UNNAMED – ? ROGER WILLIAMS (d 1722, aged 47)

Skeleton A[1374]

Lead coffin A[1372]

Inner wooden coffin A[1373]

Osteology: male aged 36–45 years at death; enamel hypoplasia; periodontal disease; intervertebral disc disease; osteophytes and Schmorl's nodes; cribra orbitalia; possible gout in left first metatarsal; healed periosteal lesions on left tibia; localised lytic lesion on frontal bone of skull (possible severe sinusitis or Pott's puffy tumour).

Coffin A[1372]/[1373] did not have a plate or any markings to identify the occupant. However, it was placed on the coffin of Frances Williams (née Jenkes) (burial A[1467]/[1466]/[1465]/[1464]) which probably dates it to post-June 1714 and makes it the last burial interred in the vault.

It seems probable that skeleton A[1374] is Roger Williams, the husband of Frances Williams. He was baptised 17 August 1675 and died aged 47 in *c* November 1722.[72] Following the death of his first wife, Frances, he married her cousin, Elizabeth Brooke, on 28 February 1714.[73] Elizabeth Brooke was the daughter of Dr Humphrey Brooke, the physician and Leveller, and his second wife, Elizabeth Brooke (née Denton). Humphrey Brooke's first wife, Elizabeth Brooke (née Walwyn, baptised 25 June 1631, d ?2 October 1666), was the oldest daughter of William Walwyn and the maternal aunt of Frances Williams.[74] The location of Roger Williams's burial is not known and he did not specify a burial location in his will, proved 19 November 1722. However, he was not buried with his father in the Williams family vault at St Mildred Poultry or with his second wife in the Brooke family vault at St Andrew Undershaft.[75]

Coffin A[677]/skeleton A[676] (b 1688, d 1721)

Attempts were made to identify those individuals found within coffins with biographic motifs (dates and/or ages, but not names) by matching the information and osteological findings with parish burial registers. However, this proved impossible in all but one case because of the extremely limited available data and the sheer number of parishes sending burials to the ground. The exception was burial A[676]/[677] (Fig 55).

The quality of coffin A[677] perhaps suggests a successful and at least moderately wealthy individual. Osteological analysis of skeleton A[676] indicated a male aged 26–35 years at death. Evidence of dental pathology included trauma (chipped tooth), caries and periodontal disease. The spine was affected by osteophytes, intervertebral disc disease and severe Schmorl's nodes. Cribra orbitalia was identified in the right orbit.

Crucially, this was the only biographic coffin motif to include the year of birth as well as death. Only one match could be found: Edward Palmer, a tailor, who died aged 32 of 'fever' in the parish of St Giles Cripplegate on 17 June 1721. He was born in the same parish on 31 December 1688, the son of 'Edward Palmer, clothworker, and Elizabeth' and brother to William and John Palmer (christened 8 May 1687 and 18 August 1698, respectively).[76] The parish register does not note the burial location of Edward Palmer in 1721 but only that the Palmers lived in the Freedom part of the parish.[77]

The name 'Edward Palmer' is associated with the tax records of an address in Sugerloaf Court, off Moor Lane, in the ward of Cripplegate Without, dated 1692–1722.[78] The address was located among the many small alleyways west of Moorfields within the Freedom part of the parish of St Giles Cripplegate (close to the modern junction of Moor Lane and New Union

Street). The name perhaps represents both Edward Palmer (1688–1721) and his father.

Burial at the New Churchyard may have been a Palmer family tradition. The Bedlam Register project (Chapters 1.2, 6.1) found five Palmers from St Giles Cripplegate who were buried at the New Churchyard 1665–90. Among these was 'Edward Palmer', a weaver who died 'aged' on 21 May 1683,[79] conceivably the grandfather of Edward Palmer (1688–1721).

5.7 'rest quietly in our Graves' – anatomical study, bodysnatching and dissection

Robert Hartle with Michael Henderson

Documentary evidence

Autopsy was a regular occurrence in Italy, France and Germany from the 13th century and surgeons were used to establish a cause of death in suspicious circumstances. In England, the dead body had been used as evidence in coroners' courts since the 12th century. Early medical autopsies were confined to prominent individuals. Oliver Cromwell was subject to an autopsy as there was uncertainty about the cause of his death in 1658. Autopsy was usually confined to examination of the soft tissue and so was less invasive or destructive than dissection.[80] As practitioners pursued the study of gross anatomy to further the understanding of the workings of the human body, more attention was paid to the connection between the sick and evidence of disease visible on a corpse. This prompted the study of morbid anatomy and an increase in dissection.[81]

Before the Anatomy Act of 1832 the only bodies that could be acquired legally for medical dissection were those of executed criminals and, despite enactments of 1540, 1565 and 1663, the number of bodies legally available to the anatomists before the Murder Act of 1752 was only six per annum.[82] However, from the early 18th century, an aspiring medical student could take classes at one of a number of medical schools in London. As anatomy schools grew in number, the demand for a regular supply increased and began to foster a lucrative market for illicit procurement.[83] In the words of one anonymous gentleman writing to the *Westminster Journal* in 1746, a surgeon had little choice but 'lay himself open and obnoxious to the Law, by robbing Hospitals and Churchyards'.[84]

Much has been written concerning the history of bodysnatching and anatomical dissection between the mid 18th century and the Anatomy Act of 1832, but little on the period contemporary with the New Churchyard.[85] In Britain the practice of bodysnatching dates back to at least the 17th century and was well established in London by the 1720s.[86] An anonymous work entitled *A view of London and Westminster*, first published in 1725, cited early examples of bodysnatching in London: 'the Corporation of *Corpse-stealers*, I am told, support themselves and Families very comfortably; and that no one should be surpriz'd at the Name of such a Society, the late *Resurrections* in St. *Saviour*'s, St. *Giles's*, and St. *Pancras's* Churchyards, are memorable Instances of this laudable Profession.'[87]

An examination of contemporary newspapers has shed light on the rapid development of this 'Corporation' and revealed early prosecutions against bodysnatching (Chapter 14.3). The earliest case is perhaps the first documented example of a bodysnatching prosecution in London: the prosecution of Joseph Bowen, gravedigger, for stealing a corpse from the New Churchyard in 1717. Benjamin Clitherow IV was not named in the trial of his gravedigger; however, he may have been suspected, since it was common for sextons and churchwardens to be complicit in such activity for the extra revenue it brought.[88]

These early bodysnatching incidents caused great alarm among the citizens of London. In an anonymous letter to the *Original Weekly Journal*, published 15 February 1717/18, the author angrily wrote:

> The sudden Resurrection of the Dead in Southwark, is become the general Subject of Conversation, and has render'd Death far more Frightful and Terrible to some People … neither common Humanity or strongest Elm, nor even the Grave are capable of Protecting the most Pious Mortal … from falling into the Hands of some Galenian Butcher or other[89]

Bowen was prosecuted, but bodysnatching cases were subject to a legal loophole: since a corpse could not legally constitute property, it could not be stolen, so the disinterment of a body did not amount to a felony.[90] It was only in cases where the deceased's belongings, such as the shroud, were taken from the grave that the crime could be punishable by deportation or death. Stealing a corpse was therefore not a felony but only a misdemeanour under common law, for which imprisonment, a fine or whipping was considered fitting punishment.

Archaeological evidence

Post-medieval bodysnatching has received limited archaeological consideration because the practice is rarely recognisable in the archaeological record.[91] There are documented early 19th-century cases of bodysnatchers removing bodies from coffins before interment and substituting weights to avoid detection;[92] possibly the earliest known example of this practice occurred in London in October 1719 (Chapter 14.3). No archaeological examples were found at the New Churchyard, but this practice was tentatively identified at Christ Church Spitalfields, where a coffin was found filled only with building rubble.[93] It would be unwise, for example, to consider the 11 empty coffins excavated at the New Churchyard as evidence of bodysnatching because of the high levels of disturbance and intercutting. However, several coffins found at the site may represent evidence of anxieties about bodysnatching, or at least the measures employed against it.

Coffin [3999] (phase 2) was found completely filled with sand above the corpse. Large stones had been placed directly on its lid and among the grave fill (Fig 56). Although the sand would have absorbed the smells and fluids of putrefaction, its primary purpose, when combined with the stones, was probably to hinder bodysnatchers. Heavily compacting grave fills or placing

Fig 56 Burial [3999]/[4000] filled with sand and covered by large stones, looking west (0.5m scale)

obstructions within them, such as branches and straw, were simple anti-bodysnatching measures documented in the late 18th and early 19th century.[94]

Other simple measures recorded in the late 18th to early 19th century included digging graves deep and using watchers or dogs to guard them. Resilient physical obstructions of the period included coffin collars, mort-stones, mort-cages, mortsafes and reinforced coffins, such as the 'patent coffin' of 1818.[95] An archaeological example of an early 19th-century mortsafe was discovered at Providence chapel and burial ground, Sandwell, West Bromwich, alongside burials covered by pine planks.[96] Early 19th-century iron-strapped coffins excavated at Christ Church Spitalfields were thought to have been intended to counter resurrections.[97]

Several excavated late 17th-century coffins were found with iron brackets. These features were structurally unnecessary and are perhaps too numerous and robust to be just decorative (Fig 57). They would certainly, however, have prevented the coffin from being easily reopened and so could represent precursors to 19th-century reinforced anti-bodysnatching coffins. A coffin with iron brackets very similar to those of [5587] is shown on the trade card of early 18th-century coffin-maker William Grinly (Fig 58).

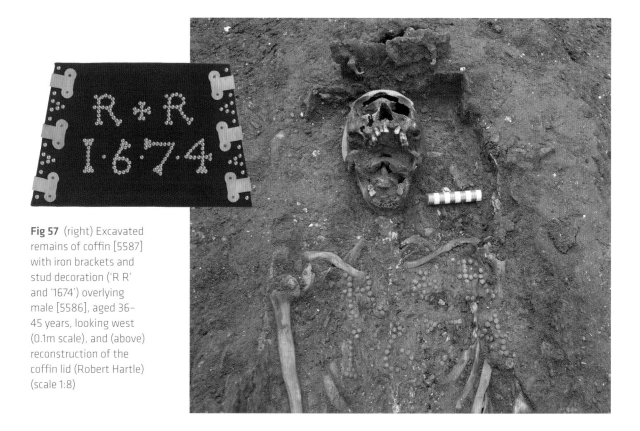

Fig 57 (right) Excavated remains of coffin [5587] with iron brackets and stud decoration ('R R' and '1674') overlying male [5586], aged 36–45 years, looking west (0.1m scale), and (above) reconstruction of the coffin lid (Robert Hartle) (scale 1:8)

What constitutes evidence of dissection or autopsy is not always easy to determine in the investigation of archaeological skeletal remains. Articulated skeletons showing evidence of saw cuts to the skull (craniotomies) and/or cuts to the thorax and spine may suggest autopsy as opposed to higher levels of fragmentation that may be associated with dissection. This is less clear for remains from the 16th and 17th century where there is an overall under-representation of archaeological evidence.[98] The skulls of two individuals from the prison ground at Oxford Castle that may date to the 16th–18th century showed evidence of multiple saw cuts.[99] Other criminals subject to anatomical study were interred in churchyards and consecrated grounds and perhaps the majority of unclaimed prisoners who died in the Poultry Compter and Ludgate prison were buried in the New Churchyard (social outcasts, Chapter 6.1).

Two individuals buried at the New Churchyard, both in coffins, had saw cuts to the skull indicating craniotomies: that of category A female [5986] (OA105C), aged 18–25 years, probably as part of an autopsy, while category B male [5328] (OA105A), aged 36–45 years, may represent autopsy or dissection (Chapter 11.2).

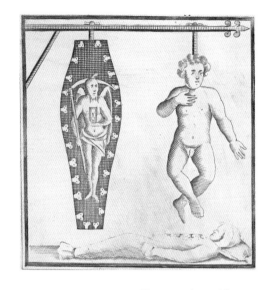

Fig 58 Trade card for William Grinly, undertaker, *c* 1730 (Trustees of the British Museum, Heal 124.38)

Notes to Chapter 5

1 Cf Betts and Weinstein 2010, 109 no. 104, 111 no. 111

2 Cf Horne 1989, 23 nos 43, 46, 48–9, 51 (illus)

3 Including Chelsea old church churchyard: Cowie et al 2008, 22–9; St Benet Sherehog churchyard: Miles and White 2008, 60–6; St Marylebone church and burial ground: Miles et al 2008, 35; St Pancras burial ground: Emery and Wooldridge 2011, 42–3

4 Miles et al 2008, 35

5 Litten 2002, 86

6 Miles and White 2008, 58

7 Litten 2002, 97–100

8 Ibid, 5–31

9 Ibid, 85–118; 1998

10 V&A, E997 to E1011–1903

11 Richardson 2001, 18 pl 2

12 Litten 2002, 96–9

13 Ibid, 90

14 Miles et al 2008, 67

15 Examples of this type have been dated 1687–1739 at sites in London, St Paul's Cathedral (Wroe-Brown 2001), St James Piccadilly extramural churchyard (Davis et al 2010) and Chelsea Old Church (Cowie et al 2008, 34), and elsewhere, Rycote chapel, Thame (Oxfordshire) (Boston 2008), and Hereford Cathedral close (Herefordshire) (Boucher et al 2015, 72)

16 The ring type can be seen on gable-lidded coffins on William Lilly's 'Hieroglyphic of the Great Plague' (Lilly 1651)

17 Reeve and Adams 1993, 82–3; Connell and Miles 2010, 10; Miles 2012, 42

18 Litten 2002, 99

19 Boucher et al 2015, 72–3

20 Bashford and Pollard 1998, 161; Brickley et al 2006, 153; McKinley 2008, 25–6

21 Litten 2002, 106–9

22 B Richardson in Miles 2012, 47–53; B Richardson in Henderson et al 2015, 70–5; Cherryson et al 2012

23 Bead identifications by Liz Goodman (MOLA) and Hazel Forsyth (MOL)

24 Gilchrist 2008, 132–9

25 Noël Hume 1974, 171–2; Cherryson et al 2012, 77–8

26 Richardson 2014

27 Noël Hume 1974, 171–2

28 St James's extramural churchyard: Davis et al 2010; New Bunhill Fields burial ground: J Pearce and B Richardson in Miles 2012, 50–3

29 B Richardson in Henderson et al 2015, 72, fig 69

30 Mytum 2004, 26–34

31 Including Sheen's burial ground: Henderson et al 2015, 71–2; Bow Baptist church: Henderson et al 2015, 71–2; St Marylebone church and burial ground: Miles et al 2008, 34; St Pancras burial ground: Emery and Wooldridge 2011, 18–20, 158–66

32 LMA, COL/CC/CLC/01/046 (J 54), 11v–12

33 LMA, P69/ANN/A/008/MS04510, item 1

34 TNA, PROB 11/240/148

35 Geological identifications by Kevin Hayward, geologist

36 Geological identification by James Wright

37 Henderson et al 2015, 17; Litten 2002, 215

38 TNA, PROB 11/393/

401; 11/381/636; LMA, P69/NIC2/A/002/MS05686

39 TNA, PROB 11/260/370

40 TNA, PROB 11/71/136

41 Malcolm 1802, 348; GBC 1822, 73

42 Evans 1811, 262

43 LMA, COL/CC/CLC/01/046 (J 54), 11v–12

44 Harding 2002, 154–7; Litten 2002, 207

45 Including Chelsea old church churchyard: Cowie et al 2008, 28–31; Sheen's burial ground: Henderson et al 2015, 65–6; Bow Baptist church: Henderson et al 2015, 41–52; St Benet Sherehog burial ground: Miles and White 2008, 54–8; St Marylebone church and burial ground: Miles et al 2008, 35–45; St Marylebone's Paddington Street north burial ground: Henderson et al 2015, 17–20

46 Colclough 2005, 222

47 Green 1888a, 3 Apr 1648, 'Cases brought before the committee: June 1646', 709; 1888b, 22 Jan 1650, 'Cases brought before the committee: Jan 1650', 1181–90; TNA, C 3/449/55, Jenkes v Clarke, dated 1650

48 LMA, P82/AND/A/010/MS06673/003, 151v: 'stranguled himselfe in his chamber'

49 De Krey 2008

50 LMA, P69/STE1/A/002/MS04449/002, 158; P69/MIC2/A/003/MS0

51 LMA, P91/LEN/A/012/MS07499/002

52 LMA, CLA/002/02/01/2153; CLC/B/050/A/003/MS01993; CLA/002/01/004, 292

53 LMA, P69/MIC2/A/003/MS04063/001, 14v; P91/LEN/A/012/MS07499/002

54 TNA, PROB 11/423/122

55 TNA, C 211/13/J1; C 142/718/144; Baggs et al 1998; Bannister 1923, 55

56 TNA, PROB 11/447/393

57 LMA, P91/LEN/A/001/MS07493

58 LMA, P91/LEN/A/003/MS07495; Carlyle 1900, 420; LMA, P69/MIL2/A/001/MS04429/001; COL/CC/CLC/01/046 (J 54), 201–201v; Milbourn 1872, 83–4

59 TNA, PROB 11/506/349; Anselment 2009

60 LMA, P69/JS2/A/002/MS09140

61 TNA, PROB 11/369/460; 11/365/71

62 LMA, P69/GIS/A/002/MS06419/010

63 LMA, P69/GIS/A/002/MS06419/007; /008, 111

64 LMA, P69/STE1/A/009/MS04455

65 LMA, P69/STE1/A/008/MS04451

66 LMA, COL/CCS/SO/01/04/016; TNA, C 7/182/68

67 TNA, C 11/20/12, Greystock v Bickley

68 TNA, PROB 11/541/129; Baggs et al 1998

69 LMA, P92/GEO/141, 56r; /142, 96v; Lilly 1771, 153

70 LMA, P69/MIC2/A/003/MS04063/001, 111v

71 LMA, P69/STE1/A/009/ MS04455; /008/MS04451

72 LMA, P69/MIC1/A/003/ MS06988/001; TNA, PROB 11/588/159

73 LMA, P91/LEN/A/008/MS07498/001

74 Bevan and Baker 2008; Hegarty 2011, 216; LMA, P69/JS2/A/003/MS09139; P91/LEN/A/002/MS07494/002

75 TNA, PROB 11/588/159; Milbourn 1872, 83–4; Rusen 1910, 14

76 LMA, P69/GIS/A/002/MS06419/011; /015; /010; /012

77 The parish of St Giles Cripplegate originally comprised two divisions, one called the Freedom and the other called the Lordship. The latter became the parish of St Luke Middlesex in 1732 (Baddeley 1888, 37).

78 LMA, CLC/525/MS11316/03, 46; /70, 82

79 LMA, P69/GIS/A/002/MS06419, 9, 92

80 Porter 1997, 176; Cherryson et al 2012, 135; Pearson and Morant 1935, 8, cited in Cherryson et al 2012, 135, 145

81 Cherryson et al 2012, 155; Roberts and Cox 2003, 315; Porter 1997, 263; Richardson 1988, 35

82 Richardson 2001, 52

83 Illustrated by late 18th-century engravings (Hogarth 1751; WL, image no. L0014659/ICV no. 10723; MOL, image no. 3262); Lane 2001, 27; Richardson 2001, 55

84 WJ, 20 Dec 1746, 1–2

85 Kausmally 2015; Dittmar and Mitchell 2015; Arnold 2007, 107–10; Emery and Wooldridge 2011, 153–5; Fowler and Powers 2012, 145–50, 201–10, 212; Miles et al 2008, 34; Richardson 2001, 22, 52–72, 99

86 Richardson 2001, 54–5

87 A view of London and Westminster 1728 repr, cited in Richardson 2001, 55

88 OWJ, 15–22 Feb 1717/18, 4 col A

89 Ibid

90 Ibid, 68

91 Molleson and Cox 1993, 203; Fowler and Powers 2012, 145–6

92 Richardson 2001, 65

93 Molleson and Cox 1993, 205

94 Richardson 2001, 81

95 Ibid, 75–99; Fowler and Powers 2012, 146

96 Craddock-Bennett 2013

97 Molleson and Cox 1993, 205; Cox 1996, 207

98 Cherryson et al 2012, 136, 137

99 Hacking 2006, 116–17, cited in Cherryson et al 2012, 137

THE NEW CHURCHYARD

CHAPTER 6

THE BURIAL POPULATION: BURIAL REGISTERS AND THE EXCAVATED SAMPLE

6.1 The written record

Registering burials

Archaeological evidence suggests that some 25,000 people are likely to have been buried at the ground between 1569 and 1739 (Chapter 5.1). Documentary evidence suggests that by the 18th century at least a basic record or tally of burials was being made by the keeper of the New Churchyard, since Benjamin Clitherow IV knew how many burials had taken place in 1729, something which Maitland published in his *History of London* in 1739.[1] Unfortunately, whatever the extent and nature of these records, they have not survived. During the late 16th to mid 18th century the City and out-parishes of London predominantly buried within their parishes but also 'imported' and 'exported' burials between themselves, as well as to grounds outside London. The New Churchyard's non-parochial status meant that all of its burials were 'imported'. Thus, no single burial record specific to the ground exists, since the registration of burials occurred at the parish where the deceased had been resident and/or had died.

This situation has left New Churchyard registrations scattered across a hundred or more parish archives. Although survival of London parish registers is impressively good, the collection of extant registers of the parishes of London held by the London Metropolitan Archives (LMA) is not complete. The level of register survival is very variable, with many lost over the centuries, for example, during disasters like the great fire of 1666 and the Blitz in World War II.

Historic recording biases mean that the surviving burial registers cannot capture the New Churchyard burial population. A key issue is lack of vital detail. Until the 19th century, there was no standardisation or requirement for burial register entries to be anything more than a brief record of the date and the name of the person to be buried. Entries might on occasion include, among other things, information on ages, gender, addresses, occupations and causes of death of those buried. Only a minority of registers contemporary with the use of the New Churchyard noted the most essential piece of information, burial location.

The second key issue is non-registration – burials not recorded in the parish registers. It has been estimated that during the parish register period as a whole (1538–1850) some 20–40% of burials went unregistered in London.[2] Non-registration occurred predominantly for two reasons: the negligence of clergymen and parish clerks not following correct procedure for compiling accurate parish registers, or non-observance of Anglican registration on religious grounds.

The process of burial registration in early modern London involved several stages. Following the report of a fatality to the parish clerk by the 'Cryer', the cause of death was established by local 'Viewers' or 'Searchers', normally two older women who visited houses to inspect the dead; they reported their findings and were duly paid 2d per body.[3] Parish clerks would then note these details in the parish registers. From the mid 16th century, information on mortality was collected and forwarded to the City of London and Privy Council.[4] Figures may have been more widely circulated but the regular publication of weekly Bills of Mortality (used in particular to track the pace and location of plague mortality) did not occur until the 17th century.[5] However, this process could break down or become considerably confused by 'exported' burials – those who died in one parish but were sent for burial in another.[6]

Cases of non-registration due to negligence may have been particularly common among the New Churchyard burials. In 1609, 1650 and 1653 the Company of Parish Clerks issued complaints to the Court of Aldermen against three of the keepers of the New Churchyard, who were 'admonished' for not checking that proper parish registration had been completed before accepting corpses for burial.[7]

Extensive infringements of the registration procedure led the Company of Parish Clerks to issue a general complaint to the Court of Aldermen on 3 December 1668 against 'sextons & grave makers who entertaine burials from any place without search or certificate or keeping any Register of yᵉ same.'[8] By the 1670s, to ensure that burial numbers were ultimately accurate, it was required that those dying in one parish but who were buried elsewhere in London were sent with a certificate issued by the exporting parish.[9] The new 'certificate system' provided the sextons or keepers of the intended burial grounds proof that the body had been 'searched' for cause of death, the details registered and that any required parish duties had been paid, so that they could then 'interr the corps' at their 'discretion'.[10]

Nevertheless, certificates were not always diligently issued by parish clerks during the late 17th and early 18th century.[11] Certificates for New Churchyard burials were recorded in the burial registers of numerous London parishes,[12] although the practice was perhaps in some cases irregular or short-lived. The parish of St Leonard Shoreditch recorded certificates issued for all its New Churchyard burials between 6 October 1685 and 5 August 1695 (92 burials), but did so only occasionally thereafter.[13] It is probable that the keepers of the New Churchyard would have simply ignored any absence of a burial certificate, thereby allowing burials which could have been 'missed' by the registration system (and are now invisible in Anglican records). The New Churchyard burial total in the year 1729, supplied by Benjamin Clitherow IV and published by Maitland, is the only total to be described as both 'register'd and unregister'd'. Although the total burial number of 270 is perhaps an estimation (or even exaggeration) on the part of the keeper, it does imply that burials were significantly higher during the ground's final decades than registered burial would suggest. The majority of the 'unregister'd' in this period may have been the city's poor; historically, the burials of the poor were more likely to go unregistered, in part due to the practice of clergymen and parish clerks refusing to register burials on account of non-payment of fees.[14] The burial of Mary Burt, a 'poor Woman', at the ground on 9 April 1738, was not apparently officially registered but her extreme age elicited comment in a newspaper (Chapter 3.7). During the 1730s, 'unregister'd' burials almost certainly included Bethlem Hospital patients, perhaps several hundred individuals (below, 'Burying the dead of Bethlem Hospital').

Burials made but not registered because of religion may also be a significant element. The New Churchyard was favoured by Dissenters until the late 17th century (Chapter 4.2). Although Nonconformist burials in London were generally included in Anglican burial registers in this period, references to the religion or denomination of the deceased were very rare. The few contemporary Nonconformist burial registers which were written and have survived were not examined as part of the Bedlam Register project (below). Thus we cannot easily know the true extent to which Dissenters used the ground or indeed absented themselves from Anglican registers.[15]

An examination of wills might find evidence of both Nonconformist and Anglican New Churchyard burials, which are otherwise missing from burial registers.

The Bedlam Register project

The database

In 2014, Crossrail's volunteer programme, the Bedlam Burial Ground Register project, produced the first list of individuals buried at the New Churchyard by conducting an extensive search of the entries contained in parish burial registers held by the London Metropolitan Archives (LMA). An early version was published online by Crossrail in 2015; a revised and updated version has been used by this publication and will also be made available online.[16]

The Bedlam Register volunteers were not able to search the entirety of the surviving records. The 124 parishes selected for examination included all the 97 intramural and 16 extramural parishes of the City of London, as well as four out-parishes of Middlesex and Surrey, and seven out-parishes of Westminster (parish localities as defined by the Bills of Mortality[17]). Ultimately, 21 parishes (17%) could not be examined (ten intramural, four extramural and seven out-parishes) due to constraints on time and resources associated with the enormity of the task. In addition, of those examined, 11 registers (11%) were not checked fully for the period 1710–39, where records survived. At least 40% of the 103 examined registers were affected by damage and/or gaps, with the mid 16th to early 17th century most greatly affected. Lastly, due to the difficulty and size of the task, it is probable that a small number of New Churchyard burials were overlooked.

The project therefore examined 103 parish registers and found 8214 individuals from 75 parishes who were recorded as buried at the site.[18] The project included a burial if, for example, it was recorded as 'at the New Churchyard' or 'at Bethlem' or 'Bethlem' (albeit, variously spelt and/or abbreviated). Entries where 'New Churchyard' might refer instead to 'new' parochial burial grounds were identified and excluded where possible, for example, burials from St Botolph Aldgate. This parish recorded burial location in its registers from 1616, the same year a new parish burial ground was consecrated in Rosemary Lane.[19] 'New Churchyard' burials appear in this burial register alongside 'Old Churchyard' until 1625. Only from 1626 are 'New Churchyard' burials at Bethlem differentiated in the register by the note 'at Bedlam' and so could be reliably included in the Bedlam Register.[20]

Some parishes undoubtedly recorded burial locations more comprehensively and accurately than others, but probably few, importantly, did so consistently over time. Of the 103 parishes examined, 30 (29%) made no reference to the ground, although some of this group would have almost certainly used the ground.

This situation is illustrated by the seven individuals buried at the ground who were identified from gravestones (Chapters 5.4, 14.2). Only two of the corresponding burial register entries noted New Churchyard burial and so were included in the Bedlam Register database. The remaining entries either did not record burial location or recorded a ground other than the New Churchyard, the latter perhaps suggesting burials redirected after registration (Mary Godfree, Chapter 8.2, 'Archaeological evidence: 1665 and later plague burials'). Similarly, there are numerous examples of individuals whose place of burial was not noted at parish registration but are known to have been buried at the New Churchyard from other documentary sources, such as Henry Jessey (Chapter 4.2).

The Bedlam Register data offer much very valuable information, in particular biographic details, and some unique insights, but the data are not a straightforward or necessarily accurate reflection of either New Churchyard usage or of burial population demographics.

Parish bias and parish use

The burials compiled in the Bedlam Register database reflect the disproportionate 'influence' of a few parishes: of the 75 parishes which recorded New Churchyard burials, just five parishes (7%) provided 61% of the total 8214 entries – St Giles Cripplegate (1819/: 22%); St Botolph Aldgate (1261/: 15%); St James Garlickhithe (783/: 10%); St Mildred Poultry (613/: 7%); and St Botolph Bishopsgate (494/: 6%) (Fig 59).[21] In contrast, 31 parishes provided just 103 or 1% of the total entries, each parish recording only between one and ten burials in the New Churchyard.

The spatial distribution of the highest contributing parishes (31 parishes contributed more than 30 burials in total) appears to show that proximity and access were both very significant factors in the choice of the New Churchyard as an extraparochial location for burial. Perhaps unsurprisingly, those parishes

Fig 59 London parishes contributing entries to the Bedlam Register database (scale 1:20,000)

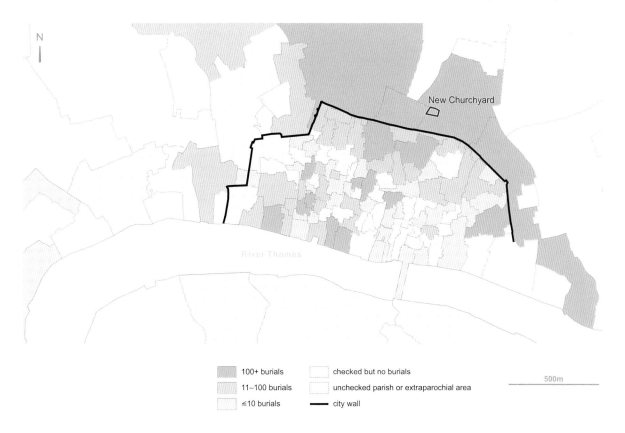

N

New Churchyard

River Thames

	100+ burials		checked but no burials
	11–100 burials		unchecked parish or extraparochial area
	≤10 burials	▬	city wall

500m

closest to the ground sent some of the highest numbers of recorded burials, in particular the three very large and populous, extramural parishes of St Botolph Bishopsgate, St Botolph Aldgate and St Giles Cripplegate.[22]

This aside, a diffuse spread of contributing parishes is seen within west and central intramural London, as well as contributing parishes immediately within the walls to the east. All burials sent to the New Churchyard would have completed their journey either via Moorfields, approaching from the west, or by Old Bethlem (modern Liverpool Street). The spatial distribution of high-contributing parishes suggests several principal routes. The parishes of west and central intramural London would have used Cheapside, then Wood Street, Coleman Street or Broad Street, passing through the city wall via Cripplegate or Moorgate, or along London Wall and Bishopsgate. By the mid 17th century an additional postern, Little Moorgate, was built toward the south-west corner of Moorfields, and would have been very convenient for completing journeys to the New Churchyard. The north-west extramural parishes would have used Redcross Street and Fore Street. The east extramural parishes would have used Minories and Houndsditch, with the east intramural parishes immediately within the city wall also using this route via Aldgate. In contrast, there are no high-contributing parishes in close proximity to Bishopsgate or Gracechurch Street. This absence is particularly notable to the south, where there are no high-contributing parishes within a *c* 300m radius of London bridge; of the 21 parishes within this approximate area, nine recorded no New Churchyard burials, while six recorded less than four burials, three between five and ten burials, one recorded 20 burials and two were not checked. This absence might be explained by the convenience of London bridge; were parishes within easy reach of the bridge more likely to send exported burials south of the Thames to the larger parish burial grounds of Southwark, rather than north to the New Churchyard?

Study of the contribution by parish suggests that these figures could broadly represent a genuine parish usage of the ground heavily influenced by proximity and access, together with parish population size, especially in the fast-growing extramural parishes. However, these data cannot be taken at face value and at least some distortion will have occurred because of the historic recording biases discussed earlier.

In addition, changes in the availability of space in parochial and non-parochial churchyards inevitably had an effect on parish use and the numbers of New Churchyard burials. In 1582, in an attempt to prevent the overuse of St Paul's churchyard, ten of the 23 parishes then using it were forbidden to do so. Some parishes took advantage of the New Churchyard to solve acute burial capacity problems; the parish of Holy Trinity Minories decided in 1602 to send all future burials to the ground, with certain exceptions, since 'our churchyard or common place of burial is but little and not sufficient to bury our dead if mortality should happen'.[23] Unfortunately, the effect on New Churchyard burial numbers created by the first example may be masked by the elevated plague deaths of 1582, and any effect from the second is not evident in the Bedlam Register because the Holy Trinity Minories parish registers were not covered by the project (presuming they recorded burial location). The largest notable fluctuation seen in the Bedlam Register results outside of plague years occurs in 1669–79 and is largely the result of changes in the burial fees of St Giles Cripplegate (Chapter 4.1). The increasing popularity of coffin burial may have also increased pressure on space (Chapter 5.2).

Chronological and demographic trends

The Bedlam Register is undoubtedly a valuable compilation, but one with limitations. The data represent essentially an incomplete sample of an incomplete and inconsistent resource (as discussed above) and not a sound basis for broader statistical conclusions and comparisons. While the Bedlam Register project recorded 8214 New Churchyard burials, it seems very unlikely that further searches would raise the total recorded number above *c* 10,000. The majority of the burials 'missing' from the 1569–1739 burial population figure of *c* 25,000 are probably due to the survival and recording biases of the written record mentioned above, with a significant minority the result of non-registration.

At first glance, Bedlam Register burial numbers between 1570 and 1729 (Fig 60) seem to represent a burial ground rising in popularity, with a period of heavy use before the numbers indicate decline and eventual closure. Between 1570 and 1620 the examined registers show a very slight increase overall and

Fig 60 New Churchyard burials by year (Old Style), as recorded 1570–1729 in the burial registers included in the Bedlam Register project (total no. individuals 8214)

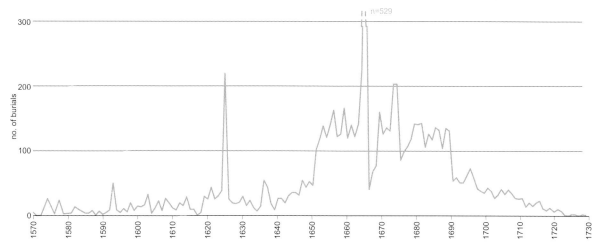

an average of 13 burials a year.[24] A gradual increase in total burial numbers is recorded in 1621–50, followed by a sharp increase in 1651–3 and sustained higher numbers, albeit with some fluctuations, between 1654 and 1689.[25] A dramatic fall in the number of burials is shown in 1690, followed by a steady decline until 1729, the year which saw the latest recorded 'Bethlem' burial discovered by the Bedlam Register project. Significant spikes in the recorded burial numbers between 1570 and 1665 appear predominantly the result of epidemics (Chapter 8.2); other smaller fluctuations may reflect parish usage, which would have varied from parish to parish, according to circumstances and pressure on space locally (above).

The Bedlam Register figures for 1570–1650 might be interpreted as reflecting the ground's rise in popularity during this period or a proportionate rise in numbers relative to the increase in the general population in this period. The recorded figures almost certainly have much to do with improvement in burial register survival rates, since many London parish registers do not survive before the early and mid 17th century. Moreover, the apparent increase in burials in the second and third quarters of the 17th century is probably not genuine but reflects the wider adoption of more detailed burial registration during those decades. For example, the parish registers of St James Garlickhithe and St Giles Cripplegate only began routinely to record burial location in, respectively, the early and mid 17th century. In particular, the apparent surge in burial numbers in 1651–3 probably reflects an enforcement of accurate recording of New Churchyard burials in response to complaints from the Company of Parish Clerks in 1650–3 (above). However, the total number of recorded burials before 1650 is just 1717, including all plague burials. Such low figures (averaging out at fewer than two a month for the first 80 years of the ground's use) seem improbable. While the broad trend of increased usage and popularity may be real, the total recorded numbers must be significantly at variance with the true numbers for this period.

Turning to the end of the century, recording biases during this period may be the source of further distortion. Many registers, which continued to maintain a very thorough record of burial location in 1690–1729, show burial numbers diminishing gradually, before stopping in either the 1710s or 1720s.[26] There are good reasons to doubt this 'pattern': the latest recorded New Churchyard burial from St Giles Cripplegate was in 1714; however, burial locations stopped being noted in the registers during 1715. Furthermore, the apparently dramatic fall in 1690 is undoubtedly a product of sample bias; the five highest contributing parishes in the Bedlam Register are all recorded as using the ground rarely or not at all after *c* 1690.

The actual pattern for the last 50 years of the ground's use is almost certainly one of greater numbers and more gradual decline. Additional research conducted for this publication suggests that further study would reflect this. For example, the unchecked burial registers of St Stephen Coleman Street contain 224 additional New Churchyard burials for the period 1689–1729 (below, 'Burying the dead of Bethlem Hospital'), and those of St Leonard Shoreditch contain several hundred New Churchyard burials in 1676–1721 (Chapter 5.6).

While no New Churchyard burials were identifiable among parish burial registers dated 1730–9, use of the ground during its last few years is clear from other documentary sources (Chapter 3.7). Although the Bedlam Register found only one burial at the ground in 1729, Maitland recorded 270 New Churchyard burials in the same year.

Burying a parish's dead – the example of St Vedast Foster Lane

The data for burials sent to the New Churchyard generated by the Bedlam Register project can be usefully compared with the overall picture of burial that emerges from an examination of a single parish's registers – in this case, St Vedast Foster Lane, included in the Bedlam Register – and that parish's relationship with the New Churchyard and other burial grounds.

The parish of St Vedast Foster Lane, near St Paul's, was by the 17th century, together with its neighbour St Michael le Querne, part of a central belt of more affluent intramural parishes.[27] One of the smaller parishes of the City, it covered an area of c 11,000m^2 (2.7 acres) and contained c 124 households in 1638.[28] The parish was characterised by taverns and prime shopfronts, and was home to the Saddlers' hall as well as jewellers and goldsmiths, centred in Cheapside and at Goldsmiths' hall immediately north of the parish. On average, c 35 burials a year were reported in the Bills of Mortality by the parish during the second half of the 17th century (excluding plague deaths).[29]

St Vedast Foster Lane recorded regular use of the New Churchyard between 1646 and 1680 (Fig 61).[30] A total of 1363 burials occurred in this period: 917 (67%) were buried in the church, 41 (3%) were buried in church vaults, and one individual was buried in the churchyard; 261 (19%) were sent to the New Churchyard, 20 (1%) to other London parish or extramural grounds, and six were buried further afield (Acton, Kent; Kingston upon Thames, Surrey; Paddington; and 'in the country'). The end of the parish's regular use of the New Churchyard in c 1680 coincides with the creation of a new parish churchyard and vault. The last recorded burial sent to the New Churchyard from the parish was recorded in May 1710, and between 1681 and 1710 only 15 New Churchyard burials are recorded.[31]

Their burial registers indicate that between 1646 and 1680 St Vedast was generally sending its poorest to the New Churchyard. During these years, most parish dependants were sent to the ground, including all 'parish children' and 'foundlings', and 43% of the parish's pensioners. The remaining pensioners were buried in the church while parish children were buried in the church's yard after 1680. In the same period, the parishioners of St Vedast sent 36% of their 'servants' to the New Churchyard, while 53% were buried in the church and 11% at other grounds.

In contrast, no clergy, military officers, 'gentlemen' or titled individuals were sent to the New Churchyard from the parish between 1646 and 1680. Moreover, only six (8%) described as 'freeman' were sent, and out of 23 entries that recorded a specific profession only one (4%) was sent (a 'clerk'); the overwhelming majority of these individuals were accommodated in the church or church vaults. Despite burial fees being double for 'strangers' (ie non-parishioners), 61% (33) of those described as such were buried in the parish while 26% (14) were sent to the New Churchyard.

Two deaths were recorded as suicides between 1646 and 1710. One was sent to the New Churchyard; the other was sent outside the parish to an unspecified ground.

Addresses were recorded for 36 individuals sent to the New Churchyard and 197 buried in the church of St Vedast Foster Lane, between 1674 and 1680. Most of the New Churchyard burials (32 or 89%) came from addresses in poorer parts of the parish (Gutter Lane and Old Change), and only three from wealthier parts (Paternoster Row and Cheapside), with one from the adjoining parish of St Michael le Querne.[32] In contrast, only a minority of those buried in the church (81 or 41%) came from poorer parts of St Vedast Foster Lane (Gutter Lane and Old Change), and the majority (107 or 54%) from St Michael le Querne or the wealthier parts of St Vedast Foster Lane (principally, Paternoster Row and Cheapside); nine (5%) came from extra-parochial addresses (including extramural parishes to the north, like St Giles Cripplegate and Harrow on the Hill).

Fig 61 New Churchyard burials sent from St Vedast Foster Lane 1646–1710, by year (Old Style), from the parish burial registers

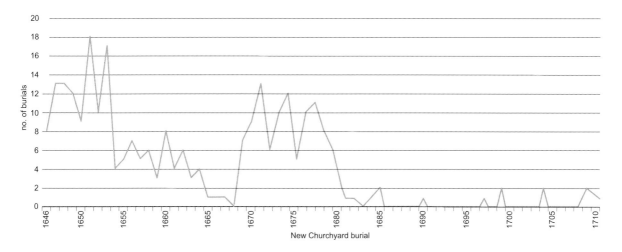

Biographic information from the Bedlam Register project

Parish burial registers provide an invaluable source of biographic information, but the level of information available prior to the 19th century is extremely variable. By its very nature, all entries recorded in the Bedlam Register database included reference to burial at the New Churchyard and at least a partial date. Almost all entries included at least a partial name. However, the presence of further notes, such as cause of death, age, occupation, family relationships or status, varied widely between parishes, over time within those parishes and even between clerks. Parish clerks may well have known the deceased, and the head of household too if that person reported the death. The cause of death was given by the searchers (above) who would have focused on symptoms, especially visible ones.

Gender/biological sex

The registers examined included 8041 entries (ie 98% of the total of 8214) that in some way indicated the gender of the individual for all ages, equated (for our purpose) with the biological sex (below, 6.2). The entries indicated the following ratio for gender: 52% (4294) male, 46% (3747) female and 2% unknown. This slight excess of males over females is similar to that recorded in the Bills of Mortality from 1657, although one would expect more females than males by the 18th century.[33]

Age at death

In total, 5654 entries (69% of the total) in some way indicated age at death, although of these only 127 gave the specific age at death. The ages variously indicated in the entries and then recorded in the Bedlam Register database – using a wide range of definitions reflecting the language of the registers – do not closely correlate with the osteological categories employed in Chapters 7 to 12 (and shown on eg Figs 70 and 71) – a very different construct (below, 6.2). However, the ages and age descriptions recorded in the database can be consolidated into the following broad groups, and so related to the osteological categories (Fig 62):

under 1 year old: recorded as 0 to 4 weeks or described as 'newborn', 'stillborn', 'chrisom' etc – in osteological terms, the <1 year old category, which includes perinatal (ie pre-term to 4 weeks post-partum);
children: recorded as 1–12 years or described as 'infant', 'child' etc – approximating to the 1–11 years old osteological category;
adolescents: recorded as 13–18 years – in osteological terms, the 12–17 years old category;
adults: recorded as 18–c 50 years or described as 'bachelor', 'spinster', 'widow',

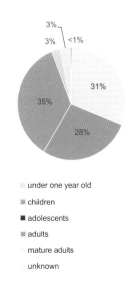

Fig 62 Breakdown of age at death, based on the Bedlam Register database

'wife' etc – approximating to the 18–45 years old osteological category; mature adults: recorded as *c* 50+ years or described as 'aged' – in osteological terms, the ≥46 years old category.

In addition, for the present purposes, those recorded as a son or daughter have been grouped with 'children' (even though the terms may have covered adolescents as well), while those with an indication of profession but no age may be fairly safely classed as 'adults'. Those described as 'apprentice' (13 individuals: seven named as apprentice to a specific person; six simply termed 'apprentice') present more of a problem. Burial registers do not indicate an age for these individuals. The age at which individuals were formally apprenticed varied over time, tending to rise overall through the medieval and early modern periods, but also might vary with the trade or occupation, gender and the individual, as could the duration of the apprenticeship (discussed further below, 'Occupation'; Chapters 7.4, 12.2). For example, Francis Jenkes was apprenticed in 1658 at the age of 18 (Chapter 5.6), Mark Daws in 1766 at the age of 14 (Chapter 13.1).

Cause of death

A total of 2669 entries (32% of the total) in some way indicated a cause of death. Among these burials 60 different causes of death were recorded, with consumption, plague and fever topping the list (Table 1). Although not precisely comparable with the 'diseases and casualties' listed in Bills of Mortality because of the varying definitions/usage of these terms over time, the New Churchyard cause of death categories and relative number of occurrences nevertheless correspond well. 'Consumption', 'fever', 'plague', 'griping', 'convulsions' and 'age' are consistently listed among the most frequent causes of death in the 17th- and 18th-century Bills of Mortality.[34]

Occupation

A total of 1210 entries (15% of the total) in some way indicated the deceased's occupation; 172 different occupations were recorded, reflecting the goods and services industries of a busy growing metropolis (Table 2). Strikingly, the largest group – servants of one sort or another – accounts for 39% (476) of the total number of recorded occupations. However, it is impossible to know how many were domestic servants: only 6% (30) of the servant group are positively identified as such, while 70% (334) are described simply as 'servant'. Of the servant group, 24% (112) also noted the occupation or livery company of their master. Some of those servants not described as domestic may actually represent apprentices, particularly considering the relatively low numbers recorded as 'apprentice' (above, 'Age at death'). Correlation with apprenticeship records could help to identify apprentices within these

Cause of death	No.	Cause of death	No.	Cause of death	No.
Consumption	416	Fits	13	Murdered	3
Plague	339	Imposthume	12	Timpany	3
Fever	281	Measles	11	Affliction	2
Gripes	206	Stone	11	Drowned	2
Convulsions	199	Suicide	11	Executed	2
Age	188	Livergrowne	10	French pox	2
Teeth	148	Suddenly	10	Griefe	2
Stillborn	145	Worms	9	Legs	2
Dropsy	105	Rising of the lights	8	Pleurisy	2
Stopping of the stomach	86	Wind	8	Scrofula	2
Smallpox	73	Lethargy	6	Ulcer	2
Dysentery/diarrhoea	63	Rupture	6	Burning jaw	1
Surfit	41	Scurvy	6	Cholic	1
Spotted fever	39	Accident	5	Falling sickness	1
Child bed	38	Overlaid	5	Fistula	1
Ricketts	38	Thrush	5	Gangreen	1
Tissick	30	Burned	4	Lunacy	1
Newborn	19	Cancer	4	Minds fever	1
Abortive	16	Vomiting	4	Palsy	1
Jaundice	15	Evil	3	Purples	1

Table 1 Recorded cause of death, ordered by number of occurrences, from the Bedlam Register database

Occupation	No.	Occupation	No.	Occupation	No.
Servant	334	Apprentice (unspecified)	13	Haberdasher	7
Servant (occupation of Master indicated, possibly apprentices)	112	Goldsmith	13	Pewterer	7
		Waterman	13	Sawyer	7
Tailor	58	Wiredrawer	11	Baker	6
Weaver	50	Currier	10	Butcher	6
Cordwainer	40	Cutler	10	Saddler	6
Porter	40	Smith	10	Vintner	6
Servant (domestic)	30	Soldier	10	Draper	5
Householder	27	Joiner	8	Dyer	5
Labourer	25	Victualler	8	Founder	5
Freeman (occupation unconfirmed)	22	Barber-surgeon	7	Glover	5
Carpenter	20	Brewer's servant	7	Nurse	5
Clothworker	19	Bricklayer	7	Pedagogue (schoolmaster)	5
		Cook	7	Seaman	5

Table 2 The 40 most commonly recorded occupations, ordered by number of occurrences, from the Bedlam Register database

'servants', but such a task is beyond the scope of this project. This dominance of 'servants' is probably explained by the relatively low fees of the ground compared with parochial grounds (Chapter 4.1). Responsibility for the burial of servants and apprentices would have lain with the families with whom they lived. Therefore, one might expect them to be buried in cheaper and less-favoured locations and (as St Vedast illustrates) not in the same location as the family.[35]

Address

A total of 1227 entries (15% of the total) in some way indicated the deceased's address. These notes were occasionally quite detailed, for example 'out of Mr Guys house in Stone Courte in Gutter Lane'; most were vaguer, for example, 'Minories'. The parish of St Botolph Aldgate was unusually diligent in recording addresses: 749 (58%) of its entries indicated an address.

Poverty and wealth

It is probable that the majority of the New Churchyard's burial population were from the poorer end of the social spectrum and that most Londoners would have considered burial at the ground to be a less prestigious option than parish burial (Chapter 4.1; above 'Burying a parish's dead – the example of St Vedast Foster Lane' and 'Occupation'; below, 'Social outcasts' and 'Burying the dead of Bethlem Hospital'). Nevertheless, a number of London's wealthy and influential citizens chose to be buried at the ground across the entire period of its use (Chapter 5.4–5.6). Among the entries recorded in the Bedlam Register database are 257 explicit indicators of social status. While the majority of these are indicative of poverty (eg 'poor') or social dependants (eg 'parish child'), a significant minority are described as gentry, either 'gentlemen' (27 or 11%) or relatives of gentlemen (46 or 18%) (Fig 63).

The burial of 'gentlemen' and their families appears to have peaked during the period 1650–80, with no such burials recorded after 1695. The number of parish children (foundlings) or those simply described as 'poor' appears to

Fig 63 Indicators of wealth and social status recorded in the Bedlam Register database (under one year old n=4; children n=81; adults n=84; mature adults n=52; unknown n=36)

under one year old (n=4)
children (n=81)
adults (n=84)
mature adults (n=52)
unknown (n=36)

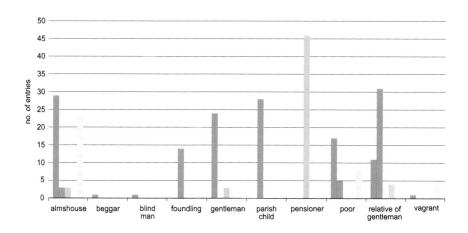

THE NEW CHURCHYARD

have tripled between 1665 and 1700, and increased further still during the early 18th century (Chapter 4.1).

Strangers

A total of 81 entries (1% of the total) in some way indicated the deceased was from outside the parish from which he or she was buried. Of these, those described as a 'stranger' were the largest in this group (38 or 47%); other entries recorded individuals from outside London but within the British Isles, for example Scotland, Wales and Cornwall, as well as individuals from the Netherlands and France (Fig 64). Here, 'stranger' need not imply 'migrant'; however, the majority of adults resident in early modern London were probably born outside London, ranging from members of the civic elite, through the professions, to the poor and actual vagrants (Chapter 7.3).[36]

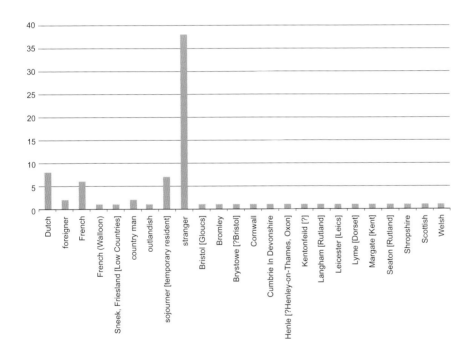

Fig 64 Strangers, from the Bedlam Register database

Social outcasts

In addition to 'lunatics' (below), the Bedlam Register included 281 individuals (3% of the total entries) who might be considered social outcasts or those at the fringes of society, whose burial in parochial or consecrated grounds may have been in some way prevented by parish officials (Fig 65). The Bedlam Register shows eight parishes sent suicides to the ground, four sent unbaptised/unchristened individuals and two sent 'bastards'. By far the largest group of social outcasts was 'prisoners', including seven children born

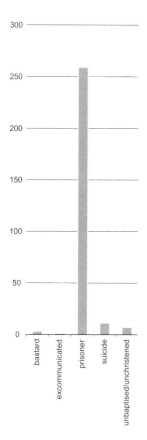

Fig 65 Social outcasts, from the Bedlam Register database

to inmates, who were sent from four parishes – St Mildred Poultry (Walbrook), St Andrew by the Wardrobe, St Michael Paternoster (Royal) and St Olave Hart Street. The prisoners sent from St Mildred between 1598 and 1698 account for 98% of the total; the majority probably came from the Poultry Compter, a small prison run by a sheriff of the City of London that was located in the parish and used to house prisoners such as vagrants, debtors and Dissenters, as well as criminals convicted of misdemeanours, including homosexuality, prostitution and drunkenness. In the early 18th century, Ludgate prison, located in the parish of St Martin Ludgate, sent all unclaimed deceased prisoners to the New Churchyard, paying the expense of coffins, transportation and burial itself;[37] however, this is not evident in the burial registers.

Burying the dead of Bethlem Hospital

The idea that the New Churchyard was used predominantly as a burial place for the lunatics of Bethlem Hospital has become an enduring modern myth,[38] and the idea that the former was owned by the latter has been a commonly held misconception (Chapter 3.1). Documentary evidence shows that the ground was used by the hospital but perhaps not as extensively as has been thought.

From the late 16th to late 17th century the original Bethlem Hospital registered the deaths of both its patients and staff in St Botolph Bishopsgate; however, it is impossible to know how many patients died and were buried during this period because the registers are neither comprehensive nor consistent. In total, 93 burial entries mention Bedlam or Bethlem (spelt variously) between 1558 and 1668.[39] Two are keepers of Bedlam: John Mell ('buried' 1 December 1579) and John Parrott (buried 22 May 1605). Another 35 refer to individuals who were 'in', 'out of' or 'from' Bedlam/Bethlem, but it is unclear if these refer to patients (Bedlam, the hospital) or addresses (Bedlam, the area). Four which mention Bedlam/Bethlem are more clearly addresses, for example, 'in the tenters at Bedlam' or 'from Bedlam Bridge'. The remaining 52 entries, dated 1575–1668, clearly identify Bedlam patients: for example, Margrett Davies, 'mad from Bedlam' (buried 16 June 1578) and David Lewis from 'Bethlem hous' (buried 29 May 1668). A further two burials refer to lunacy between 1558 and 1668 but not as if they were patients of Bethlem: Richard Springard, a 'mad-man' (buried 19 December 1575) and an unnamed 'lunatic' 'in Horseshoue alley' (buried 10 July 1650). Further burials in the registers not clearly identified as Bedlam patients have been shown to be patients by cross-referencing with other documentary sources: for example John Warde (buried 21 July 1602), only described as 'out of Bedlam', and William Ellis (buried 26 May 1618), only recorded as 'hanged himself'.[40]

THE NEW CHURCHYARD

Burial locations, however, in particular were very rarely recorded during this period. The single example for a Bethlem patient during this period suggests that at least some burials were being 'repatriated': John Mascall, a wealthy resident of St Martin Ludgate, who 'died in Bethlehem Howse' on 14 October 1620 and was returned to his parish for burial.[41] There is no evidence within the St Botolph Bishopsgate registers of any Bethlem patients being buried in local burial grounds, specifically, those of the New Churchyard and the parish church of St Botolph Bishopsgate,[42] to the immediate west and south of the original hospital respectively. We can, therefore, only speculate as to whether the original hospital used all or just one of these grounds.

The first 'lunatic' to be recorded as buried at the New Churchyard was John Newton who died 26 November 1655.[43] However, it is not known if he was a Bethlem patient or, alternatively, a suicide. It is therefore entirely possible that no Bethlem patients were buried at the New Churchyard before the hospital was relocated to Moorfields as 'New Bethlem' in 1675–6 (Fig 66).

The burial registration of the new hospital's dead was transferred to the local parish of St Stephen Coleman Street in 1676.[44] Some 720 burials were identified by the parish registers as Bethlem patients between 1676 and 1729.[45] However, this does not represent a complete record since the vast majority of burials registered in the parish before March 1684/5 are unrecognisable as patients because they were recorded only by name.[46] It is not until after March 1684/5 that patients were, with few exceptions, labelled as 'lunaticks' and therefore become evident in the burial register. In the period April 1685

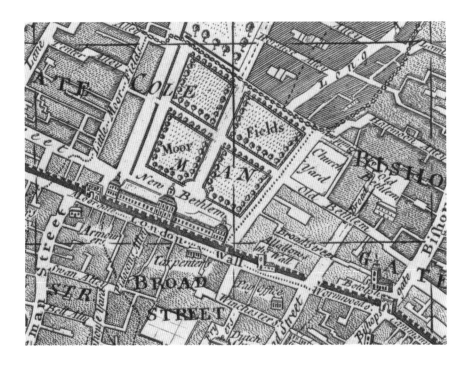

Fig 66 'Old Bethlem', 'New Bethlem' (south of 'Moor Fields') and the 'Church Yard' shown on 'London surveyed' (1742) by John Bowles; north is to the top
(Harvard Map Collection, Harvard Library, Hollis ID 010209490)

to March 1725/6 there were 671 burials identified as patients, with an average of 16 per year and a range of 7–29. These burials match very closely with deaths recorded in the Bethlem admission records which survive (with gaps) from 1683. Cross-referencing of burial registers with recorded dates of death shows that burial generally took place one to two days after death, but that death and burial did occasionally occur on the same day or were separated by as much as a week.[47]

Burial locations only appear alongside 83 (12%) of the total 720 burials identified as New Bethlem patients. Only a small minority of patients (seven of the 83 burials or 8%) appear to have been buried in St Stephen Coleman Street itself;[48] it is conceivable (but not clear) that some would have been local residents. Perhaps a larger minority of patients were buried in other parishes in and immediately surrounding the City. The registers of St Stephen only record one patient who was sent away to be buried in another parochial ground.[49] The burial records of London as a whole, however, demonstrate that patients were sent to numerous parishes during the late 17th and early 18th century, at the rate of at least two to three a year.[50] These burials were predominantly of individuals returned to their home parishes.[51] Finally, burial location notes suggest that the vast majority of patients – 90% (75/83) – were buried at the New Churchyard. It could not have been more convenient: both the burial ground and the new Bethlem Hospital fronted on to Moorfields, separated by a short walk (Fig 66). Those sent to the ground would have included nearly all patients who were not residents of London and who could not, for practical reasons, be returned home for burial.[52]

The last patient identified in the St Stephen Coleman Street registers was on 18 November 1729.[53] One might assume that patient burials continued to be registered at St Stephen but were only recorded by name, as had predominantly been the case prior to 1685. However, although patient burials continued to be recorded occasionally in the registers of numerous parishes during the 1730s,[54] no patient burial appears to have been registered at St Stephen after 1729. Moreover, it seems that the majority of patient burials of the 1730s do not appear in any of London's parish burial records. The most likely explanation for these 'missing' burials is that the majority of patients continued to be buried at the New Churchyard during the 1730s but that these burials were not officially registered and are thus invisible to the modern historian. Bethlem patient burials reappear in significant numbers immediately after the closure of the New Churchyard (Chapter 3.7). The closure appears to have necessitated new burial arrangements. The parish of St Giles Cripplegate became the default burial location for Bethlem patients from 26 March 1739[55] and St Luke Finsbury (a new parish created from the Middlesex part of St Giles Cripplegate) took over this role from March 1739/40.[56]

Archaeological evidence

Only one archaeologically excavated individual was both identifiable and described as a 'lunatic' in documentary sources: Harbert Jenkes (d 1696), who was one of several burials in vault A[556] (Chapter 5.6). No evidence has been found to indicate that he was ever a patient at Bethlem Hospital.

Undated gravestone <2543>, bearing the name 'Ann Cock' (Chapter 5.4), could belong to Anne Cock, of Stephen Coleman Street, who was 'buried in Bedlam' on 14 October 1677.[57] Alternatively, it could belong to Ann Cock of Walmer, Kent, who was admitted to Bethlem Hospital on 7 June 1712 and died there on 24 December 1712.[58] She was buried two days later and, although the location was not recorded,[59] as a non-Londoner she is perhaps more likely to have been sent to the New Churchyard than to a parish ground.

6.2   The excavated sample: the osteological evidence

Don Walker

Introduction: sample strategy and sample 'value'

From the outset of the project, it was clear from both documentary research and evaluation fieldwork that a large amount of human skeletal material would be recovered from the Broadgate ticket hall worksite, Liverpool Street (Chapter 1.1; Fig 2). Consequently, a site-specific strategy was devised by Crossrail and MOLA to address the requirements of the archaeological excavation and the construction project timetable.[60] Preliminary osteological assessment was carried out on 3354 articulated human burials from the New Churchyard.[61] These were subdivided into three categories (A, B, C) dependent on the particular retention strategy applied in different areas of the excavation (Table 3). Surviving burials located within areas of piling activity were removed and reburied by an exhumation contractor working under the supervision of an archaeologist.[62]

Category A burials were taken from 5m² zones distributed over the two main excavation areas, excavated last (Fig 67). These squares were not randomly chosen but were alternated with similarly sized squares from which burials were assessed on-site and then sent immediately for reburial (category C).[63] Burials from areas excavated previously had been retained (category A).

Category B burials were originally designated as category C burials but instead were retained as 'special cases', of particular archaeological or osteological interest. These included individuals from mass burial pit [7482]/[8473], those with grave goods, those with well-preserved or named coffins, or with notable or unusual pathological conditions.

Table 3 Numbers of burials in the preliminary osteological assessment, by category

Burial category	No.	Action
A	1971	retained
B	118	retained
C	1265	reburied
Total	3354	

a

not excavated

not excavated at burial ground level

exhumed (reburied) or 18th- to 20th-century truncation

category A zone, recorded and retained

category C zone, recorded and reburied

10m

b

category A, recorded and retained

category B, recorded and retained 'special cases'

category C, recorded and reburied

Fig 67 Spatial distribution of the excavated sample across the site:
a – the sampling zones; b – category A, B and C burials (scale 1:400)

Category A and category B burials were retained, processed and assessed in the laboratory. A further 357 burials from site A (LSS85: Chapter 1.1; Figs 2, 67) were assessed but did not form part of the analysis sample. They were added to the spatial data for the site.

At assessment, using the age criterion of molar eruption only, the 1971 individuals in category A comprised 1465 adults (74.3%) and 506 subadults (at assessment, all those less than 17 years of age) (25.7%). Spatial data showed a lack of evidence for zoning of adult or subadult individuals (Fig 68). When separated by age category at assessment, the highest numbers of subadults were aged between one month and six years at death (159/506: 31.4%), while 26.9% (136/506) were aged 13–16 years, reflecting a relatively high proportion of adolescent individuals. Neonate or foetal (under 1 month old) burials comprised 2.8% of the subadult population (14/506) and 17.2% (87/506) were aged 7–12 years. The remaining subadults (110/506: 21.7%) were too incomplete to allow them to be placed into specific age categories. There were 950 adult individuals with sufficient preservation to permit estimation of biological sex; 463 were categorised as male (48.7%) and 487 as female (51.3%).

Following assessment, all category B burials went forward for full osteological analysis. In addition, a subsample of burials was selected from category A;

Fig 68 Plan of the site showing distribution of subadult (green) and adult (light brown) burials (assessment level data) (scale 1:400)

N

adult
subadult

10m

those chosen fulfilled all of the following three criteria:

more than 65.0% complete;
in adults, sufficient survival to determine biological sex;
in subadults, sufficient survival to determine age category.

On this basis, 656 individuals were selected from category A; an additional 26 individuals had already been recorded as part of an earlier evaluation phase (=682 category A). A further 22 from category A, while not nominally meeting the preservation requirements, were considered to be of special interest and were transferred to category B (118+22=140); one category B skeleton was then excluded as it was found to be a disarticulated skull, [1459], while two burials within mass pit [7482]/[8473] had each been excavated as two separate contexts and were reassociated at the analysis stage (resulting in 140−3=137 category B). All category B data were investigated separately from category A, as category B were special cases chosen through a different, separate, selection process (above).

In the final calculation, approximately one quarter of the burials (819/3354: 24.4%) excavated from the New Churchyard went forward for full osteological analysis. The excavation allowed the investigation of the density of burial and from this a total burial population was estimated of at least 25,000 for the 170 years of use (Chapter 5.1). Thus the analysis sample probably comprised a maximum of 3.3% (819/25,000) of the original burial population. As category A lacked the selection bias of category B, which contained special cases, it was more representative of the burial population and was utilised for the majority of analyses.

The value of information retrieved from this study was enhanced by the comparative rarity of excavations of 16th- to 18th-century burial grounds in London. This has left a significant gap in our knowledge, at least with regard to the investigation of human physical remains, for the Tudor and Stuart city. Large medieval monastic cemeteries such as St Mary Spital, east of Bishopsgate, fell out of use at the Reformation.[64] There is growing evidence from excavations of late 18th- and 19th-century burial grounds, but Victorian redevelopment destroyed much of the evidence from preceding centuries. Excavations in 2005 at Royal Mint Square uncovered 238 skeletons from a burial ground used by the parish of St Botolph Aldgate; although it dated from *c* 1615 to the end of the 18th century, only 88 individuals were fully analysed.[65] Prior to Crossrail, the analysis of 231 mixed status burials from the burial ground of St Benet Sherehog (dating to the 17th–19th century) was the most significant sample of human physical remains from this early modern period.[66] A group of 17th-century pauper or epidemic graves associated with St Thomas's Hospital were excavated at New London Bridge House in 1991 and, although this produced a study of 194 individuals, the majority of the skeletons were only partially preserved.[67] Skeletal assemblages from a number of sites in London (Table 4), as well as the south-east, were used to compare prevalence rates of disease.

The size of the study sample from the New Churchyard provided an opportunity to investigate in detail a period of particular interest in the growth and development of London, spanning the reigns of monarchs from Elizabeth I to George II. The city witnessed a series of significant historic episodes, including the English Civil War, the plague and fire of 1665 and 1666, and more everyday or mundane changes, such as the opening of the first coffee houses and increased consumption of tobacco and sugar. Plague itself was no stranger to Londoners, with five major outbreaks in the late 16th and 17th centuries (1593, 1603, 1625, 1636 and 1665) (Table 14). Another serious outbreak in 1563 was at least partly responsible for the opening of the New Churchyard (Chapter 3.1).

Evidence from the archaeological excavation of the New Churchyard permitted a degree of phasing of the burial ground (Chapter 5.1). Two main phases of use were defined – 1569–c 1670 (phase 1) and c 1670–1739 (phase 2) – allowing analysis of demographic and pathological changes over time. The identification of mass burial episodes led to the possibility of comparing attritional burials (formed by the normative accumulation of dead

Table 4 Comparative London excavated samples

Site	Site address	Site code	Period of sample	No. of individuals	Reference
Bow Baptist church burial ground	Payne Road, Bow, Tower Hamlets, E3	PAY05, BBP07	post-medieval (1816–53)	416	Henderson et al 2013
City Bunhill burial ground	Golden Lane, Whitecross Street, Islington, EC1	GDA06	post-medieval (1833–53)	239	Connell and Miles 2010
St Benet Sherehog church and burial ground	1 Poultry, City of London, EC2	ONE94	post-medieval (17th century–1853)	231*	Miles and White 2008; *St Benet Sherehog
St Mary and St Michael's burial ground	Bishop Challoner Catholic collegiate school, Lukin Street, Shadwell, Tower Hamlets, E1	LUK04	post-medieval (1843–54)	705	Henderson et al 2013
St Mary Spital priory and hospital cemetery	Spitalfields Market, Lamb Street, Bishopsgate, Tower Hamlets, E1	SRP98	medieval (c 1120–1539)	5387	Connell et al 2012
St Marylebone church and burial ground	St Marylebone school, Marylebone High Street, City of Westminster, W1	MBH04	post-medieval (18th century–1850s)	301	Miles et al 2008
Sheen's burial ground	52–58 Commercial Road, Tower Hamlets, E1	CXL06	post-medieval (1763–1854)	254	Henderson et al 2013

over time) with those made as a result of catastrophe. Similar studies have previously sought to identify palaeodemographic characteristics of plague assemblages.[68] Significantly, studies of ancient DNA in human bone have now advanced to a stage where plague bacteria (*Yersinia pestis*) can be identified in archaeological remains.[69] This, together with other scientific techniques applied within the scope of this project, provided added breadth to the study (below, 'External sampling and analyses'). In addition, the Bedlam Register project, a Crossrail outreach programme, recorded the details of *c* 8000 individuals buried at the New Churchyard, providing crucial documentary evidence of the people, the lives they led and their deaths (above, 6.1).[70]

Preservation and completeness of the analysis sample

The state of preservation of bone recovered from an archaeological site is important as it influences the extent to which detailed analysis can be attempted. Poor survival hampers the ability to recover information on age, sex, metrics and pathological lesions. In category A, preservation of bone was generally good (480/682: 70.4%); only six individuals were poorly preserved (/682: 0.9%). In category B, 76.6% (105/137) were well preserved; none were poorly preserved.

The intensive use of the burial ground was reflected both in the density of burial (*c* 6–8 burials per cubic metre) and the level of truncation (Chapter 5.1). Of category A burials, 37.5% (256/682) were disturbed either during the use of the burial ground or through later works. Adults were more frequently affected than subadults, presumably due to their greater size. Unlike category A, category B burials were not selected for full analysis on the basis of completeness; this is reflected in their increased level of truncation (71/137: 51.8%). Although contained within a single defined pit, later truncation of mass burial [7482]/[8473] affected 40.5% (17/42) of the skeletons.

Redeposited disarticulated human bone was frequently encountered within graves as a result of the high level of disturbance and truncation (category A 487/682: 71.4%; category B 95/137: 69.3%) (Chapter 5.1, 'Charnel'). Some graves contained intrusive animal bone (category A 56/682: 8.2%; category B 7/137: 5.1%).

The high proportion of intercutting burials within the cemetery led to low rates of skeletal completeness overall. The greater the level of completeness, the more can be learnt from a skeleton. It is particularly important when looking at disease as many joint and infectious disorders require an appreciation of the distribution of lesions over the whole skeleton for accurate diagnosis. Category A, which was selected partially on the basis of completeness, was skewed towards a higher percentage of bones present than

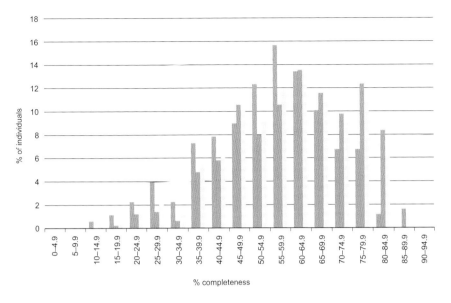

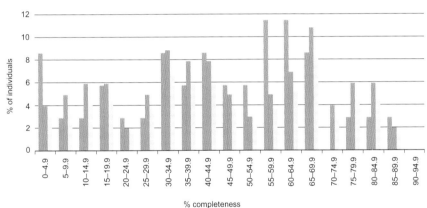

Fig 69 Skeletal completeness (%): top – for category A (n=682); bottom – for category B (n=137)

subadult

adult

all individuals

the other burials (Fig 69). Category B skeletons were not selected on the basis of completeness and thus presented a more accurate impression of overall rates (Fig 69).

Methodology at analysis

All articulated human remains from the selected analysis subsample were recorded directly on to an Oracle 9i (v9.2.0) relational database system.[71] Individuals aged below 18 years of age were classed as 'subadults'.

Assessment of biological sex was only attempted for adults. Each was assigned to one of the following six categories: male, probable male, intermediate, probable female, female, undetermined. Independent checking of DNA recovered from 18 individuals (Chapter 10.8) produced a high degree of correspondence with macroscopic methods (94.4%).

In further investigations of the health and demographic characteristics of the population, Sharon DeWitte (University of South Carolina) utilised transition analysis to estimate age at death for 354 burials from the New Churchyard analysis sample to enhance information on mortality (below, 6.3).[72]

External sampling and analyses

An integrated programme of external work was created based on the potential to enhance the osteological and archaeological analysis carried out by MOLA. The aim of this aspect of the project was to obtain a balance between the quality and quantity of data recovered and the level of destructive sampling. To this end, 40 individuals were selected for sampling on the basis of the phasing of the burial ground and the archaeological research questions. Twenty of these individuals came from mass burial pit [7482]/[8473] (located on Fig 31; Chapters 5.1, 8.2). The other 20 were selected as a sample of 'attritional' burials to compare against the suspected 'catastrophic' assemblage in the mass pit.

Two teeth were removed from the dentitions of each of the 40 skeletons. They were only selected if the same tooth on the other side of the dental arch survived. For example, the first right maxillary molar (from the upper jaw) was only sampled if the first left maxillary molar survived. Those with pathological changes or post-mortem damage were excluded. The choice of tooth also took into account the likelihood of recovering the maximum possible amount of information. In particular, Julia Beaumont (University of Bradford) and Janet Montgomery (Durham University) advised on teeth most suitable for carrying out high resolution incremental dentine analysis, on the basis of achieving greatest coverage of the childhood years. In order of preference, first and third molar, canine and third molar, and first and second molar were selected where possible.

One tooth from each of the 40 sampled individuals was chosen for pathogen DNA analysis (Chapter 8.2), carried out by Kirsten Bos, Elisabeth Nelson and Maria Spyrou (Max Planck Institute for the Science of Human History, Jena, Germany). A horizontal slice was drilled at the cemento-enamel junction and c 50mg of material removed from the innermost surface. This left the teeth largely intact and suitable for use in isotope analysis (Chapters 7.3, 10.1) and all samples were forwarded to Janet Montgomery and Ruth Morley (Durham University), where the teeth of 20 individuals were selected, ten from the mass pit [7482]/[8473] and ten from the attritional sample. Enamel taken from the teeth was submitted for strontium isotope analysis ($^{87}Sr/^{86}Sr$). Julia Beaumont and Nidia Lisic (University of Bradford) then carried out isotope analysis (carbon/nitrogen/oxygen) on the dentine of teeth from the same 20 individuals. The use of two teeth for each individual expanded the period of childhood covered by incremental analysis. Samples of rib fragments from these 20 individuals provided comparative carbon and nitrogen readings from adulthood to enhance the biographical information. Collagen (animal protein) extracted from five mass burial teeth at University of Bradford was forwarded to Stephen Hooper and James McDonald at CHRONO, Queen's University Belfast (Northern Ireland), for radiocarbon dating (Chapter 8.2).

Camilla Speller (University of York) then sampled calculus from the dentitions of eight burials from mass pit [7482]/[8473] and six from the attritional sample. In order to achieve the required biological sex coverage, six further female individuals were selected. This method produced a wide range of datasets with minimal destructive sampling. Food debris, microorganisms, plant microfossils, dust, soot and other pollutants become trapped in dental plaque and then entombed within hardened calculus deposits.[73] Next generation sequencing (shotgun metagenomics) was carried out on this material to study the oral microbiome: symbiotic microbes that at times may become unbalanced leading to, or reflecting, periods of ill health such as dental or periodontal disease. The dental calculus was also analysed through microscopy by Anita Radini (University of York) to identify inhaled micro-debris and respiratory irritants. Lifestyle factors, such as smoking, coffee consumption and exposure to industrial pollutants, were explored through gas chromatography/mass spectrometry of organic compounds by Stephen Buckley (University of York) (Chapter 10.8).

6.3 Demographic overview

Don Walker

Introduction

The New Churchyard was in use from 1569 to 1739 (Chapter 3), a period of remarkable population expansion within a growing metropolis. It is estimated there may have been 100,000 people living in London in 1580, growing to 400,000 by 1650. Problems identifying birth rates affect the reliability of these figures but cannot disguise the dramatic growth.[74] The burial records of the parishes that supplied the corpses for burial at the New Churchyard show that it was most often those of lowly status who were sent – the servants, apprentices and craft-workers (above, 6.1). Probably the majority of adults in the London population would have been born outside London and migrated as adolescents or young adults. Large-scale migration of people who may have lacked immunity to urban diseases probably increased mortality rates in newcomers when compared to London-born residents more attuned to the urban environment (Chapter 7).[75]

Age at death and sex of the osteological analysis sample

The analysis sample contained 819 burials: 605 adults and 214 subadults (Table 5).

From this point on, all analysis will deal with category A and category B as separate (sub)samples.

Table 5 Demographic profile of all burials analysed (category A and category B)

Sex	Age (years unless stated)											
	Perinatal	1–6 months	7–11 months	1–5	6–11	12–17	18–25	26–35	36–45	≥46	Adult	Total
Subadult	27	11	1	52	57	66	-	-	-	-	-	214
Male	-	-	-	-	-	-	63	73	88	35	4	263
Probable male	-	-	-	-	-	-	18	21	11	14	10	74
Female	-	-	-	-	-	-	54	47	33	20	5	159
Probable female	-	-	-	-	-	-	15	34	15	12	7	83
Intermediate	-	-	-	-	-	-	2	2	1	0	1	6
Undetermined	-	-	-	-	-	-	1	0	0	1	18	20
Total	27	11	1	52	57	66	153	177	148	82	45	819

Category A

OVERALL SEX AND AGE

Within the category A sample of 682 individuals were 503 adults (73.8%) and 179 subadults (26.2%), a similar adult to subadult ratio (2.8:1) to that observed at assessment (Table 6).

For the purposes of analysis, males were combined with probable males, and females with probable females (Table 7). There was no attempt to determine biological sex in subadult individuals, as sexually dimorphic characteristics do

Table 6 Demographic profile of all category A burials

Sex	Age (years unless stated)											
	Perinatal	1–6 months	7–11 months	1–5	6–11	12–17	18–25	26–35	36–45	≥46	Adult	Total
Subadult	23	11	1	40	51	53	-	-	-	-	-	179
Male	-	-	-	-	-	-	55	64	77	28	4	228
Probable male	-	-	-	-	-	-	15	14	9	11	6	55
Female	-	-	-	-	-	-	43	44	32	18	5	142
Probable female	-	-	-	-	-	-	11	29	13	9	6	68
Intermediate	-	-	-	-	-	-	2	2	1	0	1	6
Undetermined	-	-	-	-	-	-	0	0	0	0	4	4
Total	23	11	1	40	51	53	126	153	132	66	26	682

Age (years)	Male		Female		Intermediate		Undetermined		Total	
	n	%	n	%	n	%	n	%	n	%
18–25	70	24.7	54	25.7	2	33.3	0	-	126	25.0
26–35	78	27.6	73	34.8	2	33.3	0	-	153	30.4
36–45	86	30.4	45	21.4	1	16.7	0	-	132	26.2
≥46	39	13.8	27	12.9	0	-	0	-	66	13.1
Adult	10	3.5	11	5.2	1	16.7	4	100.0	26	5.2
Total	283		210		6		4		503	

Table 7 Demographic profile by sex and age for category A adult burials

not begin to develop until puberty. The category A sample contained 283 males and 210 females, a ratio of 1.3:1. This was an increase in the proportion of males identified at assessment where the male to female ratio was 1:1.1. It reflects a disproportionate representation of the original sample and this must be taken into account in the interpretation of the results cited here. It is possible that the more robust bone in male skeletons led to higher rates of bone survival, thus causing a greater proportion to qualify for the final analysis sample. The burial register evidence contained indications of sex in 8041 individuals: 4294 males and 3747 females, a ratio of 1.1:1 (above, 6.1).

The percentage age distribution of individuals who were sufficiently preserved to be placed into specific age categories revealed a reduction in mortality risk following the perinatal period (around the time of birth), a notable increase in early adulthood and relatively low numbers of deaths in old age (Fig 70).

The mortality profile of the New Churchyard was similar to that observed at the medieval cemetery of St Mary Spital in c 1400–1539 (period 17), in particular the attritional sample (Fig 71).[76] This was in contrast to that of the low status, 19th-century burial ground of St Mary and St Michael (in use 1843–54), where there was a significant peak in mortality between one and five years of age.[77] However, the relatively undisturbed condition of the St Mary and St Michael's burial ground significantly enhanced preservation of subadult burials. These tended to be buried in shallow graves, and are more vulnerable to later ground works, such as at the New Churchyard. Therefore, subadults, and especially infants, may be under-represented in the New Churchyard as a result

Fig 70 Distribution (%) of aged individuals (n=656) from category A

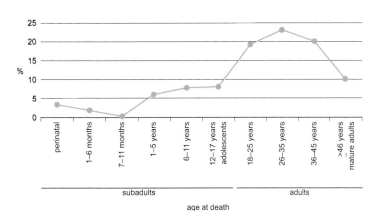

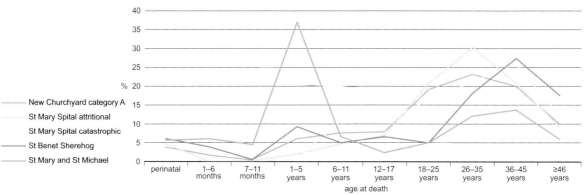

Fig 71 Distribution (%) of aged individuals in the New Churchyard category A sample (n=656) compared with St Mary Spital *c* 1400–1539 attritional sample (n=514) and catastrophic sample (n=122), 17th- to 19th-century St Benet Sherehog (n=181) and 19th-century St Mary and St Michael (n=665)

Legend:
— New Churchyard category A
St Mary Spital attritional
St Mary Spital catastrophic
— St Benet Sherehog
— St Mary and St Michael

of poor preservation rather than accurately reflecting the original burial population. The mortality curve of the 17th- to 19th-century burial ground of St Benet Sherehog reflects higher survival rates in young adulthood when compared to the New Churchyard which may have contained a relatively high proportion of vulnerable, poor migrants from rural areas, lacking immunity to infections common to urban centres.[78] St Benet Sherehog contained both high- and low-status burials and as such appears to have had a greater overall life expectancy.

At the New Churchyard, mortality was higher in the 1–5 age group when compared to the perinatal period but lower than that in the later subadult categories (Fig 72). This makes an interesting comparison with John Graunt's (1620–74) life table, published in his book *Natural and political observations … upon the Bills of Mortality*, in which he calculated that 60% of the London-born population died before reaching the age of 17 years.[79] This reflects a common problem in apparent under-representation of subadults in archaeological samples and in our understanding of the lives and health of children in the past. It must also be acknowledged that infant mortality varied significantly between London parishes, and not just on the basis of wealth, so the data from the New Churchyard present an average of rates obscuring degrees of parochial variability.[80] When formulated in years, there was a distinct peak in perinatal mortality (23/179: 12.8% of subadults) (Fig 72).

The perinatal mortality peak observed at the New Churchyard was reflected in data from the attritional burial sample from St Mary Spital, *c* 1400–1539, and contrasted with the 19th-century (1843–54) burial ground of St Mary and St Michael which peaked around one year of age (Fig 73).

In those subadults assigned a gestational age (ie during development of the foetus), age at death peaked at 40 weeks (Fig 74). The majority of perinatal deaths occurred at 36–40 weeks (18/23: 78.3%), probably the result of still-birth and death at birth or soon after.

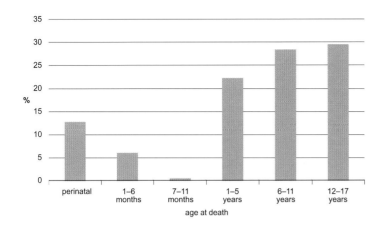

Fig 72 Subadult age at death (%) for category A (n=179): top – by age group; bottom – in years

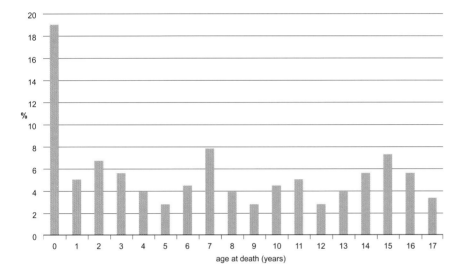

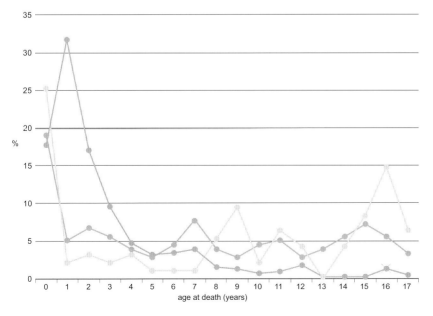

Fig 73 Subadult age at death in years (%) in the New Churchyard category A sample (n=179) compared with St Mary Spital c 1400–1539 attritional sample (n=95) and 19th-century St Mary and St Michael (n=406)

New Churchyard category A
St Mary Spital attritional
St Mary and St Michael

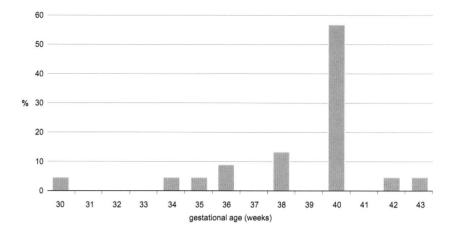

Fig 74 Perinatal age at death (%) in gestational weeks from category A (n=23)

gestational age (weeks)

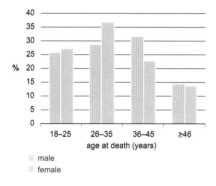

Fig 75 Adult male burials (n=273) and female burials (n=199) age distribution (%) from category A

age at death (years)

male
female

In those adults who could be placed into specific age categories, the mortality pattern by sex was broadly similar, although a greater proportion of females died between 26 and 35 years of age when compared to males (Fig 75). The position was reversed in the next age category (36–45 years). This may reflect increased risk of female death during the main childbearing years.

PHASES 1 AND 2 COMPARED

Phasing of the New Churchyard allowed the burials to be divided into two periods of use: phase 1, 1569–c 1670, and phase 2, c 1670–1739. The comparative mortality curves revealed broadly similar patterns with death rates peaking in middle age (Fig 76). When divided by sex, the only variation by phase occurred in males, with an increase in the number of those living into older age (≥46 years) in the period following the great plague of 1665 (phase 1: 15/145, 10.3%; phase 2: 24/128, 18.8%).[81]

The 17th-century Bills of Mortality show that approximately 35% of deaths were neonatal or infantile, while at least 7% were 'aged' (over c 60 years of age).[82] For a period when a large proportion of deaths must have occurred in childhood, the evidence from the New Churchyard implies that many of the original burial population were missing from the excavated sample. Children were either buried elsewhere or perhaps more likely placed in shallower graves, more vulnerable to casual disturbance both during the use of the burial ground and subsequent groundworks. Nevertheless, investigating any shifts in the relative proportions of different age groups over time was still

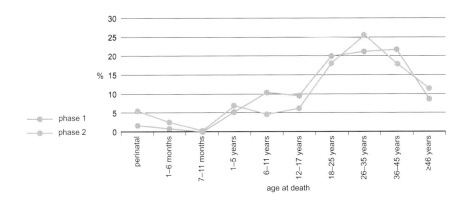

Fig 76 Distribution of aged individuals (%) from category A, phase 1 (n=353) and phase 2 (n=303)

worthwhile (Fig 77). In subadults, the low mortality rates in those aged less than one year of age in phase 1 when compared to phase 2 (phase 1: 9/99, 9.1%; phase 2: 26/80, 32.5%)[83] accorded with Razzell and Spence's conclusions that low infant and child mortality, as well as migration, fed population growth in the 16th and early 17th centuries.[84] We cannot dismiss the possibility that at least some of the increase in perinatal and infant mortality in phase 2 was the result of less disturbance of later burials; earlier burials would be more vulnerable to damage from later grave digging. However, the differences between the two phases may still signify an increase in infant mortality and by implication a greater risk to the health of the very young following the great plague.

Such a rise in risk levels to young children in the second half of the 17th century has been postulated in population studies and attributed to the dangers of urbanisation, including

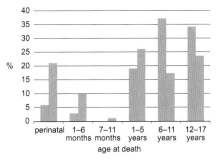

Fig 77 Subadult age at death (%) from category A in phase 1 (n=99) and phase 2 (n=80): top – by age group; bottom – in years

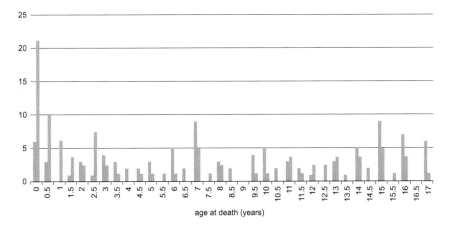

compromised sanitary conditions and overcrowding.[85] Newton compared the infant mortality rates in Cheapside and Clerkenwell for the period 1550–1750 and found that by the final quarter of the 17th century more than 300 per 1000 infants were dying, twice the rate of the first quarter. In fact, the records suggest that mortality was increasing in all areas of the city, where everyday commerce provided fertile conditions for the spread of infectious disease in both crowded and less crowded areas. By the third and fourth decades of the 18th century, infant death was particularly common.[86] Perhaps the similar rate of infant deaths at St Benet Sherehog reflects this and demonstrates that mortality was influenced more by urban living than by status.[87] At the same time, a significant increase in evidence of childhood rickets (vitamin D deficiency) at the New Churchyard does suggest increasingly reduced access to sunlight in the crowded urban environment (Chapter 12.1). It may also be that cultural or socio-economic conditions altered child-rearing habits in poorer areas of London, perhaps leading to an increasingly indoor existence for young children. In contrast, the reaction of some of the wealthier classes was to send infants to the country to live with wetnurses. Feeding practices, particularly for newborns, can of course impact on mortality rates (Chapter 12.1).

In contrast to the rise in infant mortality, there was an equally dramatic reduction over time in the mortality of those aged between six and 17 years (phase 1: 71/353, 20.1%; phase 2: 33/303, 10.9%[88]). In the absence of evidence of decreases in traumatic or metabolic conditions, this may reflect a reduction in vulnerability to mortality from infectious disease. Perhaps a greater proportion of the dead from poorer communities were now buried elsewhere, such as in the new burial ground at Bunhill Fields, opened in 1665 (Chapter 3.1). The poor – whether London-born, long-term residents or recent migrants – tended to live in the more cramped and unhealthy areas of town, where conditions encouraged the spread of typically 'urban' infectious diseases, such as tuberculosis (Chapter 7).

The relative importance of apprenticeships in pre-Civil War towns influenced the sex ratio, with a higher number of men living in London; however, by 1700 women probably outnumbered men.[89] This change was not observed in the demographic analysis of the analysed individuals from the New Churchyard and it is likely that the variation in sex ratio was too subtle to be observed in the osteological subsample.

Included within the category A sample were 22 individuals from a group of 11 burial pits (OA105E) (Fig 31) in the west half of the burial ground that contained a total of 109 individuals (Chapter 8.2). The studied sample contained 12 adults and ten subadults, a ratio of 1.2:1 (Table 8). This small catastrophic sample contrasts with that of the majority of the burial ground that contained chiefly attritional burials.

Sex	Perinatal	1–6 months	7–11 months	1–5	6–11	12–17	18–25	26–35	36–45	≥46	Adult	Total
Subadult	0	0	0	2	4	4	-	-	-	-	-	10
Male	-	-	-	-	-	-	2	1	3	1	0	7
Probable male	-	-	-	-	-	-	1	0	1	0	0	2
Female	-	-	-	-	-	-	0	1	0	1	0	2
Probable female	-	-	-	-	-	-	0	1	0	0	0	1
Intermediate	-	-	-	-	-	-	0	0	0	0	0	0
Undetermined	-	-	-	-	-	-	0	0	0	0	0	0
Total	0	0	0	2	4	4	3	3	4	2	0	22

Table 8 Demographic profile of category A burials from a group of 11 burial pits (phase 1, OA105E)

Category B

Category B contained 137 individuals recovered from areas of the burial ground where skeletons were nominally assigned for immediate reburial (category C). They were instead retained as 'special cases', of particular archaeological or osteological interest (above, 6.2). Far from being a random, representative sample of the overall excavated burial population, category B contained a biased selection of individuals based on predetermined factors. Unlike category A, the demographic profile is unrelated to that of the actual burial sample (Table 9).

Category B contained 102 adults and 35 subadults. It was possible to determine biological sex in 86 adults: 54 males and 32 females (Table 10). The mortality curve was similar to that from category A, showing a broadly similar spread of age ranges, though based on a much smaller, and biased, sample (cf Figs 70, 78).

Table 9 Demographic profile of burials from category B

Sex	Perinatal	1–6 months	7–11 months	1–5	6–11	12–17	18–25	26–35	36–45	≥46	Adult	Total
Subadult	4	0	0	12	6	13	-	-	-	-	-	35
Male	-	-	-	-	-	-	8	9	11	7	0	35
Probable male	-	-	-	-	-	-	3	7	2	3	4	19
Female	-	-	-	-	-	-	11	3	1	2	0	17
Probable female	-	-	-	-	-	-	4	5	2	3	1	15
Intermediate	-	-	-	-	-	-	0	0	0	0	0	0
Undetermined	-	-	-	-	-	-	1	0	0	1	14	16
Total	4	0	0	12	6	13	27	24	16	16	19	137

Table 10 Demographic profile by sex and age for category B adult burials

Age (years)	Male		Female		Intermediate		Undetermined		Total	
	n	%	n	%	n	%	n	%	n	%
18–25	11	20.4	15	46.9	0	0.0	1	6.3	27	26.5
26–35	16	29.6	8	25.0	0	0.0	0	0.0	24	23.5
36–45	13	24.1	3	9.4	0	0.0	0	0.0	16	15.7
≥46	10	18.5	5	15.6	0	0.0	1	6.3	16	15.7
Adult	4	7.4	1	3.1	0	0.0	14	87.5	19	18.6
Total	54		32		0		16		102	

Fig 78 Distribution (%) of aged individuals (n=118) from category B

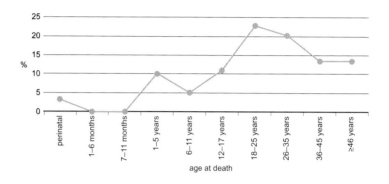

The category B sample included all individuals excavated from the mass burial pit, [7482]/[8473], in the centre of the south half of the ground (phase 1: Fig 31; Chapter 8.2), containing a minimum number of 42 individuals (Table 11). Later disturbance had removed at least half of the pit as first dug, suggesting it may originally have contained at least 100 individuals. The burials from this mass pit comprised 26 adults and 16 subadults, a ratio of 1.6:1; this compares to a ratio of 2.8:1 in the category A sample. Although this suggests there were

Table 11 Demographic profile of burials from mass burial pit [7482]/[8473] (phase 1)

Sex	Age (years unless stated)											
	Perinatal	1–6 months	7–11 months	1–5	6–11	12–17	18–25	26–35	36–45	≥46	Adult	Total
Subadult	1	0	0	6	3	6	-	-	-	-	-	16
Male	-	-	-	-	-	-	0	2	0	0	0	2
Probable male	-	-	-	-	-	-	2	3	0	1	1	7
Female	-	-	-	-	-	-	3	1	0	1	0	5
Probable female	-	-	-	-	-	-	3	3	0	1	0	7
Intermediate	-	-	-	-	-	-	0	0	0	0	0	0
Undetermined	-	-	-	-	-	-	1	0	0	0	4	5
Total	1	0	0	6	3	6	9	9	0	3	5	42

larger proportions of subadults within the mass burial, the result was not statistically significant. In mass pit [7482]/[8473], child burials were included at various depths, reflecting the speed with which the pit had to be filled. This variable extra depth of burial may explain the improved preservation and apparent greater number of subadults.

The mortality profile of mass pit [7482]/[8473] reflects the higher proportion of subadult individuals when compared to category A, in particular in the 1–5 years age group (Figs 79, 80). However, the small sample size hampered comparative analysis with the remainder of the burial ground.

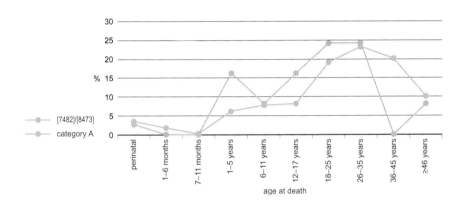

Fig 79 Distribution (%) of aged individuals from mass burial pit [7482]/[8473] (n=42) compared with category A (n=656)

LIVING LONGER? – DEMOGRAPHIC TRENDS IN LONDON USING TRANSITION ANALYSIS

Sharon DeWitte

Previous research into the life expectancy of those within the population who reach adulthood (termed 'adult survivorship') used skeletal samples from a variety of medieval burial grounds in London and found evidence of improvements in adult survivorship and, by inference, health following the Black Death of 1349–50 compared to conditions before the epidemic (ie *c* 1000–*c* 1250 vs *c* 1350–*c* 1540).[90] To determine whether the previously observed improvements in survivorship following the Black Death persisted beyond *c* 1540 in the face of increasing urbanisation, repeated plague outbreaks and on the eve of industrialisation in London, the same methodology was applied to a sample from the New Churchyard.[91] Previous research used transition analysis to estimate adult ages at death, a method developed to avoid limitations associated with the conventional methods of age estimation most commonly used in bioarchaeology (including elsewhere in this report).[92] Skeletal markers of age are recorded and transition analysis applied, which yields point estimates of age for the oldest adults, rather than a broad (terminal) age (eg ≥46) and avoids 'age mimicry' (whereby estimated ages are biased toward a known-age reference sample). This means that patterns of survival and mortality at later ages, which might be obscured using conventional approaches, can potentially be assessed.

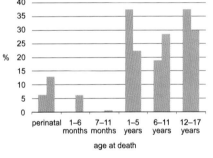

Fig 80 Subadult age at death by age group (%) from mass burial pit [7482]/[8473] (n=16) compared with category A (n=179)

Ages were estimated using transition analysis for a sample of 354 individuals above the age of 15 years from the New Churchyard (phase 1: 1569–*c* 1670, n=194: phase 2: *c* 1670–1739, n=160). These estimates were used in combination with previously obtained data from several London cemeteries: St Nicholas Shambles (GPO, 11th–12th centuries, n=128), Guildhall Yard (GYE, *c* 1050–*c* 1230, n=39), St Mary Graces (MIN86, *c* 1350–1538, n=109) and St Mary Spital (SRP98, periods 14 and 15, *c* 1120–*c* 1250, n=379; period 17, *c* 1400–1539, n=201).[93] These samples exclude the mass pit burials and other category B individuals from the New Churchyard, later 14th-century plague burials from St Mary Graces and catastrophic burials from St Mary Spital in order to ensure that the results reflect normal mortality patterns as closely as possible rather than being biased by the over-representation of pathological individuals or victims of crisis mortality.[94]

Kaplan-Meier survival analysis (a non-parametric approach that allows for the estimation of survivorship and variation thereof within or between populations) was then used on this dataset to assess temporal trends in survivorship across the following broad time periods: 1000–1250, 1350–1540, 1569–1670 and 1670–1739. The results show a significant variation in mean survival time across the four time periods ($p<0.001$) (Table 12). The highest survivorship is seen in the immediate post-Black Death period, *c* 1350–*c* 1540; the associated 95% confidence interval for that period does not overlap with those of any other time periods. This is consistent with previous findings of elevated survivorship following the Black Death.[95] Interestingly, survivorship drops again from this high level in 1569–*c* 1670, and then increases slightly in *c* 1670–1739. There is, however, substantial overlap in the 95% confidence intervals for mean survival times in the *c* 1000–*c* 1250, *c* 1569–*c* 1670 and *c* 1670–*c* 1739 time periods (Table 12). Furthermore, survival analysis of just those three time periods (ie excluding *c* 1350–*c* 1540) does not reveal a significant difference in survivorship between them ($p=0.37$).

These results might indicate that improvements in survivorship and, thus, health were relatively short-lived in the aftermath of the Black Death; the apparent gains might have been lost as the population and available resources achieved a new equilibrium following the epidemic. The apparent decline in survivorship from 1569 onwards might be a product of the socio-economic composition of the New Churchyard, which contained a majority of lower-status burials (above, 6.1). It is possible that in the period 1569–1739 there were substantial differences in survivorship between high and low status/rich and poor people in London, as has been found for the 18th–19th centuries.[96] Thus, the patterns observed here might reflect conditions among the poor rather than a general decline in survivorship in the broader population.

Table 12 Kaplan-Meier survival analysis for London in the medieval and early modern periods (data from St Nicholas Shambles, Guildhall Yard, St Mary Graces, St Mary Spital and the New Churchyard)

Time period	Mean survival time (years) ($p<0.001$)	95% confidence interval
c 1000–*c* 1250	34.2	32.6–35.8
c 1350–*c* 1540	39.9	37.6–42.2
c 1569–*c* 1670	32.4	30.6–34.7
c 1670–*c* 1739	35.1	32.6–37.5

THE NEW CHURCHYARD

Notes to Chapter 6

1 Maitland 1739, 741

2 Razzell 2011; Boulton 2014

3 Picard 2004, 100

4 Razzell 2011, 46

5 Finlay 1981, 118; WL, Bills of Mortality

6 Boulton 2014

7 LMA, COL/CA/01/01/ 032 (Rep 29), 58v; /064 (Rep 60), 256v; /066 (Rep 62), 403v

8 LMA, COL/CA/01/01/ 078 (Rep 74), 34v

9 Burial certificates had been used previously, chiefly to help accurately record plague burials (Razzell 2011, 47), eg 'the clerk do send with every corps to be buried in the new burying place [Bunhill Fields], a certificate with the name of the party deceased', Oct 1665; LMA, P69/SEP/ B/001/MS03149/002, 83

10 Adams 1971, 59–60

11 LMA, COL/CA/01/01 /096 (Rep 92), 50–1

12 LMA, P69/DIO/A/001/ MS017602, Rebecca Thompson 'removed by certificate to Bethelem' 19 Aug 1685; New Churchyard burials recorded 'by certificate' in the burial register of St Vedast Foster Lane, 1681–1709: Littledale 1903, 219–62

13 LMA, P91/LEN/A/012/ MS07499/002 (a parish absent from Bedlam Register database)

14 Razzell 2000, 8, 16

15 Boulton and Schwarz 2010, 32

16 Bedlam Register; Chapter 1.2, n 4

17 Cummins et al 2013, 6

18 Eg noted as buried 'at the New Churchyard at Bedlam' or 'at Bethlem ground'

19 Miles and Bekvalac 2014, 31

20 LMA, P69/BOT2/A/ 015/MS09222

21 The burial numbers of St Mildred Poultry were greatly elevated by prisoner burials (253

22 With average annual burials in 1657–64 of 514 (St Botolph Bishopsgate), 731 (St Botolph Aldgate) and 1126 (St Giles Cripplegate): *Collection* 1759

23 Harding 1989, 118–19; 2002, 97

24 Excluding recorded plague deaths

25 Averaging only 135 burials a year for 1651– 89 (excluding recorded plague deaths)

26 Eg St Vedast Foster Lane and St Peter le Poor Broad Street

27 Cummins et al 2013, 10–12

28 Dale 1931, 60–1

29 *Collection* 1759; St Vedast was united with the neighbouring parish of St Michael le Querne in 1670, after both churches were destroyed in the great fire and only the former was rebuilt

30 Old Style years; Littledale 1903, 173–219

31 Old Style years; ibid, 219–62

32 Dale 1931, 60–1

33 *Collection* 1759

34 Ibid

35 Harding 1989, 123; 2002, 97

36 Earle 1994, 38–54

37 *Prison* [?1725], 59–60

38 Tindall 2016, 88, 136

39 LMA, P69/BOT4/A/ 001/MS04515/001–4

40 Andrews et al 1997, 122

41 See LMA, P69/BOT4/ A/001/MS04515/001, 14 Oct 1620; and 1582 London Subsidy Roll: Farringdon Ward Within in Lang 1993, 224–36

42 An additional churchyard was built in 1615–17 (Chapter 3.3)

43 LMA, P69/STE1/A/ 002/MS04449/002

44 Andrews et al 1997, 340; the Bedlam Register project incorporated only three St Stephen Coleman Street burial registers (dated 1558–

1689 and 1711–23: LMA, P69/STE1/A/ 002/MS04449/001–002 and P69/STE1/A/009/ MS04455; and that dated 1689–1812 has been analysed by the author: LMA, P69/ STE1/A/008/MS04451/ 001)

45 Thomas Tymes was the 'first Lunatick in new Bedlam' and was 'buryed' 2 Aug 1676 (LMA, P69/STE1/A/ 002/MS04449/002).

46 Twenty-four deaths are recorded in the admissions register in 1684 (Old Style years); four appear not to have been recorded in the burial register of St Stephen Coleman Street, 17 are listed only by name and only three are listed as 'lunaticks' (BRH, ARA-01).

47 BRH, ARA-01; LMA, P69/STE1/A/002/ MS04449/001; /009/MS04455; /008/ MS04451/001

48 Four burials in the parish churchyard, two in vaults and one in the church

49 Thomas Yates, whose death and burial was recorded in St Stephen Coleman Street on 5 Apr 1712 as 'dyed of feaver in Bethlem' and 'at St Lawrance Jewry' respectively (LMA, P69/ STE1/A/009/MS04455; /008/MS04451/ 001), and then recorded in St Lawrence Jewry as buried in the 'middle isle' on 8 Apr 1712 (LMA, P69/LAW1/A/ 002/MS06975).

50 Most, if not all, of this group were double registered: once in the registers of St Stephen Coleman Street, but without any indication of burial location, and again in the register of the parish of burial, which only intermittently noted that the individual had come from Bethlem Hospital.

51 Eg William Miles, a joiner of St Andrew

Holborn, who died on 1 Jan 1698/9 (BRH, ARA-01, 260), burial registered 2 Jan 1698/9 in St Stephen Coleman Street without any note on location (LMA, P69/STE1/A/008/MS04 451/001) and in St Andrew Holborn on 8 Jan 1698/9 as 'William Miles from Bethlem' (LMA, P82/AND/A/ 010/MS06673/007); Dorothy Howard 'off St Paul Shadwell', died on 16 Mar 1697/8 (BRH, ARA-01, 201), burial registered on 16 Mar 1697/8 in St Stephen Coleman Street without any note on location (LMA, P69/STE1/A/ 008/MS04451/001) and in St Paul Shadwell on 21 Mar 1697/8 as 'Dorothy Howard from St Stephen Coleman Street by certificate' (LMA, P93/PAU3/033).

52 Eg John Langley of Little Horsted (Sussex) who 'Dyed Lunatick in Bethlam' on 1 Feb 1722/3 (BRH, ARA-05, 106; LMA, P69/STE1/ A/009/MS04455) and was recorded as a 'Lunatick bu[ried] at Bethlem' on the same day (LMA, P69/STE1/ A/008/MS04451/001); most patients from outside London came from the home counties, but others came from as far away as Glasgow (Lanarkshire), Bangor (Caernarfonshire) and Falmouth (Cornwall), with one patient noted as 'from Bermudas' (BRH, ARA-01, 238, 252, 277 and 222).

53 Mary Clark who 'dyed Lunatick in Bethlem' and was 'buried' (LMA, P69/STE1/A/008/MS04 451/001).

54 Eg Christopher Lockman, d 30 Jan 1736/7 (BRH, ARA-04, 335), buried in St George Bloomsbury 2 Feb 1736/7 (LMA, P82/GEO1/056); Robert Preston, d 24 Oct 1736 (BRH, ARA-05, 338), buried in All Hallows the Great 27 Oct 1736 (LMA, P69/ ALH7/A/002/MS05161)

55 Twenty-two Bethlem patients were recorded alongside the note 'from Bedlam' in the burial register between 26 Mar 1739 and 7 Feb 1739/40: eg Jane Chissell of Henley-on-Thames (Oxfordshire) d 6 Nov 1739 (BRH, ARA-05, 61), buried in St Giles Cripplegate 10 Nov 1739 (LMA, P69/GIS/A/002/MS06419/017); occasional burials also appear in other parishes during this period, eg William Meacham, d 7 Oct 1739 (BRH, ARA-05, 62), buried St Dunstan in the West 10 Oct 1739 (LMA, P69/ DUN2/A/018/MS10350)

56 Mary Green, d 4 Mar 1740 (BRH, ARA-05, 59), buried at St Luke Finsbury 6 Mar 1739/40 (LMA, P76/LUK/001)

57 LMA, P69/STE1/A/002/MS04449/002

58 BRH, ARA-03, 217

59 LMA, P69/STE1/A/008/MS04451/001; /009/MS04455

60 Crossrail 2014

61 Carty et al 2016

62 Carver 2012

63 Carty et al 2016

64 Connell et al 2012

65 Miles and Bekvalac 2014

66 *St Benet Sherehog*

67 *St Thomas's Hospital*

68 Margerison and Knüsel 2002; Gowland and Chamberlain 2005

69 Bos et al 2011

70 Bedlam Register; Chapter 1.2, n 4

71 Connell and Rauxloh 2007; Powers 2008

72 DeWitte 2010; 2014a; 2014b; 2014c; DeWitte and Slavin 2013

73 Warinner et al 2015

74 Finlay 1981, 51, 56

75 Roberts and Cox 2003, 293, 296–7; Newton 2011, 260, 265

76 Connell et al 2012, 34

77 Henderson et al 2013, 101

78 *St Benet Sherehog*; Roberts and Cox 2003, 293–4

79 Glass 1950, 60

80 Finlay 1981, 101–3

81 χ^2=3.92 df=1, p≤0.05

82 Benjamin and Graunt 1964, 18, 21, 23, 52

83 χ^2=11.74 df=1, p≤0.001

84 Razzell and Spence 2007, 271

85 Houston 1996, 144

86 Porter 1991, 13; Newton 2011, 260, 265, 268

87 *St Benet Sherehog*

88 χ^2=11.74, df=1, p≤0.001

89 Finlay 1981, 140–1

90 DeWitte 2014b; 2014c

91 DeWitte 2016

92 Boldsen et al 2002

93 DeWitte 2014b; 2014c

94 Grainger and Phillpotts 2011; Connell et al 2012

95 DeWitte 2014c

96 DeWitte et al 2016

THE NEW CHURCHYARD

CHAPTER 7

LIVING AND WORKING IN LONDON

7.1 Population growth, housing and the urban environment

Niamh Carty and Don Walker

Our interpretation of the results of osteological analysis of past populations can be significantly enhanced by an interpretation of the environment and conditions in which people lived and worked. For those buried in the New Churchyard, this was, ultimately, the London metropolis, where the urban experience must have differed increasingly from that of rural life.

This was a time of significant change for London and those who lived there. Population growth was fed by migration from within this country and from abroad; London became the number one destination in England for emigrants from Europe. Work opportunities in the 16th and 17th centuries appear to have been filled rapidly by migrants.[1] As Clark states, 'immigration rates were substantial, as more and more people from England and abroad came to the city to take advantage of its economic, political and cultural attractions'.[2] By 1715, the population of the capital was probably over 600,000 and London had become the largest city in Western Europe. By the turn of the 18th century, almost 10% of the population of England and Wales counted London as home.[3] London was a pre-industrial city during the period in which the New Churchyard was in use, but population growth would have a lasting impact on living standards for the city's inhabitants.[4]

London presented a changed landscape in *c* 1550 after the suppression of the monasteries: religious landlords were replaced by aristocratic ones, mansions were carved out of religious precincts, monastic churches were demolished or turned into parish churches and land became available for new building.[5] From the last quarter of the 16th century there was a great increase in house building, including over any remaining open spaces and, in particular, for rent, as seen in the new streets of Spitalfields, east of Bishopsgate.[6] Brick was replacing stone, particularly in prestigious buildings, but most houses were still timber-framed with wattle and daub walls. In some areas of town rich and poor lived side by side. At the turn of the century, the surveyor Ralph Treswell's descriptions of properties ranged from one-room and two-room plan houses, to medium-sized and larger houses. One-room plan houses had a room on two floors; two-room plan houses doubled up as workrooms and shops. Upper-storey jetties protruded into the airspace above the streets, blocking sunlight and bringing houses on opposite sides of the street closer together. Those streets were generally narrow; lanes and courts were cramped.[7]

Merry and Baker's work on marriage duty tax assessments from 1695 in the parishes of wealthy Cheapside and poorer Aldgate showed that larger households contained greater numbers of apprentices and servants – apprentices commonly lodged with their masters, as might servants. The city centre parishes of Cheapside, rather than suburban Aldgate, housed the majority of unmarried people and single parent families.[8] It became common to take in lodgers and their families, both in the centre and the suburbs; just under half of properties contained two or more households.[9]

Urban living in the 17th and 18th centuries was generally associated with low standards of health and high rates of mortality when compared to rural areas.[10] This would have particularly affected the most vulnerable in society, the poorer classes. With so many people coming to London to find work, slum areas grew quickly. Poor families with children born in London and those who migrated to the city sought accommodation in the capital's overcrowded streets and alleys. Many lived near their place of work, in ramshackle tenements or in damp cellars, with no sanitation or fresh air. For the poor, the standard home was a single rented room, which sometimes doubled as a workshop.[11] Increases in manufacturing and home-based occupations such as textile working would have resulted in long hours spent indoors. Busy mothers perhaps could not afford their work to be interrupted by their child's demands. Babies were often swaddled and bound tightly in strips of cloth to restrict their movements; this may have resulted in many developing rickets (Chapter 12.1).[12] Despite this, London was still surrounded by accessible green fields, and fresh air, for those with time for recreation.[13]

Sanitation had been a concern of the city since the 12th century: private cesspits were regulated, 'common' or public privies were provided in busy parts of the capital. Legislation attempted remedies; a Bill of Sewers, for example, was passed in 1531 to establish a systematic cleaning and drainage of the city.[14] Cleanliness, however, would always be difficult to enforce in crowded alleyways lined with multistorey and multi-tenanted 'slums' and their overflowing cesspits. Animal waste, rubbish and blocked drains could cause perilous slippery conditions and pedestrians were also exposed to filth thrown from the windows of the projecting upper storeys.[15] Hugh Peter, a Puritan minister who spent some time in Amsterdam in the 1630s, criticised the state of London's streets. He wrote that in the city 'we see most beastly durtie streets', which fouled clothes and shoes and caused dirt to be carried into houses, in contrast to the cleanliness of their Dutch counterparts.[16] Piped water was not generally available, and garden or backyard wells, where these existed, were often dug close to privy cesspits. Otherwise, water had to be bought or fetched from the local conduit or pump, which would have been vulnerable to contamination.[17]

7.2   Environmental pollution

Niamh Carty

The environment in which an individual lives, with occupational hazards and domestic pollution, can have a huge impact on health, particularly in relation to susceptibility and exposure to infectious disease. Inside and outside the city walls, the increased population accounted for many new problems that Londoners had to face, including environmental pollution in the form of overcrowding and cramped living conditions, and the transmission of new and existing infectious diseases.[18] The immune status of new immigrants to the city could have resulted in them being more susceptible or conceivably more robust than their London-born peers, 'contingent on the nature of the diseases they encountered, and the epidemiology of their native environment' (Chapter 12.2).[19]

Living conditions in the city and growing trade with the rest of the world from the 16th century onwards created an ideal environment for an increase in infectious disease epidemics.[20] These included not only plague, which recurred at frequent intervals, but also influenza, scarlet fever, tuberculosis, typhus, typhoid, diphtheria, measles, whooping cough and smallpox. As a result, it was not uncommon for London to lose 10% or more of its total population to epidemic disease outbreaks in any given decade. During the 18th century, more people died in London than were baptised every year; it was only the steady flow of migrants to London that prevented the population declining dramatically (below, 7.3).[21]

The main fuel burnt during this period was sea coal, which had an influence on the levels of smog and general aerial pollution in the atmosphere.[22] Wood was becoming a scarce resource, due to the high cost of road transportation into London and limited timber resources near the navigable rivers in south-east England.[23] The move to sea coal led to complaints about fuel emissions, with Queen Elizabeth so 'grieved and annoyed with the taste and smoke of sea cooles' that in 1578 the Company of Brewers promised to use only wood in their brewing operations in the future'.[24] Sea coal remained unpopular into the 17th century in London, 'so during times of wood shortage it was the poor who were obliged to change over to this cheaper and dirtier source of heat'. The rich did not favour the use of it, but there was greater acceptance of its use after the death of Elizabeth I. By that time, 50,000 metric tonnes of sea coal a year were being used in London.[25] Hugh Platt wrote in *A fire of coal-balles* in 1603 that smoke from burning coal caused damage to plants and buildings in the City of London.[26]

John Evelyn, the writer and diarist, among others, wrote treatises in the 17th century on the topics of smog and smoke in the city, the associated risks and the possible solutions.[27] In 1661 Evelyn presented Charles II with a pamphlet in which he compared London unfavourably with cities on the Continent, complaining of the overcrowding, poor planning and pollution caused by smoke and sulphur. A wide variety of occupations contributed to these noisome conditions, including salt- and glue-makers, bakers, brewers, soap-boilers and slaughterhouses. Evelyn blamed domestic pollution produced by the acrid and sulphurous smoke of sea-coal fires for deaths from pulmonary and tubercular disorders, claiming that this accounted for nearly half of all deaths in the city. A multitude of smoking chimneys must have shrouded the crowded streets and courts in smog.[28]

This period also saw the characteristic wide climatic variability and effects of the 'Little Ice Age'.[29] Mean temperatures in England were probably a degree or two less than at the end of the 20th century; extreme weather events such as storms became more frequent, with wide oscillations in rainfall and some summers that may have been extremely wet.[30] This climate may have impacted on food supply with changes in diet and the availability of fresh food affecting the health of Londoners (Chapter 10). A reduction in the rate of rickets recorded in the London Bills of Mortality in the early 18th century may reflect an improvement in climate.[31]

Pollution – domestic and occupational – is particularly relevant when examining the respiratory health of those buried at the New Churchyard. Evidence for inflammation and infection of the respiratory systems may be present in the form of active or healed lesions to the visceral (lung-facing) surfaces of the ribs and maxillary sinus cavities reflecting chronic sinusitis. Both of these conditions would have been directly impacted by the levels of pollution.[32] The most abundant opportunistic pathogens detected within dental calculus DNA were those species which are commonly found within the healthy oral microbiome or respiratory tract, but which may occasionally result in acute infections in immunocompromised individuals. Examples of such opportunistic pathogens included bacteria such as *Streptococcus pneumoniae*, *Streptococcus pyogenes* and *Haemophilus influenzae*, which can cause upper and lower respiratory infections (Chapter 10.8).

The French envoy Honoré de Courtin was afflicted with a bad cough shortly after he arrived in London in 1665 and complained bitterly about the 'vapours du charbon de terre'.[33] By the early 1600s, the College of Physicians in London had determined that the areas which saw an expansion of poor-quality housing, which attracted the city's poor due to low rents, had higher rates of disease, and physicians shifted their emphasis to encompass the patient's living environment.[34] Graunt's analysis of the Bills of Mortality determined that 19% of deaths in the 17th century were directly attributed to consumption and coughs.[35] Graunt also made the link between the built environment and disease in 1662 in his *Natural observations*, particularly the relationship between (as he put it) the 'waxing and waning of diseases' and the quality of the built environment.[36] By the 18th century occupational hazards were having an impact on the health of Londoners: 'industrial diseases were rife, silicosis destroyed potters, chimney sweeps got cancer, and lead poisoning killed paint makers'.[37]

Only some 15% of the entrants in the Bedlam Register database had evidence of occupation; of the more specific named trades, some of the most common involved the textile and clothing industries: tailors (58), weavers (50) and clothworkers (19) (Chapter 6.1; Table 2). Correlation of such evidence with specific individuals is not possible. However, male [8198] from mass burial pit [7482]/[8473], who died between 18 and 25 years of age, was found to have a relatively high number of sheep wool fibres encased within his dental calculus; he may have lived and/or worked with wool or perhaps close to livestock. All 20 individuals analysed in this study (Chapter 10.8) had microscopic fragments of charcoal trapped within their dental calculus, no doubt as a result of everyday exposure to burning fires. Female [175], who died aged 36–45 years, had a particularly high concentration of charcoal when compared to the others, suggesting exposure to unusual levels of pollutant during occupational activity, rather than normal domestic living. There was no skeletal evidence that this affected her health.

All of the 20 individuals investigated using a range of isotopes and trace elements experienced what by modern standards is regarded as a high level of lead exposure during childhood and may have suffered subclinical and possibly clinical effects (below, 7.3).[38]

Neoplastic disease

Niamh Carty

Neoplastic disease is a generic term for a large group of diseases that can affect any part of the body. A defining feature of these diseases is the formation of abnormal cells that grow beyond their usual boundaries, and which can then metastasise or spread to adjoining parts of the body.[39] Modern clinical evidence indicates that a principal contributor to many types of cancer, particularly in younger individuals, is the environment, with outdoor air pollution in urban settings as well as indoor air pollution possible factors (above).[40] This has been demonstrated through multi-generation migrant studies showing adaptation to the cancer risk of the host country.[41]

Neoplastic disease was found in 27 category A individuals from the New Churchyard (/682: 4.0%), 1.7% of subadults (3/179) and 4.8% of adults (24/503). The distribution of adult males and females affected by neoplastic

	Subadult			Male		
Table 13 Crude prevalence of neoplastic disease by type for category A and category B burials	No. of individuals	No. affected	%	No. of individuals	No. affected	%
Category A	179			283		
Osteoma (including button osteoma)		0	-		6	2.1
Osteoid osteoma		0	-		2	0.7
Osteochondroma		1	0.6		2	0.7
Meningioma		1	0.6		0	-
Bone cyst		1	0.6		4	1.4
Metastatic carcinoma (osteoblastic)		0	-		0	-
Category B	35			54		
Osteoma (including button osteoma)		0	-		3	5.6
Osteochondroma		0	-		2	3.7
Metastatic carcinoma (osteoblastic)		0	-		1	1.9

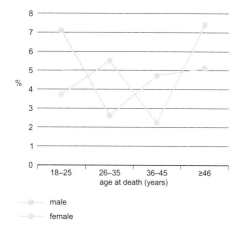

male

female

Fig 81 Crude prevalence of neoplastic disease by age for category A males (n=273) and females (n=199)

disease varies across age groupings, but was very similar across the population with 4.9% (14/283) of males affected and 4.3% (9/210) of females in the total group (Table 13; Fig 81).

Adult male [1551] displayed a rare perineurial cyst also known as a Tarlov cyst; these represent fluid-filled sacs that affect the nerve roots in the spine and particularly the sacrum. Usually asymptomatic, some cysts result in progressive thinning of the surrounding bone and in dry bone are characterised by the gradual destructive lesions and regions of marked bone thinning revealed on radiographs (Fig 82).[42]

Metastatic bone tumours represent the most common form of bone tumours, with metastatic carcinomas the most prevalent, reflecting the spread of cancerous cells through the blood to the bone.[43] Female [5012], aged 36–45 years, had widespread remodelled florid, osteoblastic and lytic lesions across the right ilium and ischium of the pelvis. Radiographs revealed multiple areas of increased density. These bone changes were consistent with an osteoblastic metastatic carcinoma.

There were both bone forming and bone eroding lesions primarily located bilaterally (both sides) on the upper axial skeleton of adult male [3293], aged 26–35 years. There were lesions of thick, light brown-coloured, new

| Female | | | Adult | | | Total | | |
No. of individuals	No. affected	%	No. of individuals	No. affected	%	No. of individuals	No. affected	%
210			503			682		
	5	2.4		12	2.4		12	1.8
	0	-		2	0.4		2	0.3
	0	-		2	0.4		3	0.4
	0	-		0	-		1	0.1
	2	1.0		6	1.2		7	1.0
	1	0.5		0	-		1	0.1
32			102			137		
	0	-		3	2.9		3	2.2
	0	-		2	2.0		2	1.5
	0	-		1	1.0		1	0.7

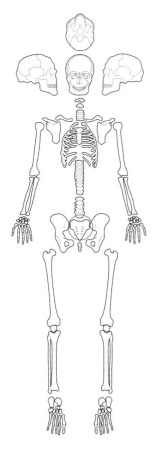

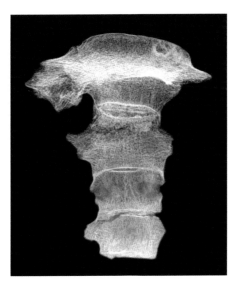

Fig 82 Sacrum of adult male [1551] in (left) radiograph and (right) photograph, displaying evidence of a possible Tarlov cyst (scale c 1:2)

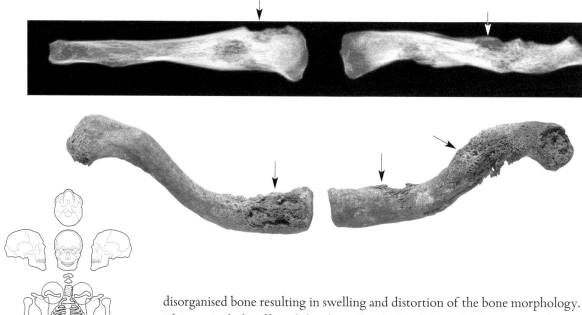

Fig 83 (top) Radiograph and (bottom) photograph of adult male [3293] displaying both clavicles showing evidence for metastatic carcinoma (scale *c* 1:2)

disorganised bone resulting in swelling and distortion of the bone morphology. This particularly affected the clavicular shafts of the collar bones, scapular or shoulder blades and mandibular rami (part of the lower jaw bone which articulates with the upper jaw). Lytic lesions were present to the internal and outer surfaces of the frontal and parietal bones of the skull, clavicles, scapulae, mandible, manubrium (sternum of the rib cage), right ulna and left radius (lower arm). The sternal rib ends were inflamed with osteoblastic lytic lesions (Fig 83). Radiographs revealed destructive lesions consistent with metastasis. Similar bone changes identified in skeleton [605] from the 17th- to 19th-century Aldgate burial ground were attributed to prostate cancer.[44]

7.3 Migration from the country into London

Don Walker

For much of its history London has attracted migrants from other parts of Britain, Continental Europe and beyond. While many travelled from other urban centres, it was those from rural settlements who would have experienced the most significant changes in living and working environments. Being raised in the countryside may have provided certain health advantages when compared to crowded towns, but migration to London would have increased the risk of exposure to 'urban' communicable diseases such as tuberculosis. Indeed, a much higher number of people died each year in London than were born there: large-scale immigration was a necessity.[45] Whereas infants and young children buried within the New Churchyard were probably born in London, a high proportion of the adults would have been born outside London and migrated in adolescence or early adulthood. With an estimated net annual influx of 8000 people between 1650 and 1750, London was a city where adapting to the crowded, polluted environment was a key factor affecting levels of mortality and morbidity.[46]

While industry remained small-scale and largely focused in rural areas during the early 16th century, trade depressions and harvest failures in the south of England led to increasing migration from the countryside into urban centres. The lives of those who worked on the land were hard and laborious, subject to the vagaries of weather and without prospect of attaining anything approaching wealth. Life in towns must have seemed attractive to all classes and London in particular was a draw.[47]

As in previous periods, it was the young, both rich and poor, who migrated to London, those in their 20s and especially teenagers. Long-distance apprentice migration was not uncommon in the 16th century, with many travelling more than 200km to reach London.[48] Clark identified two subdivisions of migrants prior to the Civil War of the 1640s: servants, apprentices and 'would-be spouses' who tended to travel to a nearby village or town; and longer-travelling 'subsistence' migrants, seeking to escape destitution by finding relief or casual employment. Many of the latter were young male vagrants who came to London from all over England.[49] There is some evidence to suggest a fall in large-scale subsistence migration following the Restoration of 1660, partly as a result of a decrease in urban mortality and rising agricultural output. The plight of the poor was mitigated by improved living conditions and rising real wages. A reduction in the role of apprenticeships by the beginning of the 18th century must also have played a part in the falling numbers of young migrants.[50] A possible reduction in subsistence migration did not mean a fall in migration overall, which continued at a high rate in the later 17th and into the 18th century. London offered economic opportunities that pulled in those seeking to improve their circumstances, including gentry, professionals and the middling classes, attracted by recreational pursuits, investment opportunites and marriage prospects. This, allied to booming trade, led to the economic growth that sustained the rapidly rising population.[51]

There was scant direct evidence in the Bedlam Register database of those who had moved to London from elsewhere, even though migrants of one sort or another probably accounted for the majority of adult residents. Many would have become assimilated as Londoners and been buried in London parish and non-parochial burial grounds. Of the 82 names identified as coming from outside London, 38 (46.3%) were simply noted as 'strangers' (Chapter 6.1; Fig 64). Where origins were given, most came from the south of Britain or the Midlands, although there were also nine Dutch, seven French and one Scot. In many cases the origins of the deceased may have been simply omitted or not known. Therefore, it is difficult to identify and individualise those who moved to London, even with the aid of burial registers. Nevertheless, recently developed techniques of isotope analysis can be used to estimate the origins of a select few and, while this may not be able to tell us exactly where someone was raised, it can normally identify those who were brought up outside London.

Isotope evidence on migration

Janet Montgomery, with Julia Beaumont, Nidia Lisic, Ruth Morley, Geoff Nowell, Chris Ottley, Joanne Peterkin

The mobility and diet of 20 individuals were investigated using a range of isotopes and trace elements: ten (three subadults, three females, four males) from mass burial pit [7482]/[8473] and ten (one subadult, two females, seven males) from the attritional sample (six from phase 1, four from phase 2).[52] Nine of this small dataset have a combined strontium and oxygen isotope profile that is inconsistent with childhood residence in London (mass pit 5; phase 1 x 3, phase 2 x 1); all of these clear migrants are males or subadults except for a single female aged 26–35 ([4307], phase 2). Ten individuals are consistent with origins in south or north England. One subadult, [8219], aged 12–17 years, from the mass pit, is most likely to have originated outside Britain in a warmer climate. Isotope values, however, are not exclusive to any specific location, and there are many other places in Europe and beyond where strontium and oxygen isotopes would be indistinguishable from those of Londoners; migrants from these places would be invisible in the dataset.

Statistical analysis of the data between mass pit and attritional groups and between males and females found few significant differences in origins or diet (Chapter 10.1). A male aged 26–35 years from the mass pit appears to have consumed a very different diet during childhood and his isotope profile suggests he originated in a rural population, possibly in north England. Several individuals show a gradual shift during their lifetime towards a diet typical for urban London; this is clearly seen in migrant male [8216] aged 18–25 years. Two female burials from the mass pit, [8101] and [8223], have almost identical isotope profiles which strongly support shared origins and life histories.

The data from the New Churchyard provide a rich body of evidence for individual life histories during the late 16th to 18th centuries. The results raise new questions, both for the period and for what the techniques used can tell us about humans in the past.

7.4 Apprentices and servants

Michael Henderson and Don Walker

The Bedlam Register database contained a large proportion of servants, some of whom may have been apprentices (Chapter 6.1). This is reflected in the relatively large number of adolescents and young adults in the burial sample under study. These people formed an important constituent of London's economy. A plethora of domestic servants, chiefly women and girls, maintained London's households; only the wealthy employed more than a single male servant.

Women tended to come to London at an earlier age than men and to work in domestic service for a period to save money before returning home.[53] They might be employed as maids or, if references allowed, teachers; the less fortunate had to survive as barmaids, hawkers of goods or prostitutes.[54] Boys with some means (usually from their parents), and occasionally girls, might purchase a place in a master's household as an apprentice. Demand for servants and apprentices was created by the need for new entrants to fill roles vacated by those who fell victim to the urban environment (above). Of the approximately 15% of entries in the Bedlam Register database that had some evidence of occupation, a large proportion (39%) were described as servants (Chapter 6.1; Table 2). High numbers of deaths in the young, prior to marriage, suppressed natural population growth, adding to migratory pull and perhaps helping to maintain endemic pools of infection within the city.[55]

Apprenticeships were paid for by parents; in 1700, premiums could range from £10 to £40 and so were available only to families who could afford them.[56] During the medieval period, the wealthy could afford apprenticeships to grocers, drapers, haberdashers, mercers and merchant tailors, and in the gold-working and shipbuilding industries. In the 16th century, apprentices could be taken on at a high cost by one of the 12 great companies, although there were concessions for poorer families; orphans may have found a role through the Justice of the Peace or overseers of the poor.[57] Francis Jenkes, apprenticed at 18 years of age in 1658 to the Fishmongers' Company, was from a Shropshire gentry family (Chapter 5.6). For children of husbandmen, labourers and craftsmen, the smaller metal, leather and wood crafts such as coopers and hosiers, felt-makers and weavers, carpenters, farriers and smiths, as well as the building industry, may have been an option. Over the 16th and 17th centuries apprenticeship ceased to be both the predominant mode of entry into the London workforce and a key facilitator of social mobility.[58]

By 1600 there are thought to have been approximately 30,000 apprentices working in the metropolis in a very wide range of trades.[59] Youths normally entered into apprenticeships between the ages of 14 and 18, for a period of seven to ten or more years. The earliest an apprenticeship could end was at 24 years of age, although it was frequently extended. On completion, apprentices who had been enrolled could become citizens of the City of London; many masters and apprentices avoided the expense of formal enrolment.[60]

Many boys would have had some education or work experience prior to being apprenticed. A master could have more than one apprentice at any time in his household; apprentices slept in the shop or house. Contracts outlined strict rules to abide by, and life could be hard. Maltreatment was not infrequent and was one reason for apprentices failing to complete their term. Whipping was an approved form of discipline, and apprentices could be mistreated in other ways. If they left their master's service before completion of their term they could be ordered to leave the city, or risk punishment as a vagrant.[61] The physical working hours were long, from dawn to dusk; before the Industrial Revolution, this was likely to be 5am to 8pm depending on daylight.[62] Around 60% never completed their terms of service; some died, and others fled (Chapter 12.2).[63]

Girls could also be apprenticed in the medieval and early modern periods, but this was much rarer. Their entry into apprenticeships (eg to embroiderers, silk thread-makers, tailors, brewers) might take place earlier than boys', and cost less; there were no female guilds and women rarely became full guild members.[64]

Young people who could not afford apprenticeships went into service. Skilled or unskilled, servants might be domestic and part of the household, or work in, for example, the victualling trades; in both cases this was generally on a contractual basis. Whether living-out in cheap rented rooms on meagre wages or living-in with room and board and wages (at least when trained), servants probably had little job security.[65] Beneath apprentices and live-in servants there was an underemployed class of labourers and servants who eked out a bare existence, often relying on seasonal work to feed their families. The poor who begged or were considered to be vagrants were placed in early forms of workhouses or, if too sick, were sent to St Bartholomew's and St Thomas's Hospitals (Chapter 11.2).

Approximately 50% of individuals excavated from the New Churchyard died between 12 and 30 years of age. While it is not possible to determine from the present study what proportion of these were migrants, or apprentices or servants, it is likely that as a whole the group were relatively poor and vulnerable to ill health (above, 7.3; Chapter 12.2, 12.3).[66] It is also interesting to observe the manner in which plague epidemics disproportionately affected mortality rates in some age groups. Model life tables of London parishes for the years of severe plague epidemics commonly identified excess mortality in children (above that experienced by the age group in non-plague years) and particularly in those aged 10–19 years. This was especially true of wealthier parishes, suggesting that apprentices and servants in those parishes may have suffered higher rates of mortality during epidemics when compared to the remainder of the population.[67] Rates of bone fracture were also high in those who died between 18 and 25 years of age, particularly for males, and were probably work- or accident-related (Chapter 11.1).

Notes to Chapter 7

1   Cummins et al 2013, 35

2   Clark 2015, 8

3   Harding 1990; Craig 2000

4   Hardy 1993, 65; Roberts and Cox 2003, 293–4, 358

5   Wright 2010; 2014

6   Harward et al 2015, 23–55, 94–125, 325–31 and passim

7   Schofield 1984, 129–61; Picard 2003, 3, 7–8; Schofield 2011, 30–3, 60–113

8   Merry and Baker 2009, 227

9   Ibid, 213

10 Houston 1996, 144

11 Payne 2008, 27–8

12 Roberts and Manchester 2012, 238; Mays 2003, 151; Porter 1991, 143; Picard 2003, 94

13 Picard 2004, 63

14 Clark 2015, 8

15 Rawcliffe 2013, 116–75 esp 140–7

16 H Peter 1651, cited in Porter 2012b, 24

17 Rawcliffe 2013, 226–7; Harward et al 2015, 251–62

18 Brimblecombe 1987, 22; Clark 2015, 8; Roberts and Cox 2003, 344–5

19 Landers 1993, 48; Roberts and Cox 2003, 294; Davenport et al 2010, 1

20 Cox 1993, 74–5

21 Clark 2015, 9

22 Te Brake 1975, 338

23 Clark 2015, 8; Te Brake 1975, 343; Brimblecombe 1987, 29

24 Te Brake 1975, 341

25 Brimblecombe 1987, 22, 30

26 Ibid, 30–1

27 J Evelyn's *Fumifugium* in Brimblecombe 1987, 39–40

28 Bray [1901], 350

29 Which lasted from approximately 1564 to 1730; Reiter 2000, 1

30 Brimblecombe 1987, 23

31 Roberts and Cox 2003, 209

32 Laumbach and Kippen 2012, 4

33 Porter 2012b, 25

34 J Champion 1993, 35; Hardy 1993, 67

35 J Graunt cited in Porter 2012b, 105

36 J Champion 1993, 35

37 Porter 1991, 14

38 There was no significant difference between lead exposure in the mass pit and attritional groups (Montgomery et al 2016).

39 Clapp et al 2008

40 Rothman et al 2001; Dockery et al 1993; Lichtenstein et al 2000

41 Kolonel et al 2004

42 Acosta et al 2003; Tarlov 1970

43 Ortner 2003, 503

44 Royal Mint Square: Miles and Bekvalac 2014, 33

45 Earle 1994, 38

46 Ibid, 38–9

47 Ibid, 38–54

48 Ibid, 46–7

49 Clark 1979, 59; Clark and Souden 1987, 29–34; Earle 1994, 49

50 Landers 1993, 44–6, 48

51 Earle 1994, 51–2

52 Montgomery et al 2016

53 Earle 1994, 41

54 Landers 1993, 181–2; Bucholz and Ward 2012, 74–6

55 Newton 2011, 260, 265

56 Bucholz and Ward 2012, 79

57 Lewis 2016, 140–1

58 Earle 1994, 60

59 Bucholz and Ward 2012, 269

60 Hanawalt 1993, 129–41, 144–6

61 Porter 1991, 85–6; Porter 2011, 156

62 Lewis 2016, 143

63 Bucholz and Ward 2012, 80

64 Hanawalt 1993, 142–4

65 Ibid, 173–95

66 Landers 1993, 48

67 Finlay 1981, 126–30

CHAPTER 8

'LONDON, LYING SICKE OF THE PLAGUE'[1]

8.1 The disease, origins and responses

Don Walker

The disease and its effects

Perhaps of all the diseases we know of from historical texts, it is plague that is the most notorious (Fig 84). This is chiefly due to its virulence, the high mortality rate, the large numbers of individuals affected and the widespread, pandemic nature of the infection. The disease itself is a bacterial infection, of a type referred to as a zoonosis because it primarily affects animals, specifically rodents and the fleas that feed on them.[2] The bacterium responsible is *Yersinia pestis* which belongs to a group of microbes that commonly cause haemorrhagic sepsis (tissue damage associated with bleeding) in animals. The disease is spread in rodent populations by the injection of infected saliva from the feeding tube of the flea (*Xenopsylla cheopis*) while it is feasting on the blood of the host. While these fleas do not naturally choose

Fig 84 Title page from Thomas Dekker's plague pamphlet, *A rod for run-awayes* (1625) (Wilson 1925, 158–9)

(Guildhall Library, City of London)

humans as hosts, they will abandon dead animals and alight on any person in the vicinity in the absence of other live rodents on which to feed. A further flea, *Pulex irritans*, plays an important role in the spread of the disease as it feeds on both humans and rodents.[3]

Clinically, plague is normally considered an acute infection which resolves rapidly, resulting either in the death or the survival of the affected individual. This means that skeletons do not show evidence of plague as it acts too quickly for the bone to react and remodel. In humans, three different expressions of the disease are known – bubonic, septicaemic and pneumonic. The bubonic form appears about four to five days after infection and affects the lymphatic system, presenting in the lymph nodes closest to the site of the flea bite, either the neck, under the arm or in the groin. Characteristic large painful red swellings, or buboes, appear. These then turn black as the disease progresses with symptoms including fever, chills, malaise and muscle cramping. In untreated cases the mortality rate is 60–70%. Septicaemic plague involves infection of the bloodstream and can develop from the bubonic form or can arise independently. It causes tissue death (necrosis) in the extremities, such as the nose, fingers and toes. The mortality rate is higher than that of the bubonic form with death caused by diffuse haemorrhage. The third form is pneumonic plague which affects the lungs and is the only expression of the disease that can spread directly between humans, by droplet infection during coughing and sneezing. It can also develop from the bubonic and septicaemic forms. Pneumonic plague damages the respiratory system leading to pneumonia and the production of bloody sputum. In the absence of antibiotics all sufferers die within two to five days.[4]

The exact origins of plague in humans are uncertain, with the earliest identification of the infection coming from 5000 year old remains in Siberia. The highly virulent bubonic strain of the disease spread by fleas is thought to have developed about 3000 years ago.[5] The widespread geographical distribution of outbreaks has permitted the identification of three historical pandemics. The first, in the 6th–8th centuries AD, affected the Eastern Roman Empire and the coastal Mediterranean, but did not spread as far as north-west Europe. During the second, the disease spread from Asia through marine trade routes into Europe and, for the first time, into England in 1348.[6] Plague probably appeared in London in November 1348, and land was prepared at West Smithfield and East Smithfield to provide burial for the high number of casualties expected. The city was severely affected with between a third and a half of Londoners dying; England's population as a whole was similarly devastated.[7]

The plague returned again in 1361 and continued to reappear for the next three centuries, with ten recorded outbreaks in the 15th century alone.[8] Outbreaks occurred at regular intervals until the pandemic faded from

Western Europe in the early 18th century. The third pandemic began in the late 19th century in China, and still affects areas of Asia, Africa and the Americas, though causing far lower rates of mortality, perhaps due to improved standards of hygiene, reduced close contact with rodents and the use of antibiotics.[9]

Living with plague in the 16th and 17th centuries

Following four outbreaks of plague in the first half of the 16th century, a particularly severe epidemic in 1563, where perhaps more than 20% of the population succumbed, was at least in part responsible for the decision to open the New Churchyard (Chapter 3.1; below, 8.2). The parish burial grounds were filling up and an overflow burial ground beyond the city walls would relieve pressure on space. There followed five further major outbreaks up to the end of the second pandemic (Table 14).[10]

It has been claimed that the high profile afforded to plague, together with its concentrated spread in urban centres, has led to an unwarranted focus on the disease at the expense of others, such as influenza, with just 15% of overall deaths recorded as plague between 1580 and 1650 (cf Chapter 9.1).[11] However, throughout the 16th and 17th centuries, plague was a frequent visitor to the city, with an outbreak occurring every 10–30 years, about once in every generation. Anyone who lived to middle age had direct experience of the disease and its frequency must have caused a certain familiarity and a common anxiety. At the same time, migration and the fertility of the population helped to mitigate the long-term effects of these high mortality episodes.[12]

The effects of plague were known, as were the procedures to be followed during epidemics. To a large degree this was due to the publication of plague orders, first produced for London in 1583. These were released during outbreaks and provided a set of rules to follow to try to prevent the spread of the disease and reduce the number of deaths. The orders covered quarantine regulations, disposal of bedding, house hygiene, treatments, medicines and other preventative

Table 14 Early modern plague outbreaks in London

Year	Plague burials	All burials	Estimated total population	Plague mortality %
City and Liberties				
1563[1]	17,404	20,372	85,000	20.5
1592[2]	15,003	25,886	128,000–150,000	7.1–8.3
1593[3]	10,662	17,844		
1603[3]	30,561	38,244	144,000–167,000	18.3–21.2
City, Liberties and out-parishes				
1625[4]	35,417	54,265	209,000–244,000	14.5–16.9
1636[4]	10,410	23,369	286,000–333,000	3.1–3.6
1665[1]	55,797	80,696	459,000	12.2

[1] Slack 1986, 62 table 7 'Major epidemics in London, 1563–1665'
[2] Creighton 1891, 341–4
[3] Finlay 1981, appendix 1, The London Bills of Mortality, 155 table A1.1 'The City and Liberties'
[4] Finlay 1981, appendix 1, The London Bills of Mortality, 156 table A1.2 'The City, Liberties and out-parishes'

advice, including pomander recipes. Unlike in some countries on the Continent, little effort was invested in setting up specialist plague houses and instead sufferers tended to be kept in their own homes. When a case was confirmed, the victim and all others in the house, even if they were just visiting, were confined for a minimum of 28 days. The house was then daubed with a cross and the inscription 'Lord have mercy upon us'. The parish authorities were responsible for providing provisions, with the aim of preventing starvation or attempts to break out in search of food.[13] Many of the plague orders would have improved hygiene and reduced interpersonal contact, so removing some of the conditions that encouraged the spread of the disease. Orders regarding the use of pomanders and other strong-smelling potions, and the smoking of tobacco, were designed to combat the miasma, the smells thought to be responsible for disease. These were ineffective and may even have led to false confidence and people unnecessarily exposing themselves to plague.

Those who could, fled London. The wealthy, with resources and contacts, could more easily move out, and it was the poor who were generally left behind. As animals were believed to carry plague, the mayor ordered the killing of cats and dogs. Daniel Defoe claimed that during the great plague of 1665, 40,000 dogs and five times as many cats were slaughtered.[14] Shops closed and purging fires were lit to burn the disease out of the air. Among the meagre traffic remaining in the city must have been the carts collecting and then carrying the dead to burial grounds and common graves, including those at the New Churchyard.[15]

The great plague of 1665 was the final serious outbreak of plague in London. The last plague death to be recorded in the Bills of Mortality was in 1679, although occasional deaths may have been registered thereafter, such as Mary Floyd, a spinster of the parish of St Andrew by the Wardrobe, who 'dyed of the Plague' and was buried on 8 July 1690 (burial location not noted).[16] It is possible that there were other isolated episodes (misidentified as typhus, accidentally or intentionally) until the general ending of the second plague pandemic in the 1730s.[17]

8.2 Burial of plague victims at the New Churchyard

Robert Hartle

Documentary evidence

Parish registers and burial numbers

The location of the New Churchyard outside the city walls made it ideally placed to serve both city parishes and extramural pesthouses in times of crisis.[18] Data in London's parish burial registers extracted for the Bedlam Register project record plague victims buried at the ground in 25 of the 93 years between 1581 and 1674 (Chapter 6.1). Some trends are discernible

Fig 85 Deaths and burials, 1570–1679: top – London deaths (from Bills of Mortality); bottom – New Churchyard burials (from the Bedlam Register database, Old Style)

within these records. In the majority of these years only a few plague burials were recorded; however, noticeable rises were recorded in 1603 and 1636, and dramatic rises in 1625 and 1665, all of which correlate with the worst 17th-century London plague outbreaks (Table 14; Fig 85).[19] New Churchyard plague numbers also appear representative of relatively small rises in plague deaths documented during the years 1606–10, 1630 and 1640–7 (Fig 85).[20]

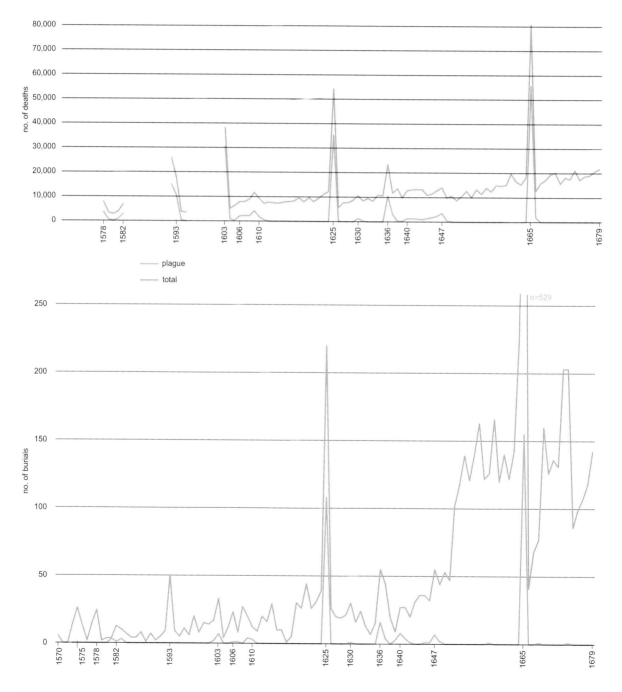

These figures, however, are undoubtedly under-representations because of the incomplete and inconsistent nature of the registers, as well as other factors, such as the practice of deliberately under-registering plague victims during this period.[21]

Moreover, since only a limited number of parishes recorded both burial location and cause of death during epidemics, these figures certainly represent a biased picture and, therefore, are not representative of London plague mortality or burial practice as a whole. For example, the smaller outbreaks of 1636 and 1637 are represented by only three and one parishes respectively, while only one, seven and nine parishes are represented in the New Churchyard plague burial figures during the major outbreaks of 1603, 1625 and 1665 respectively (Fig 86). In particular, the figures for the outbreak of 1625 are dominated by burials from St James Garlickhithe, which contributed 86 (80%) of the 108 recorded 1625 New Churchyard plague burials (Fig 87). Such figures seem disproportionate and probably indicate that burial registration in St James Garlickhithe during the crisis of 1625 was unusually diligent and comprehensive.

A somewhat clearer picture may be gained by examining the total number of recorded burials alongside those recorded as plague. The Bills of Mortality and other documentary sources tell us that a significant plague outbreak occurred in 1593 and that smaller outbreaks occurred in 1574, 1578 and 1582.[22] However, no plague victims were noted among those buried at the ground during 1574, 1578 and 1593, and only one during 1582. There are, nevertheless, significant spikes in total burial numbers in these years (Fig 85); these figures almost certainly represent plague burials sent to the ground but simply not recorded

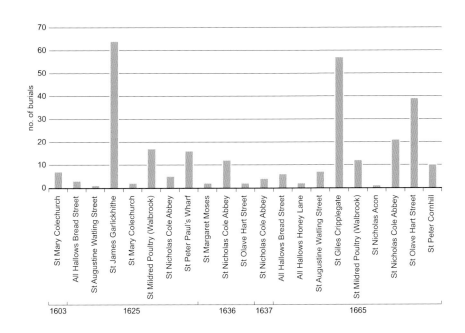

Fig 86 Major plague burial years at the New Churchyard by contributing parish (from the Bedlam Register database, Old Style)

as such. Some parishes which would have probably contributed large numbers of burials during plague outbreaks did not keep detailed records until later in the history of the burial ground. For example, the neighbouring parish of St Giles Cripplegate, which sent large numbers of plague burials to the ground in 1665, very rarely recorded burial location alongside cause of death before 1653. Parish responses to the increased demands placed on the burial registration process during epidemics evidently varied between parishes and with time, with some not recording either burial location or cause of death. St Olave Hart Street routinely recorded both burial location and plague deaths from 1633 and recorded a relatively large number of plague burials sent to the ground in 1665. Before 1633, however, plague burials were rarely noted and burial locations only occasionally. During 1625, despite a surge in mortality, the number of burial locations noted is significantly reduced and the parish register attributes no deaths to plague, whereas the Bill of Mortality for that year, based on figures contributed by the parish clerk, records 266 deaths of which 195 were said to be plague.[23]

The London plagues of 1603, 1625 and 1665 were of roughly equal lethality, with deaths running at five to six times their usual level; the plague of 1593 saw deaths running at 4.6 times normal, and in both 1578 and 1636 deaths were 2.5 times normal.[24] Total burials at the New Churchyard show the following approximate pattern: deaths ran at six times normal in 1578, five times normal in 1593, 6.5 times normal in 1625, 3.5 times normal in 1636–7 and four times normal in 1665.[25] These figures appear to imply that the ratio of New Churchyard plague to total deaths was broadly similar to that of London as a whole throughout the early modern period. However, such estimates for the New Churchyard should not be taken entirely at face value, due to the problems inherent in the records, particularly for the period 1569–1650 (Chapter 6.1).

Contemporary accounts of plague outbreaks in London and responses, including use of the New Churchyard

Large public gatherings were invariably prohibited during bad outbreaks and the burial ground's pulpit sermons, like those at St Paul's,[26] were for obvious reasons no exception. The New Churchyard was closed to the public several times during the early 17th century due to plague burial. On 19 May 1625 the Court of Aldermen was informed that the Whit Sunday sermon would be preached at Christ Church due to the 'sickness'.[27] In 1626 the sermon was preached at the Mercers' chapel 'in regard of the greate multitude of people that were buryed the last summer of the plague in the said churche yarde [the New Churchyard]'.[28] It is estimated that around 35,000 Londoners died of the plague in 1625 (Fig 85).[29] Plague deaths in 1625 were largely contained within the months of July–September, with a peak in mid August,[30] a pattern which appears to be matched by recorded New Churchyard plague burials which show a peak in the third week of August (Fig 87).[31] The Whit Sunday sermon was relocated again in 1636–8 (below).

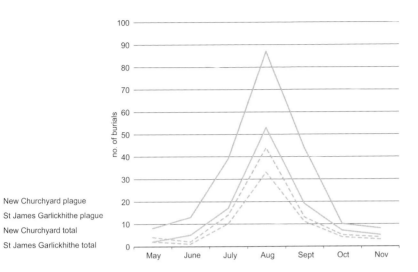

Fig 87 New Churchyard total and plague burials recorded from May to November 1625, from the Bedlam Register database, showing total and plague burials sent from the parish of St James Garlickhithe

Documentary evidence for the use of the New Churchyard during the great plague of 1665–6 benefits from the better survival rates of contemporary records, among which are a higher number of references specifically to the New Churchyard. The great plague began in London in late 1664, but mortality soared from mid July 1665 and was at its worst between the last week of August and the third week of September.[32] Although nearly 70,000 deaths from the plague were recorded during 1665, it has been suggested that the true figure may have been nearer 100,000 or 20% of London's population.[33] Defoe's *A journal of the plague year*, published in 1722, indicates the New Churchyard among a list of plague burial sites: 'a piece of ground in Moorfields, by the going into the street which is now called Old Bethlem'.[34]

In his book *God's terrible voice in the city by plague and fire*, first published in 1667, Thomas Vincent describes London in August 1665:

In August how dreadful is the increase. … Now the cloud is very black, and the storm comes down upon us very sharp. Now Death rides triumphantly upon his pale Horse through our street. … Now we could hardly go forth, but we should meet with many Coffins …

Vincent described the epidemic during the first half of September:

Now the grave doth open its mouth without measure. Multitudes! Multitudes! In the valey of the shadow of death, thronging daily into eternity; the church yards now are strufft so full with dead corpses, that they are in many places swell'd two or three feet higher that they were before; and new ground is broken up to bury the dead.[35]

One of the 'spectacles' Vincent encountered during August was a woman 'with a little Coffin under her arm, carrying it to the new Church-yard'.[36] When Samuel Pepys recorded that on Wednesday 30 August 1665 he 'walked towards Moorefields' to see if he could see 'any dead corps going to the grave', he was almost certainly referring to burials at the New Churchyard.[37]

Burial registers recorded 155 plague victims sent to the New Churchyard 25 March 1665–24 March 1665/6 and that the ground was predominantly used for plague burial between late July and the first week of September 1665, when nearly 7000 deaths in London were attributed to the plague.[38] Despite adopting pit burial in response to high demand, the keeper of the New Churchyard could not avoid a crisis of capacity. The following entry from the repertories of the Court of Aldermen, dated 6 September 1665, paints a vivid picture:

> This Court being now informed of the noisome stenches arising from the great multitude of dead bodyes buryed in the new Churchyard in Bethlem during this mortality … doth order that Mr Clitherowe Keeper of the said Churchyard shall not henceforth make any Pitts for burials durng this said visitation and only in single graves of sufficient depth and in such convenient places from whence noe annoyance may arise; And that (at his owne charge) hee cause such quantity of fresh mould to bee forthwith laid on the places complained of as may effectually smother and suppresse the stenches or annoyances likewaise cause all the bones lying above the ground to bee buryed and pieces of coffin boards to bee burnt this evening in the midst of the said Churchyard.[39]

A very similar scene depicting pit burial in an extramural London parish churchyard is part of an engraving for a plague broadsheet attributed to John Dunstall and dated 1666 (Fig 88). This shows three square, or perhaps rectangular, pits filled with neatly stacked predominantly coffined burials. The Plague Orders of 1 July 1665 stipulated that plague burials had to be at least six foot (nearly 2m) deep,[40] perhaps a reaction to earlier pits lying closer to the surface and causing problems.

Burial numbers had begun to fall in the first week of September, but burial registers show a drastic reduction in New Churchyard burials after the prohibition of pit burial in the second week of September. A further note in the repertories dated 25 October 1665 confirms that the keeper obeyed the order to

Fig 88 Detail of plague broadsheet comprising nine scenes relating to the 1665 plague, by John Dunstall, 1666
(Museum of London)

cease pit burial.[41] Relatively few burials took place at the ground between 10 September 1665 and 31 December 1665 (91 burials, 29 recorded as plague). Only 44 burials (two recorded as plague) are recorded at the ground 1 January 1665/6–31 December 1666 and the ground appears to have been 'rested' until 1669, with total numbers of burials running at half their average during 1667–9.

During the final months of 1665 those parishes previously using the New Churchyard had little choice but to redirect any burials they could not accommodate to other grounds. Urgent preparations of a new ground 'neare Bunhill', now known as Bunhill Fields, were ordered in early September 1665:

> Upon complaint of the Churchwardens & Inhabitants of Sundry parishes of this Citty that their Churchyards and also the new Churchyard in Bethlem are in this great Mortality surcharged with dead Corps, and noe place there remayning for further Burialls … It is ordered by this court … to treat with Mr Tindall (the Cittye's tenant of ffinsbury fields) … intending a peece of ground neere Bunhill to bee speedily sett out and prepared for a Burying place …[42]

The opening of Bunhill Fields came too late for the September peak of the great plague. The Bunhill ground, however, was walled by 19 October and was taking burials by at least mid October, when weekly plague deaths were declining but still numbered in the thousands.[43] The extensive use of the New Churchyard by the parish of St Michael Queenhithe to relieve its own grounds came to an end on 1 October 1665; between 15 October 1665 and April 1666 there are numerous mentions of 'Tindalls new ground' and

'Tindalls new ground near bone hill', but only three burials are noted at the New Churchyard.[44] The intention to redirect plague burials from the New Churchyard to Bunhill Fields is also reflected in the parish records of St Sepulchre. On 3 October 1665 the vestry minutes book records that the churchwardens were to 'consider and agree with the bearers for the carrying of the corpses to the new churchyard in Moorfields' but on 9 October arrangements were discussed for burials to be sent to the 'new burying place in Finsbury Fields'.[45] Further grounds mentioned in parish registers between September 1665 and mid 1666 (eg the 'new ground', 'new ground in Shoreditch', 'new ground neare the windmills' and 'new ground at Bunhill') could refer either to Bunhill Fields or to other new parochial grounds.[46]

Mass or common graves, including the New Churchyard

The idea of foregoing normal burial practice in favour of mass or common graves seems to have been novel in 17th-century London, particularly opening a large trench or pit and leaving it open until filled with successive burials.[47] There are, however, archaeological precedents for such a response in the Black Death cemetery of East Smithfield.[48] Of course, the main motive for digging mass graves was for reasons of practicality and hygiene, which in times of mass mortality could outweigh personal and communal sensitivities. A mass grave could achieve the rapid accommodation of the maximum number of burials in one space. However, parishes may also have been driven to it to save money, since burial of the dead during epidemics represented a massive financial burden. By the height of the 1665–6 epidemic, for example, many families could not contribute to the cost of burial and the expense became increasingly shouldered by the parish.[49]

Contemporary sources show that pit burial of plague victims did occur in London during the 1603 and 1625 epidemics.[50] In 1603 Balmford wrote of 'open graves, where sundry are buried together' and Dekker wrote of graves where 'Threescore' were 'thrust all together into one close room: a little noisome room, not fully ten foot [3.05m] square'.[51] To Dekker the 1625 outbreak revealed 'the earth [as a] great warehouse, which is piled up with winding-sheets', and he observed that in many churchyards they were 'compelled to dig Graves like little Cellars, piling up forty or fifty in a Pit'.[52] Dekker's mention of piled 'winding-sheets' is particularly notable for its indication that plague victims were buried uncoffined. John Taylor, the 'water poet', wrote that 'fifty corpses scarce one grave doth fill' when describing burial during the 1625 epidemic.[53]

Evidence for mass burial in pits at the New Churchyard is perhaps contained in the burial registers of St Peter Cornhill. The parish recorded 'New Churchyard' burials between 1585 and 1669, and from the 1580s to 1666 used the term 'pit' to describe some burials.[54] Seven 'New Churchyard' burials were recorded in 1625; the first, dated 17 July, was recorded as 'in New Ch Yard', but the rest, dated 19 July to 25 August, were each recorded as 'pit in New Churchyarde'. This may suggest that pit mass burial was adopted at the ground in late July 1625 and used until at least late August, the peak of plague deaths that year.

Further evidence of early to mid 17th-century plague burial practices exists in the parish burial registers of St Peter Paul's Wharf, which are highly unusual because they contain occasional years when mode of burial was recorded.[55] These periods coincide with two years with elevated plague deaths, 1625 and 1640. During 1625 the parish made use of its churchyard and church but also sent burials to other grounds: 22 individuals, or 23% of the total that year, were sent to the New Churchyard. These burials fell almost exclusively in the months of August to October, during the epidemic's summer peak and decline, and 15 were recorded as 'plague'. In about a third of these burials no detail is given, but the remaining two thirds indicate how the body was sent to the ground. Although no entries indicate the type of grave (ie pit or single burial), among the New Churchyard group coffined individuals were a small minority (18% of the total). In contrast, church and churchyard burials in 1625 were mainly coffined and in single or, at most, double graves. This difference could indicate that this parish was sending their poorest uncoffined to the New Churchyard in 1625.

The numbers of New Churchyard plague burials recorded per year between 1625 and 1665 are very small relative to the outbreaks of those years (Fig 85). It is possible that for most of this period plague burials could have been accommodated in single graves. If so, they would be indistinguishable archaeologically from the general burial population. The continuation of 'normal' burial practice in all but the worst epidemics is supported in documentary sources. A woodcut from *London's lamentation* exemplifies the desire and efforts of Londoners to maintain normal funeral practices during the period of sustained elevated plague deaths in the 1640s, in contrast to the 'crueltie' of irregular and undignified burial in rural areas (Fig 89).[56] The burial register of St Peter Paul's Wharf for the year 1640 shows that coffin burial had become the norm even among plague victims. Of the eight burials which were sent to the New Churchyard from the parish in 1640 (24% of a total of 33 parish burials that year), seven were identified as plague victims (70% (7/10) of the parish plague victims). Of the parish's plague victims, 80% (8/10) were buried in coffins, including five of the plague victims buried at the New Churchyard (71%).[57]

Although registers record 16 and four plague victims in 1636 and 1637 respectively, total burial numbers hint at a greater use of the ground for plague burial during these years. Other documentary sources suggest this: on 1 June 1636, the Court of Star Chamber drafted an order to the Lord Mayor

Fig 89 Title page of
London's lamentation,
dated 1641
(Museum of London)

of London (Christopher Clitherow) to arrange for the imminent (5 June) New Churchyard Whit Sunday sermon to be preached this year in the Guildhall chapel 'in regard those who die of the plague out of all the adjoining parishes are usually buried there'.[58] The sermon was again relocated in 1637–8.[59] Although no reason was noted, it was, presumably, to avoid the unpleasantness of a burial ground both recently and heavily used.

St Peter Cornhill recorded ten 'New Churchyard' burials between 7 July and 18 August 1665 (all 'plague' deaths).[60] Those between 7 July and 13 August were recorded as 'in the new churchyard', but the last burial, on 18 August, was recorded as 'pitt in the new churchyard'. This could indicate that the burial ground adopted mass burial for plague victims sometime in mid August, a date supported by other contemporary documentary sources and the general pattern of burials as indicated by the Bedlam Register project as a whole.

Parish records provide some evidence of pit burial in London during 1665 to add to that of the New Churchyard. St Dunstan in the West and St Bride's Fleet Street both began digging pits in August 1665.[61] However, perhaps the most famous account of pit burial during the summer of 1665 is not a contemporary account but that of Defoe.[62] He notes further pit burial in various locations across London: at the 'upper end of Hand Alley, in Bishopsgate Street', at St Botolph Aldgate and in 'Finsbury, in the parish of Cripplegate'. According to Defoe, pits in the parish churchyard of St Botolph Aldgate were initially dug in early August and by mid August were being dug large enough to take 'all that the cart brought in a week' (200–400 bodies).[63]

The scenes of panic and chaos described by Defoe during pit burial at the height of the 1665 epidemic in September have been the basis for the popular image of 1665 plague burial which has endured since the 18th century. Defoe tells us that the 'great pit' dug at Aldgate was filled between 4 and 20 September with 1114 bodies, 'some wrapt up in linen sheets, some in rags, some little other than naked' since 'coffins were not to be had for the prodigious numbers that fell in such a calamity as this'. Moreover, they were not 'decently laid in' but were 'thrown' in or 'shot into the pit promiscuously' from carts.[64]

However, Defoe's descriptions must be approached with some caution because his book was published nearly 60 years after the events it chronicles and he himself was only five years old at the time of the great plague. Thus, it is not a genuine memoir but a popular historical novel, perhaps sensationalising or emphasising details to excite the reader. Even if Defoe's account of the 'great pit' at Aldgate is accurate, it may only genuinely reflect burial practice in one churchyard in one period. Defoe's Aldgate example occurred in the worst week of the 1665 plague, perhaps when a greater degree of panic and disorder led to increasingly hurried burial.

No archaeological evidence has yet been found to support Defoe's description of chaotic pit burial in September 1665 (below).

Archaeological evidence: the excavated mass or common graves

Burial pit group

Eleven pits (OA105E) were found clustered in a roughly trapezoidal-shaped area that would have lain in the western centre of the ground at its fullest extent (Fig 90). Taken together, the 11 pits covered an area at least 18m by 18m, but it is impossible to fully define the extent of the area occupied by them. Further pits perhaps once existed between or to the north and west of those recorded to the south and east (XSM10), forming a continuous area with those identified to the north (site A; Fig 2). However, while the outlying pits of this postulated group were discernible, any in the centre would have been truncated by modern construction or, in areas of archaeological survival, could have been obscured by later grave cuts. The pits contained a total of 109 individuals; the osteological study sample (XSM10) contained 12 adults and ten subadults (Chapter 6.3; Table 8).

Each pit was aligned east–west, the alignment generally adhered to in the period 1569–c 1670 (phase 1) (Chapter 5.1; Fig 31). They appear to have been dug in a series of rows; this certainly seems to be the case with the north pits. Each pit contained between five and 17 individuals, with an average of ten individuals per pit. Each was dug to a similar size, 2m long by 1m wide on average. This allowed two individuals to be accommodated side by side at the

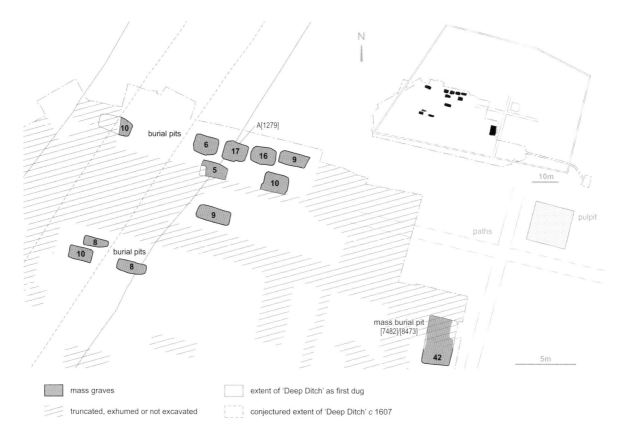

mass graves

truncated, exhumed or not excavated

extent of 'Deep Ditch' as first dug

conjectured extent of 'Deep Ditch' c 1607

Fig 90 Location of mass graves excavated in the New Churchyard, with number of recorded individuals indicated (scale 1:300; inset, 1:1500)

base of the cut, with further pairs placed in layers above (Fig 91). The depth of the pits was unclear because of truncation to the top of the cuts by later graves. Only 23 individuals or 21% were coffined, in plain wooden coffins. The construction and shape of the coffins was not discernible. The remaining individuals may well have been buried in shrouds. The presence of soil between many of the burials in this group implies that each represents more than just a single burial event. Burials were likely 'layered', perhaps over a period of a week or more, with soil placed over each new layer interred for reasons of safety and hygiene. Dating evidence is not sufficient to determine in what order the pits were dug, nor is it possible to say if they were all dug within a single month or even a single year. It is feasible that they were dug during the course of successive but less significant plague outbreaks (such as those of 1636 and 1637), rather than during severe epidemics (such as 1625) (Table 14).

The pits were located in an area on the west side of the site, an area which only became part of the burial ground after c 1607 (the infilling of the deep ditch) (Fig 90). As a group, they are stratigraphically later than the deep ditch infilling. Only a small number of burials (n=18: two coffined and 16 uncoffined) took place in this area before the digging of this pit group.

Fig 91 Uncoffined burials A[1433] and A[1434] within pit burial A[1201], one of the group of 11 excavated burial pits, looking west (0.5m scale)

Material from the fills comprised a medium-sized pottery assemblage, dated *c* 1550–*c* 1700, with a *terminus post quem* (TPQ) of *c* 1580, together with residual medieval pottery, and a single fragment of window glass (TPQ *c* 1500). The pit fills are consistently dated by the pottery to the last quarter of the 16th century, with no evidence of later sources of supply (totals: site A – SC 42, ENV 25, 968g; the site, XSM10 SC 13, ENV 10, 490g). Burials below and pre-dating the pits (OA105B and OA105D) were dated by small to medium assemblages of pottery of *c* 1480–*c* 1700 with a TPQ of *c* 1580; burials made above the pits could be either phase 1 (OA105F) or phase 2 (OA106).

The north line of pits (at site A) included pit A[1279] (Fig 90); three individuals from this pit were sampled for radiocarbon dating (Table 16; below). Ancient DNA analysis was not carried out on any burials from the pit group. Burial pit A[1279] was over the ditch as it was originally cut, early 16th century; however, the width of the ditch when it was infilled was not determinable (the dumped material of the infill was archaeologically indistinguishable from the burial ground consolidation dumping of *c* 1569–70; Chapter 3.3).

Mass burial pit

This large burial pit was located in the centre of the south half of the ground (Figs 31, 90) which was in use from 1569. Like the group of 11 pits (above), burial pit [7482]/[8473] was dug on the east–west alignment typical of the period 1569–*c* 1670 (phase 1) (Chapter 5.1; Fig 31). The section of the pit which survived modern truncation covered an area of 2.3m² and contained 42 *in situ* burials (Fig 92); all 42 individuals, 26 adults and 16 subadults, were included in the osteological study (Chapter 6.3; Figs 79, 80; Table 11). However, traces of the pit cut found to the north showed that this section represents only the south end and no more than 50% of the pit. Therefore, it can be estimated that the entire pit is likely to have originally contained at least 90–100 burials.

The number of coffins was difficult to determine confidently due to extreme slumping and poor preservation. However, traces of wood found beneath and between skeletons, together with body positioning, suggest that perhaps 26 (62%) of the burials in pit [7482]/[8473] were coffined. The use of some kind of shroud or fabric containment for the remaining bodies is likely, but was not evidenced by shroud pins or traces of fabric. Burials in pit [7482]/[8473] had been 'laid in' with a certain amount of care and were deliberately stacked in order to use the available space most efficiently (Fig 93). Stacks containing only coffined individuals were up to six deep, while stacks with a mix of coffined and uncoffined individuals were up to eight deep. To fit the coffins in neatly, and to maximise the use of space, the orientation of the head end of

each coffin was alternated. To fill any remaining gaps, further coffins were placed along the edges of the pit, perpendicular to the rest.

Burials were not sorted by size or into coffined/uncoffined. Smaller coffined and uncoffined child burials, as well as uncoffined adult burials, were not just laid on top but were found tucked between adult coffined burials deeper in the pit. This may indicate some degree of haste and that individuals were put into the pit in roughly the same order as they had been delivered to the site. Nevertheless, care appears to have been taken to arrange the stacks so that no child burial or uncoffined adult burial was crushed by the weight of a coffined burial.

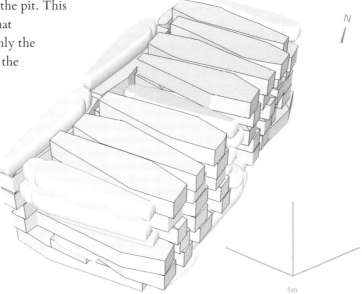

Fig 93 Three-dimensional reconstruction of mass burial pit [7482]/[8473], showing burials found (green) and conjectured, viewed from the south-east (scale 1:50)

In contrast to the pit group (OA105E), the absence of any soil between the burials or other material, such as lime or sawdust, suggests that the pit was filled within a short period of time, perhaps in a single day.

The top of the pit and the contemporary ground surface had been truncated by later burials and modern activity, so its original depth is unknown (Fig 92). However, although the decay and collapse of coffins had compressed the burials to no more than 300mm thick at the centre of the pit, it can be estimated that the stacks would have originally been *c* 1.5–1.8m deep, based on the number of coffined individuals per stack (six) and approximation of coffin depth (250–300mm).

Pit [7482]/[8473] bears a strong likeness to the pits filled with neatly stacked, predominantly coffined, burials shown in Dunstall's engraving published in 1666 (Figs 88, cf 95). Pit [7482]/[8473] would not have been much more than 2m deep. This depth would still have required a ladder for access, as seen in Dunstall's engraving and, because of the soft burial ground soil, this is probably the maximum depth that gravediggers could dig without risking the sides of the pit collapsing on them. It is very likely that this pit would also have produced 'noisome stenches' (as described in the aftermath of plague pit burial at the ground in 1665); some pits at the New Churchyard may have lain closer to the surface than was legal in the later 17th century.

Pit [7482]/[8473] truncated one coffined burial, [7557]/[7558], and one uncoffined burial, [7085], both undated (but phase 1 on stratigraphic/ alignment grounds). Five coffined burials which were later than the pit were undated (phase 1 or phase 2).

Dating evidence is provided by the coffins and coffin furniture, together with finds from the pit fills, [7483] and [7989]: a small pottery assemblage dated *c* 1550–*c* 1610 with a TPQ of *c* 1580 (25 SC, 25 ENV, 630g); and a complete cylindrical phial in natural green glass, of the kind used for medicinal preparations, dating to *c* 1670–*c* 1800 but here considered intrusive (below).

Although nearly all of the coffins were plain, coffin [8201] was recognisable as a flat-lidded 'single break' or shouldered type, a form which appeared in the last quarter of the 16th century and was ubiquitous from *c* 1650 (Chapter 5.2; Fig 94).[65] Gable-lidded or 'ridged' coffins, as seen on Fig 84, were the predominant form in medieval England and into the 16th century.[66] However, the flat-lidded coffin began to be favoured by London parishes by the early 17th century where overcrowding was an issue, since its shape allowed burials to be stacked and so was less wasteful of space.[67] The only example of coffin furniture, a coffin grip or handle found near the head end of coffin [8106], was of a type thought previously to have been in use *c* 1650–*c* 1750; the earliest intrinsically dated example known comes from the New Churchyard, from coffin [5587], which was marked '1674' by studs (Fig 57).

Fig 94 Coffined burial [8200]/[8201], with coffin highlighted, looking north-west

Identifying plague through ancient DNA analysis

Kirsten Bos, Elisabeth Nelson and Maria Spyrou

Recent developments in ancient DNA sequencing techniques, together with work on the East and West Smithfield emergency Black Death burial grounds, demonstrated it was possible to reconstruct genomes of the *Yersinia pestis* pathogen in archaeological tooth samples from medieval London.[68] Until now, no DNA studies had been carried out on 16th- to 17th-century Londoners who might have been exposed to or fallen victim to the plague. Genomic data of *Yersinia pestis* from this period would contribute to our understanding of the history and evolution of plague, and infectious diseases in general.

To determine the presence of *Yersinia pestis*, we performed an initial screening of this population using small amounts of material retrieved from the pulp cavity of the teeth from 20 individuals from the mass burial pit, [7482]/[8473]. Five teeth from five different individuals had indications of the presence of plague, though the screening was based on the presence of a single gene (Table 15). Through shotgun sequencing we confirmed that the samples from the five individuals were pathogen-positive. This reveals that all five individuals had the plague bacterium circulating in their bloodstreams at the time of death, supporting the conclusion that they died of plague during an epidemic crisis. Through ongoing genomic analyses, we hope to understand better the relationship between this strain of plague and those from other areas of Europe. This information may provide important details relating to the mechanisms by which plague persisted in Europe after the Black Death.

Table 15 Plague-positive individuals from mass burial pit [7482]/[8473]

Context	Sex	Age (years)
[8052]	undetermined	18–25
[8103]	female	18–25
[8127]	(subadult)	6–11
[8198]	male	18–25
[8216]	male	18–25

Radiocarbon dating of the excavated burial pits

Derek Hamilton and Peter Marshall

A total of eight samples from well-preserved individuals in common or mass graves in the New Churchyard were taken for radiocarbon dating (Table 16). All samples were pre-treated, combusted, graphitised and measured by accelerator mass spectrometry. Five samples were taken from tooth material from individuals within the mass pit, [7482]/[8473], and submitted to the 14CHRONO Centre, The Queen's University, Belfast (UBA).[69] Three further samples were taken from human bone from burial pit A[1279] (OA105E) and submitted to the Scottish Universities Environmental Research Centre (SUERC), East Kilbride.[70]

Individual calibrations suggest calendar ages fall between the 15th and 18th centuries and show strongly bimodal results ('posterior distributions'). This is due to the shape of the calibration curve between *c* 1450 and *c* 1650 which consists of two periods of rapidly changing radiocarbon concentrations separated by a pronounced wiggle. Combining the radiocarbon dates with stratigraphic information provides a model that refines the posterior distributions (below).

STABLE ISOTOPE ANALYSIS

Stable isotope analysis ($\delta^{13}C$ and $\delta^{15}N$) was undertaken on the human bone and teeth material (with the exception of UBA-32526, which was fully

Table 16 Radiocarbon dates for eight individuals buried in mass graves at the New Churchyard

Laboratory no.	Context	Description	Radiocarbon determination (years BP)	^{13}C (‰)	^{15}N (‰)	C:N	% marine (±10%)
Mass burial pit [7482]/[8473]: tooth collagen							
UBA-32525	[8147]	male aged 26–35 years	442±43	-19.44	12.22	2.85	13
UBA-32526	[8193]	female aged ≥46 years	224±32	-	-	-	
UBA-32527	[8219]	subadult aged 12–17 years	355±31	-20.01	11.36	2.83	11
UBA-32528	[8198]*	male aged 18–25 years	424±39	-19.54	10.98	2.82	17
UBA-32529	[8216]*	male aged 18–25 years	370±33	-19.42	11.84	2.80	19
Burial pit A[1279]: bone collagen							
SUERC-70950	A[1362]	female aged 18–25 years	381±33	-19.0	12.1	3.2	24
SUERC-70954	A[1381]	male aged 36–45 years	386±33	-19.3	12.2	3.2	20
SUERC-70955	A[1394]	female aged 18–25 years	363±33	-19.3	11.3	3.2	20

* plague-positive individuals (Table 15)

The results have been calibrated from the conventional radiocarbon ages (Stuiver and Polach 1977) and are quoted in accordance with the international standard known as the Trondheim convention (Stuiver and Kra 1986). The calibrations were calculated according to the maximum intercept method (Stuiver and Reimer 1986) using the datasets published by Reimer et al (2013) and the computer program OxCal v4.2 (Bronk Ramsey 1995; 1998; 2001; 2009a) combusted for radiocarbon dating). While the C:N values for the SUERC dates fall within the range (2.9–3.5[71]) often used to judge whether bone preservation was sufficiently good to have confidence in the accuracy of the radiocarbon determinations,[72] those from UBA are just at or below the lower limit of the range. The small samples afforded by using tooth collagen and the slightly low C:N ratios may have resulted in the higher than expected variability within the radiocarbon ages from what is purportedly a single event (mass burial pit [7482]/[8473]; above).

The $\delta^{13}C$ and $\delta^{15}N$ values from the majority of the burials from these two pits suggest these individuals had a predominately terrestrial-based diet, but were consuming marine and/or freshwater protein,[73] as is typical of many post-medieval sites in England. If an individual has taken up carbon from a reservoir not in equilibrium with the terrestrial biosphere,[74] there can be implications for determining the actual date of death.[75]

It is possible to 'correct' radiocarbon ages for material whose protein has come from both terrestrial and marine sources.[76] It should be stressed that this marine correction is essentially a modelled radiocarbon calibration that uses a mixture of the internationally agreed calibration curves IntCal13 and Marine13.[77] It is a modelled calibration because there is more than one way to determine the percentage of diet that derived from terrestrial/marine resources. As such, the results will vary slightly depending on the method used.

The more common method of calculating the percentage of the diet that was marine uses linear interpolation of the $\delta^{13}C$ values between two endmembers: one that is indicative of a purely terrestrial diet and the other purely marine. Linear interpolation was used here (Table 16, % marine) with -12.5‰ and -21.0‰ as the end members for the $\delta^{13}C$, where -21.0‰ was the equivalent of 100% terrestrial and -12.5‰ was equal to 100% marine.[78] These percentages can be used in OxCal to 'mix' the percentage of the IntCal13 terrestrial calibration curve with the Marine13 calibration curve during the calibration process. While the quantities of non-terrestrial protein are generally viewed as being insufficient to affect the radiocarbon dates, a sensitivity analysis was run assuming any reservoir offset is due to the consumption of marine protein.

BAYESIAN MODELLING AND DISCUSSION

Bayesian statistics provides a method of allowing the scientific dates to be considered with archaeological information to constrain the calibrated calendar ages and quantify the uncertainties of the estimates.[79] The chronological modelling has been undertaken using OxCal v4.2[80] and the internationally agreed calibration curve of the northern hemisphere.[81] The modelling produces posterior density estimates; highest posterior density intervals are used to summarise the distributions and are given in italics (Table 17) to highlight the fact that they are modelled rather than absolute and may change given a different set of parameters or 'prior' beliefs. Both plague pits are modelled in the same way, but independently of one another. The constraints used here are the documented dates for the establishment of the burial ground in 1569 and its closure to burial in 1739. An alternative model was produced for pit A[1279] using 1607 as a TPQ.

The model assumes the buried individuals all died at the same time, or within an extremely short period of time (ie within days or weeks of one another), and uses the combine function in OxCal to combine the probabilities derived from calibration, which results in a single date estimate for the event. The five radiocarbon results from the burials from mass pit [7482]/[8473] are not statistically consistent (T'=23.9; v=4; T'(5%)=9.5).[82] Given the strong evidence for the individuals having died at about the same time, this suggests the potential presence of outliers. Outlier analysis[83] identified UBA-32526 as a misfit (88% probability of being an outlier) and it was excluded from further modelling. The remaining four radiocarbon results are statistically consistent (T'=3.9; v=3; T'(5%)=7.8), and could be the same age. The resulting model has good agreement (Acomb=89.3%; n=4; An=35.4%). It provides an estimate for the date of the mass pit of *cal AD 1590–1620 (95% probability)*, and probably *cal AD 1600–15 (68% probability)*, suggesting the mass pit dates to a plague outbreak in the opening decades of the 17th century.

The three radiocarbon measurements from pit A[1279] are statistically consistent and could be the same age (T'=0.3; vs=2; T'(5%)=6.0). The model has good agreement (Acomb=130.4%; n=3; An=40.8%). It estimates the date of pit A[1279] to be *cal AD 1575–1630 (95% probability)*, and probably *cal AD 1600–20 (68% probability)*. This suggests burial pit A[1279] probably dates to the opening decades of the 17th century.

Table 17 Modelled dates for the radiocarbon-dated burial pits

Model in text	68% probability unless otherwise indicated	95% probability
Mass burial pit [7482]/[8473]	*cal AD 1600–15*	*cal AD 1590–1620*
Burial pit A[1279]	*cal AD 1600–20*	*cal AD 1575–1630*
Mass burial pit [7482]/[8473] marine corrected	*cal AD 1570–1605 (46%)* or *cal AD 1610–30 (22%)*	*cal AD 1560–1635*
Burial pit A[1279] marine corrected	*cal AD 1565–95 (25%)* or *cal AD 1615–45 (43%)*	*cal AD 1565–1650*
Burial pit A[1279] marine corrected with AD 1607 TPQ	*cal AD 1620–45*	*cal AD 1605–55*

A formal comparison of the two probabilities using the order function in OxCal suggests there is a 52% probability that mass pit [7482]/[8473] is earlier than pit A[1279]. Therefore, the dating suggests the two pits are very closely related in time, and may be coeval.

The alternative version of the modelling, which constrained the dates between AD 1607 and AD 1739 for pit A[1279], had limited effect on the posterior distributions. Effectively the ranges were truncated at 1607 and ended as in the primary model (Table 17).

MARINE RESERVOIR SENSITIVITY ANALYSIS

A second pair of models was constructed that included the percentage marine diet correction for the radiocarbon ages (Table 17). The local reservoir correction (ΔR) for the results was derived from the 14CHRONO Marine Reservoir Database[84] and is -31±56 ^{14}C years. These models both have good agreement: the combined result for mass pit [7482]/[8473] (Acomb=96.4%; n=4; An=35.4%) estimates it dates to *cal AD 1560–1635 (95% probability)*; the combined result for burial pit A[1279] (Acomb=123.1%; n=3; An=40.8%) estimates it dates to *cal AD 1565–1650 (95% probability)*. However, the inclusion of the potential marine dietary offset has resulted in a significant decrease in the precision of the results (*≤46%*: Table 17).

The alternative form of the marine corrected model, that is using 1607 as the lower constraint, had a relatively significant effect on the final probabilities for pit A[1279]. The estimated date for this burial pit is *cal AD 1605–55 (95% probability)*, and probably *cal AD 1620–45 (68% probability)*.

Conclusion: the date of the excavated mass or common graves

The date of the burial pits – pit A[1279] from the north line of pits and mass pit [7482]/[8473] – is of particular interest, both in relation to one another and to the known dates of plague events in London. It had been suggested that these pits might relate to the plague of 1665. However, even the most imprecise estimates – marine corrected and constrained by a TPQ of 1569 – resulting from modelling of the radiocarbon dates failed to incorporate this date at 95% probability (above; Table 17). The potential marine reservoir offset makes it difficult to separate confidently the dating as it might relate to severe plague outbreaks in 1603, 1625 and 1636 (Fig 85). The initial models – uncorrected and constrained by a TPQ of 1569 – would support the earlier two events. By imposing a TPQ of 1607 on burial pit A[1279], the earliest event is automatically discarded and the model agrees most with the events in 1625 and 1636; the radiocarbon dating and modelling are not able to resolve between these two possible dates.

Pit burial is confirmed by documentary evidence in London in 1603, 1625 and 1665, and in the New Churchyard in 1665 and ?1625 (above). Parish registers show heavy use of the New Churchyard in every major plague outbreak (above; Fig 85; cf Table 14). The Whit Sunday sermon was moved from the New Churchyard in 1625–6 and 1636–8 because of plague burial (above).

The problems of dating burials in a dense burial ground by finds recovered from grave fills are demonstrated in the case of mass grave [7482]/[8473]. While finds evidence initially suggested a date after *c* 1650, based on the glass phial and coffin grip, the radiocarbon dating and modelling suggests that the phial is certainly intrusive, introduced to the fill by later grave cuts and/or modern truncation, as also may be the coffin grip (cf above; Chapter 5.2).

Pit [7482]/[8473] was filled as a single event (Fig 95). The high success rate in identification of *Yersinia pestis* DNA supports the interpretation that at least most of the individuals buried in the mass pit died of plague during an epidemic crisis. This pit might represent the south-west corner of a cluster of burial pits dug at the centre of the burial ground and associated with a particular outbreak of plague; if so, the other associated pits would have been removed by Broad Street Station. The mass pit (and any other contemporary pits) may have been deliberately located near the pulpit for reasons of available space. Until the *c* 1640s, the area surrounding the pulpit was

Fig 95 A conjectural reconstruction of the burial of plague victims in the mass grave ([7482]/[8473]) dug in the New Churchyard, close to the south gate (artist Faith Vardy)

THE NEW CHURCHYARD

probably one of the least dense areas of the burial ground, particularly before new space was made available following the expansion of the ground in *c* 1607. The area surrounding the pulpit was probably less well used than the remaining ground, perhaps kept clear in order to accommodate audiences attending the sermons and largely reserved for burial monuments (Chapters 3.2, 5.5). A lower density of burials surrounding the pulpit in the main cemetery at St Mary Spital was seen archaeologically and this area became associated in particular with monuments and child burials.[85]

The character and scale of the group of burial pits to the north-west is strikingly reminiscent of what we know historically about plague burials in London from Dekker and, specifically, at the New Churchyard in 1625 from burial registers regarding the mainly uncoffined burial of plague victims (above). In the first half of the 17th century, this area could have been the least dense part of the ground and therefore the most logical place for digging a series of pits (some at least in lines) for burials.

Archaeological evidence: 1665 and later plague burials

Plague burial at the New Churchyard during the 1665 epidemic is amply attested by the documentary sources (above; Fig 86), but none of the excavated individual or common graves have been dated to this event. The burial pits excavated in the south part of the ground are associated with earlier outbreak(s) (Fig 90); common graves associated with the 1665 epidemic may have been located in the (unexcavated) north of the ground, in less-used areas away from the south gate.

An *ex situ* headstone (Fig 96) found reused within possible burial structure [1639]/[1640] was matched with an entry in the burial register of St Giles Cripplegate, which recorded the death of Mary Godfree who died of the plague on 2 September 1665. During the 16th and 17th centuries, the large, poor suburbs north of the city, including St Giles Cripplegate, were always among the areas hardest hit by plague epidemics and often saw the first rises in mortality.[86] The entries for burials at the parish during the height of the epidemic in August and September take up 101 and 54 pages, respectively.[87] Mary Godfree's entry reads: 'ff Mary dau[ghter] of[blank] Godfrey dec[ease]d Plague Above 2'.[88] The abbreviation 'ff' notes that the deceased was from the Freedom part of the parish. 'Above' may indicate burial in the ground of the pesthouse or (more likely) around the church (the upper churchyard), but in either case this is evidently incorrect and did not take place.[89] The error may have been a result of the general administrative chaos: the parish clerk, the sexton and two churchwardens all

<664>

Fig 96 Limestone headstone <664> of Mary Godfree (d 1665) (scale *c* 1:4)

died from the plague. Alternatively, her burial may have been redirected on the day of interment to the New Churchyard for reasons of space. Interestingly, the date of her burial is just four days before the prohibition of pit burial at the New Churchyard. Since the headstone was removed from its original location, it is impossible to know if it originally marked a single grave or, alternatively, a mass grave which contained Mary Godfree and others.

In the following century, there was no clear evidence of the mass graves of the late 1730s (Chapter 3.7). However, some of the burials at the top of the burial ground sequence were so tightly packed that they could as equally represent stacks arranged in rows as they could burials neatly stacked in pits and are therefore indistinguishable archaeologically.

Notes to Chapter 8

1   Dekker 1603

2   Aufderheide and Rodríguez-Martín 1998, 195; Achtman et al 1999

3   Roberts and Cox 2003, 266

4   Aufderheide and Rodríguez-Martín 1998, 196; Roberts and Cox 2003, 266

5   Rasmussen et al 2015

6   Aufderheide and Rodríguez-Martín 1998, 197; Roberts and Cox 2003, 266

7   Aufderheide and Rodríguez-Martín 1998, 197; Grainger et al 2008, 28; Sloane 2011, 22–3, 33–4, 103–11; Pfizenmaier 2016, 17–28

8   Bucholz and Ward 2012, 312–13

9   Aufderheide and Rodríguez-Martín 1998, 197–8; Bucholz and Ward 2012, 318–19

10 Bucholz and Ward 2012, 313

11 Houston 1996, 146

12 Finlay 1981, 112

13 Porter 2012b, 109–10

14 Carpenter 1896, 47, 114

15 Bucholz and Ward 2012, 312, 316

16 LMA, P69/AND1/A/ 009/MS04507/001

17 Cummins et al 2013, 4

18 LMA, COL/CA/01/01 /023 (Rep 21), 415v

19 Bedlam Register; Chapter 1.2, n 4

20 London Bills of Mortality figures: City and Liberties – 1578–95, Creighton 1891, 341–4, 353–4; 1603, Finlay 1981, 155; City, Liberties and out-parishes – 1604–79, Maitland 1739, 736–9

21 Cummins et al 2013

22 Creighton 1891, 339, 341–4, 353–4

23 Collection, 39

24 Cummins et al 2013, 16; Creighton 1891, 341–4

25 Averages based on the five years which preceded outbreaks or, in the case of 1578 where data is more limited, on the following two years.

26 Morrissey 2011, 6; Fuller 1626

27 LMA, COL/CA/01/01/ 043 (Rep 39), 213

28 LMA, COL/CA/01/01/ 044 (Rep 40), 203v

29 Harding 1993

30 Shrewsbury 1970, 327–8

31 Porter 2012a, 51

32 Harding 1993; Pepys diary, 31 Aug 1665

33 Porter 2012a, 71–4

34 Defoe 1986, 241–2

35 Vincent 1811, 16–19

36 Ibid, 17–18

37 Pepys diary, 30 Aug 1665

38 Porter 2012a, 51–2

39 LMA, COL/CA/01/01/ 074 (Rep 70), 153v

40 Defoe 1986, 62

41 LMA, COL/CA/01 /01/074 (Rep 70), 156

42 LMA, COL/CA/01/01/ 074 (Rep 70), 153v

43 Defoe 1986, 240; Harding 1993; 2002, 99; Maitland 1739, 1370; Strype 1720, ii(4), 54; LMA, COL/CA/01/ 01/074 (Rep 70), 155v

44 LMA, P69/MIC6/A/ 001/MS09147

45 LMA, P69/SEP/B/001/ MS03149/002, 82–3: I am indebted to Val Southon for this reference

46 Harding 2002, 99; LMA, P69/AUG/A/ 001/MS08872/002, 12 Sept and 21 Nov 1665; P69/MIL2/A/001/MS04 429/001, Oct 1665; P69/NIC2/A/002/MS0 5686, 9 Sept 1665; P69/ NIC1/A/001/MS17621, 3 Mar 1665

47 Harding 1993

48 Grainger et al 2008; Sloane 2011, 53–5, 90– 103; Pfizenmaier 2016, 22–3

49 Harding 1993, 53–64; 2002, 67

50 Harding 2002, 65

51 Balmford 1603, 32; Dekker 1603 quoted in Evans 1988, 336

52 Dekker 1625 quoted in Wilson 1925, 139 and 158–9

53 Taylor 1630

54 Many 'pit' burials clearly refer to corpses buried in multiple

graves or plots, eg Susan Yonge, 'widd[ow]', buried 15 Dec 1615 'in her pitt in the Chancell by her husband', and Walter Persy, buried 3 Oct 1599, in 'the infants pit in the East Church Yard' (LMA, P69/PET1/ A/001/MS08820). However, it is not clear if the term was ever used for single burials/grave cuts.

55 LMA, P69/PET3/A/ 001/MS05721/001

56 BL, E.166.(10)

57 LMA, P69/PET3/A/ 001/MS05721/001

58 Cal S P Dom 1635–6, vol 325, 1–9 June 1636, p 524

59 LMA, COL/CHD/CT/ 01/001, 50v, 140 and 217

60 LMA, P69/PET1/A/ 001/MS08820

61 Harding 1993, 53–64; 2002, 66

62 Defoe 1986

63 Ibid, 78–9, 241

64 Ibid, 77–81

65 Litten 2002, 96–9

66 Ibid, 96–7

67 Harding 2002, 142

68 Bos et al 2011; Schuenemann et al 2011

69 Methods detailed in Reimer et al 2015

70 Methods detailed in Dunbar et al 2016

71 DeNiro 1985

72 Masters 1987; Tuross et al 1988

73 Chisholm et al 1982; Schoeninger et al 1983

74 Lanting and van der Plicht 1998

75 Bayliss et al 2004

76 Cook et al 2015

77 Reimer et al 2013

78 Arneborg et al 1999

79 Buck et al 1996

80 Bronk Ramsey 1995; 2009a

81 IntCal13: Reimer et al 2013

82 Ward and Wilson 1978

83 Christen 1994; Bronk Ramsey 2009b

84 *14CHRONO*

85 Connell et al 2012, 5, 7, fig 3

86 Cummins et al 2013, 3, 9

87 LMA, P69/GIS/A/002/ MS06419

88 LMA, P69/GIS/A/002/ MS06419/006

89 Baddeley 1888, 20–1

CHAPTER 9

OTHER INFECTIOUS DISEASE

Niamh Carty

9.1 Introduction

Infectious disease represents either an inflammatory response by the body to attack from bacteria or a virus, or a secondary response to a wound or injury such as a fracture.[1] The appearance and severity of an infectious disease depends on the ability of a pathogen to damage the host as well as the immune response of the host to resist the pathogen.[2] The majority of deaths in the (pre-antibiotic) early modern period were probably from infectious disease rather than from accidents, old age or other illnesses.[3] The Bedlam Register database reveals that a range of infections affected the population, with consumption (tuberculosis) the most frequent cause of recorded death, followed by plague and fever (which may indicate an infectious disease) (Fig 97; Chapter 6.1).

The likelihood of catching an infection can be related to underlying health problems, reduced immune and nutritional status, and the ease at which it can be passed from human to human. The increased population and the cramped living conditions of many, especially the poor, during this period would

Fig 97 Incidence of infectious disease recorded in the Bedlam Register database (n=1188)

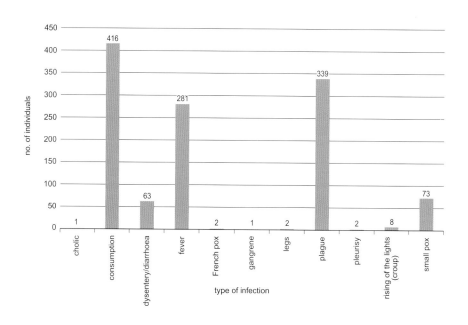

have helped disease spread and probably contributed to the several outbreaks of plague in the 16th and 17th centuries (Chapters 7, 8).[4] Contemporary knowledge about the spread of disease meant that during the early 18th century poor patients could neither gain entry nor receive treatment at one of the city's voluntary hospitals if they showed any symptoms for any infectious disease.[5]

Many diseases, particularly acute diseases such as smallpox, plague or typhus responsible for many deaths at this time, would not leave any traces on the skeleton. This is especially the case where the patient recovers quickly or death occurs rapidly before the infection can spread to the bone. Bone lesions are usually manifestations of a response to chronic long-lasting infections. These are usually bacterial rather than viral infections and include diseases such as tuberculosis (TB) and leprosy, and treponemal diseases such as syphilis.[6]

The most commonly encountered evidence of infectious disease amongst the category A burials from the New Churchyard comprised non-specific periostitis – inflammation of the periosteal tissue that surrounds bone (Table 18).[7] This affected 20.2% of individuals (138/682). Non-specific infections may result from many different processes including dietary and general stresses. These changes were more prevalent than specific diseases where a cause could be determined, such as TB or syphilis.[8] It is also possible that those who died from specific infections such as TB and syphilis did not survive long enough for the disease to show any bony changes, but that plenty of individuals lived long enough to display less severe infectious bone changes.[9]

There was an almost equal distribution between males (82/283: 29.0%) and females (56/210: 26.7%) affected by both specific and non-specific infectious disease (Fig 98). When examined by age at death, there were a lower number of females recorded in the older age categories. Perhaps females were less susceptible to infectious disease or able to tolerate stress better due to an enhanced immune status?[10]

There was no difference in the adult crude prevalence rates of infectious disease between phase 1, pre-*c* 1670, and phase 2, post-*c* 1670. However, there was almost double the number of subadults in phase 1 (20/99: 20.2%) compared to phase 2 (11/80: 13.8%) with evidence of infection. Caution must be exercised when extrapolating from small samples, but this appears to suggest that there was less stress from or exposure to infectious disease in the subadults who died during the period *c* 1670–1739 and more in this age group in the period before *c* 1670; was this related in the earlier period to working from a young age and in an urban and insecure environment, particularly as apprentices (Chapters 6.1, 7.4, 12.2)?[11]

The highest rates of subadult infectious disease for both phase 1 and phase 2

Table 18 Crude prevalence of infectious disease for category A and category B burials

	Subadult			Male		
	No. of individuals	No. affected	%	No. of individuals	No. affected	%
Category A	179			283		
Non-specific periostitis		18	10.1		69	24.4
Non-specific osteomyelitis		1	0.6		3	1.1
Non-specific osteitis		0	-		4	1.4
Tuberculosis		3	1.7		2	0.7
Treponemal disease		0	-		3	1.1
Category B	35			54		
Non-specific periostitis		2	5.7		15	27.8
Non-specific osteomyelitis		2	5.7		0	-
Non-specific osteitis		0	-		0	-
Tuberculosis		2	5.7		3	5.6
Treponemal disease		0	-		4	7.4

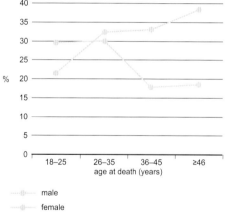

Fig 98 Crude prevalence of infectious disease by age for category A males (n=273) and females (n=199)

were recorded in the 6–11 years and 12–17 years age categories. Lewis has noted a rate of infection in urban subadults (in a pooled sample from across England) in the period AD 900–1550 of 7.1% (57/806) aged 6.6–9.9 years, 8.6% (63/732) aged 10–13.9 years and 11.9% (76/641) aged 14–16.9 years.[12] This would suggest that the 20.2% rate in phase 1 at the New Churchyard is high in comparison.

9.2 Non-specific disease

Non-specific infectious disease refers to a skeletal response to an unknown bacterial or viral infection in bone. Evidence of non-specific infectious disease was found in 150 category A individuals in the New Churchyard (/682: 22.0%), 10.6% of subadults (19/179) and 26.0% of adults (131/503). There was an increase with age in the males and a decrease in the female sample (Fig 99).

Overall crude prevalence rates between phase 1 (93/368: 25.3%) and phase 2 (82/314: 26.1%) show a higher rate of females were affected in phase 2 (27/113: 23.9%) than phase 1 (28/97: 28.9%). In contrast, subadults had a higher crude prevalence in phase 1 (16/99: 16.2%) than phase 2 (7/80: 8.8%). The rate of 16.2% (16/99) for subadults from phase 1 was much higher than in later assemblages, possibly reflecting increased stresses in this period,

Female			Adult			Total		
No. of individuals	No. affected	%	No. of individuals	No. affected	%	No. of individuals	No. affected	%
210			503			682		
	49	23.3		120	23.9		138	20.2
	1	0.5		4	0.8		5	0.7
	1	0.5		5	1.0		5	0.7
	2	1.0		4	0.8		7	1.0
	2	1.0		2	0.4		5	0.7
32			102			137		
	3	9.4		18	17.6		20	14.6
	0	-		0	-		2	1.5
	0	-		2	2.0		2	1.5
	2	6.3		4	3.9		6	4.4
	1	3.1		7	6.9		7	5.1

particularly for children who can be especially vulnerable to infectious disease (Chapter 12.1). There were 10.3% (8/78) of subadults affected at 18th- to 19th-century St Marylebone church and burial ground,[13] 10.4% (21/202) at 19th-century (1816–53) Bow Baptist church burial ground and 11.2% (49/437) at 19th-century (1843–54) St Mary and St Michael's burial ground (Table 4).[14]

A comparison of infectious disease rates in assemblages with an 18th- to 19th-century date range from low rates of 1.1% (4/360) at Kingston upon Thames[15] and 3.9% (10/254) at Sheen's burial ground[16] to higher rates of 12.0% (11/92) at St George's church, Canterbury (Kent),[17] 20.2% (84/416) at Bow Baptist,[18] 21.6% (65/301) at St Marylebone[19] and 23.7% (167/705) at St Mary and St Michael[20] indicate that the overall rates of non-specific stress in both phase 1 and phase 2 are similar to sites of a slightly later date.

Pathogenic bacteria detected within the dental calculus DNA were dominated by those species associated with the progression of periodontal disease. The most abundant periodontal pathogens were *Tannerella forsythia*, *Treponema denticola*, *Porphyromonas gingivalis*, the so-called 'red complex' of oral bacteria, with other periodontal pathogens such as *Filifactor alocis* and *Fusobacterium nucleatum* present at lower frequencies. Opportunistic pathogens (organisms capable of causing disease when the host's resistance is compromised) were also detected (Chapter 10.8).

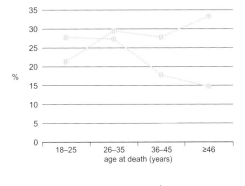

········ male
········ female

Fig 99 Crude prevalence of non-specific infectious disease by age for category A males (n=273) and females (n=199)

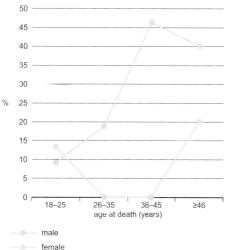

Fig 100 Crude prevalence of periostitis by age for category A males (n=273) and females (n=199)

Periostitis

New bone growth to the outer surfaces of bones (periostitis) represents a skeletal reaction to inflammation of the periosteum (dense layer of tissue) that surrounds a bone.[21] This can occur through extension of an adjacent soft tissue infection, as a manifestation of a generalised disease or by involvement of the surface of the bone from osteitis or osteomyelitis.[22] Evidence of non-specific periostitis was recorded in 20.2% of category A individuals (138/682), 10.6% of subadults (19/179) and 23.9% of adults (120/503). Females had a higher rate (49/210: 23.3%) than males (69/283: 24.4%), but males showed an increase with age while no females aged 26–45 years were affected (Fig 100). This was comparable to evidence from the medieval period: in the overall sample at St Mary Spital overall crude prevalence was 22.4% (1204/5387).[23] Similar rates were also recorded at the later Bow Baptist (63/416: 15.1%) and St Mary and St Michael (167/705: 23.7%).[24]

Almost double the amount of subadults were affected in phase 1 (14/99: 14.1%) compared to phase 2 (6/80: 7.5%).

The majority of periosteal lesions were healed (92/158: 58.2%) with 28.5% of all non-specific periosteal lesions active at the time of death (45/158) and 9.5% comprising mixed lesions that were both active and healing, perhaps suggesting a long-standing infection (15/158).

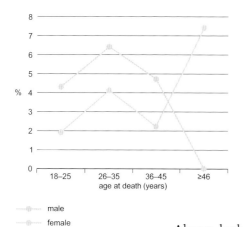

Fig 101 Crude prevalence of rib lesions by age for category A males (n=273) and females (n=199)

Rib lesions

New bone formation on the visceral (lung-facing) surfaces of the ribs represents an inflammatory response to direct contact with a lung infection.[25] These changes may signify a non-specific indicator of TB.[26] Evidence of rib lesions was found in 23 (/682: 3.4%) category A individuals from the New Churchyard, 1.7% of subadults (3/179) and 4.0% of adults (20/503). There was a similar rate between males (12/283: 4.2%) and females (8/210: 3.8%), although females demonstrated a higher prevalence than males in the older age category (Fig 101).

Almost double the amount of individuals were affected in phase 2 (16/314: 5.1%) compared to phase 1 (11/368: 3.0%). This may reflect increasing industrialisation, pollution and access to tobacco, and associated respiratory problems, in the late 17th and early 18th century (Chapters 7.2, 12.3). The rates of rib lesions are similar to those at St Marylebone, which had 4.0% (12/301) affected, with higher rates recorded at Bow Baptist (9.9%: 41/416)

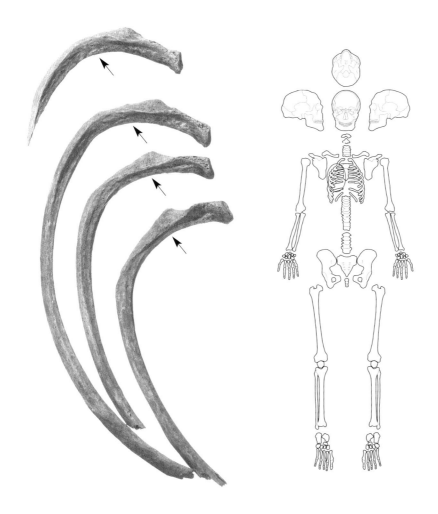

Fig 102 Adult male [5218], showing the active infection on the visceral surface of the right ribs (arrowed) (scale *c* 1:2)

and St Mary and St Michael (11.9%: 84/705).[27]

An adult male, [5218], aged 36–45 years, had thick plaques of white, porous new bone to the visceral surfaces of multiple ribs located at the rib angles, indicating an active infection (Fig 102); this individual also had evidence of habitual clay pipe smoking.

Sinusitis

Chronic infection of the paranasal sinuses may reflect recurring inflammation of the periosteum immediately underlying the mucosa lining of the maxillary sinuses in the nasal cavity.[28]

Evidence of maxillary sinusitis was found in 20 category A individuals from the New Churchyard (20/682: 2.9%), 1.1% of subadults (2/179) and 3.6% of adults (18/503). There were slightly more females (9/210: 4.3%) than males (9/283: 3.2%) affected, which may reflect the role of women in households, with large amounts of time spent indoors in smoky environments. However,

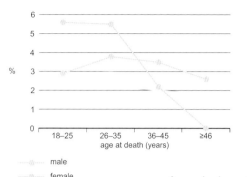

Fig 103 Crude
prevalence of sinusitis
by age for category A
males (n=273) and
females (n=199)

the male rate is more steady across all age categories and the female rate drops as age progresses (Fig 103). Both males and females showed the highest frequency of sinusitis in the 18–35 years age ranges. A higher overall rate of sinusitis was recorded in phase 1 (12/368: 3.3%) compared to phase 2 (6/214: 2.8%).

These rates are higher than crude prevalence rates recorded from the overall sample from St Mary Spital (8/607: 1.7%) and in *c* 1400–1539 (period 17) (8/607: 1.3%), and also from the later Bow Baptist which had a rate of 0.5% (2/416) and St Mary and St Michael 1.7% (12/705). However, a comparison of rates between sites may be hampered by differing levels of preservation and the survival of intact crania.[29]

There was a large bulbous, lobular bone growth in the right maxillary sinus of adult male [516], aged ≥46 years, indicting a chronic sinusitis infection (Fig 104). This may also be associated with a periapical abscess at the socket of the right first maxillary molar. Approximately 10–12% of cases of inflammatory maxillary sinus disease represent a spread from a dental infection.[30]

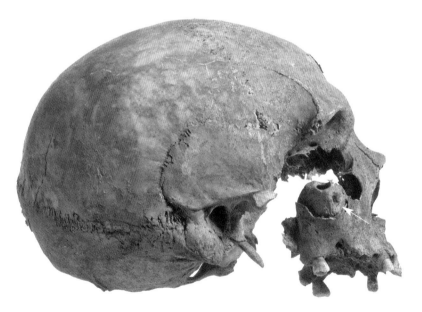
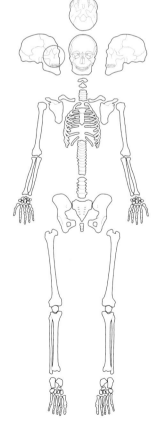

Fig 104 Adult male
[516], showing a large
growth in the right
maxillary sinus
(arrowed) (scale *c* 1:2)

Osteomyelitis

Osteomyelitis representing inflammation of bone (osteitis) and of internal bone marrow (myelitis) is caused by a pus-producing bacterial infection.[31] This commonly results from the introduction of pyogenic bacteria into bone following a compound fracture. However, other infectious agents, including viruses, fungi and multi-celled parasites, can also infect bone marrow.[32]

Evidence of osteomyelitis was found in only five category A individuals (/682: 0.7%) including 0.6% of subadults (1/179) and four adults (/503: 0.8%). There were more males than females affected and both showed an increased prevalence with age (Fig 105). These rates were comparable with evidence from the overall sample from St Mary Spital (30/5387: 0.6%).[33] Low rates of osteomyelitis were also recorded at later Sheen's burial ground (1/254: 0.4%) and Bow Baptist (5/416: 1.2%).[34]

Of particular note were the severe and widespread bone lesions observed in subadult [5193], aged *c* ten years old, that suggested a diagnosis of infantile cortical hyperostosis or Caffey's disease, characterised by extensive sub-periosteal new bone formation. The mandible was thickened and covered in a plaque of disorganised, spongy new bone growth and there was erosion of the left temporomandibular joint surfaces that would have restricted movement of the jaw (Fig 106). The distal (end farthest away from the body) shaft of the left humerus (upper arm) and proximal (end nearest the body midline) right radius and ulna (elbow) were expanded through osteomyelitis, with evidence of active and healed lesions suggesting a long-standing infection (Fig 106). Radiographs revealed moderate thickening of the long bone shafts. The distal right radius was swollen with plaques of pitted new bone but sparing the joint of the wrist. Porous lesions were present on the first cervical vertebrae of the upper spine with lytic destruction to the anterior body of the second cervical vertebrae and destruction of the left articular facets between the second and third vertebrae. Active lytic erosions were present on the sternal ends of two left ribs and the scapulae (shoulder blades) had destructive changes to the acromial spines and active new bone formation on the blades. Radiographs showed irregular thickening to the superior (head-facing) aspects of the scapulae.

Caffey's disease normally begins in infants younger than five months and has an average age of onset of nine to ten weeks.[35] While the exact aetiology (cause) is unknown, the disease may result from a viral infection passed on from a mother via the placenta, a genetic defect, abnormalities in vitamin levels, trauma, arterial abnormality or an allergic reaction to collagen.[36] The disease may be associated with fever, joint swelling and pain. While the bone manifestations

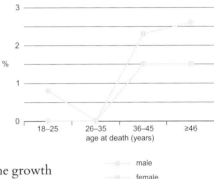

Fig 105 Crude prevalence of osteomyelitis by age for category A males (n=273) and females (n=199)

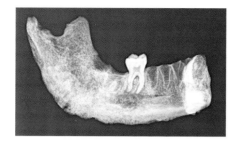

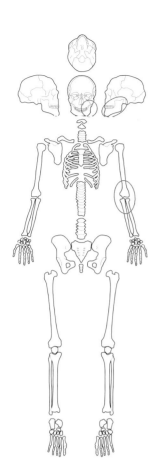

Fig 106 Subadult [5193], displaying evidence for Caffey's disease (arrowed): top left – radiograph of the left mandible (mediolateral view); bottom left – the mandible; right– left elbow joint (scale *c* 1:2)

may gradually subside over a few months or years, the disease can persist and recur intermittently.[37] Skeletal changes occurring over the age of two years, as in this individual, may represent a reoccurrence of the disease.[38]

Osteitis

Expansive changes to the bone shaft diagnostic of non-specific osteitis were recorded in five category A individuals (/682: 0.7%), 1.0% (5/503) of adults, affecting more males (4/283: 1.4%) than females (1/210: 0.5%). There was a peak in the 18–25 age category for both sexes. Almost double the number of individuals were affected in phase 2 (5/314: 1.6%) than phase 1 (2/368: 0.5%) (Fig 107).

Again, these rates are comparable to those recorded in the overall sample from St Mary Spital (50/5387: 0.9%).[39] Similar rates were also recorded at Sheen's burial ground (2/254: 0.8%), Bow Baptist (3/416: 0.7%) and St Mary and St Michael (2/705: 0.3%).[40]

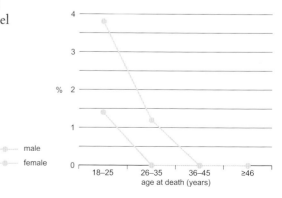

Fig 107 Crude prevalence of osteitis by age for category A males (n=273) and females (n=199)

9.3 Specific disease

No evidence for pathogens associated with epidemic diseases such as bubonic plague, tuberculosis or syphilis was identified within the metagenomic data. Although some DNA sequences from other respiratory diseases (eg whooping cough) were recovered from the metagenomic data, these were at extremely low abundance and would require further deep sequencing to conclusively identify these as the causative agents of disease (Chapter 10.8).

Tuberculosis

Tuberculosis (TB) is an infectious disease caused by bacteria of the mycobacterium complex, most often *Mycobacterium tuberculosis* and *Mycobacterium bovis*.[41] It is contracted via inhalation of bacteria-laden exhaled droplets from an infected person. Primary TB usually occurs in childhood and in people who have never been exposed to the infection before. The primary lesions affect the lungs or intestines and tend to heal unless the person dies in the acute stages of the disease.[42] Skeletal involvement is low, ranging 1–9%, with a focus in the spine and weight-bearing joints such as the hip and knee.[43]

In 1667, approximately 20% of all deaths in London were recorded as having been due to consumption. Morton in 1720 described consumptions resulting from bloody flux, breastfeeding with an inadequate diet, scurvy and diabetes, in addition to pulmonary consumptions that bear a closer resemblance to TB.[44] Although the term may have covered a wide range of conditions, it often meant TB.[45] References to the king's evil or scrofula (or swelling of the lymph nodes) also relate to cases of TB, which could be cured by the king's touch.[46] The indiscriminate nature of the disease meant that both rich and poor would have been at risk; however, poor nutrition and overcrowded living conditions with poor sanitation would have exacerbated the spread (Chapters 7, 10). In the next century the disease rose to epidemic proportions.[47]

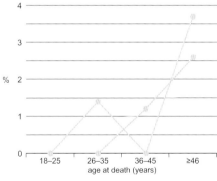

Fig 108 Crude prevalence of tuberculosis by age for category A males (n=273) and females (n=199)

Evidence of bone changes diagnostic of TB were found in seven category A individuals (/682: 1.0%), 0.8% of adults (4/503) and 1.7% of subadults (3/179). Seven category B individuals (/137: 5.1%), 4.9% of adults (5/102) and 5.7% of subadults (2/35) were also affected. There were slightly more females affected (2/210: 1.0%) than males (2/283: 0.7%), with both sexes showing an increased prevalence with age (Fig 108). A higher rate was recorded in phase 2 (10/314: 3.2%) compared to phase 1 (4/368: 1.1%).

Tuberculosis was widespread in London from the medieval period. The overall crude prevalence rate recorded at St Mary Spital was 1.9% (100/5387)

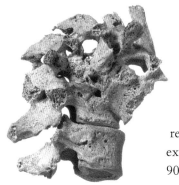

with the majority dying between *c* 1200 and *c* 1400; the lowest overall TB rates were recorded in *c* 1400–1539 (6/650: 0.9%).[48] In the later, post-medieval, period, rates of 1.9% (8/416) were recorded at Bow Baptist and 0.7% (5/705) at St Mary and St Michael.[49]

There were extensive deformities in the spine of female [8178], aged 26–35 years. The bodies of the fifth to the ninth thoracic vertebrae (lower back) were largely destroyed through erosive lesions. This had resulted in the anterior collapse into the tenth thoracic vertebra with extensive remodelling, fusion and a severe anterior kyphosis of approximately 90° known as Pott's disease, pathognomic of TB (Fig 109).[50]

Syphilis

Acquired venereal syphilis is an acute or chronic treponemal disease characterised by a primary lesion or chancre (painless ulcer). This affects the skin and mucous membranes with long periods of latency.[51] A third of untreated patients go on to develop the tertiary stage symptoms that include Charcot joints (a weight-bearing joint with progressive degeneration), gumma (soft, non-cancerous growth) of the skin, skeletal system, liver or spleen, neurological disorders or lesions in the cardiovascular or central nervous system. The disease can also cross the placenta to infect a developing foetus.[52] Syphilis may have had a hugely debilitating impact on the lives of those affected. As well as the impact on physical appearance, neurosyphilis may result in delirium, dementia, mania, psychosis, personality change and/or depression.[53]

Syphilis, known in England as the 'French Pox', was a significant health problem during the early modern era. However, deaths attributed to the disease in the Bills of Mortality are relatively few in number; bribes were quite often paid to ensure that family members were not recorded as dying of the pox in the bills.[54] There was a rise in prevalence during the mid 17th century, with a decline in the 18th century although it remained commonplace.[55]

Venereal syphilis is usually transmitted by sexual contact. Contemporary observers such as Friano degli Ubaldini of Bologna believed it was passed on 'through eating and through drinking and through sexual activity'; Girolamo Fracastoro of Verona, the 16th-century Italian physician and scholar, pointed not only to his 'seeds of contagion' but also, like many others, to 'astronomical causes'.[56] Women were frequently blamed for the contagion, for example, the 'wicked' wet-nurse was often accused of passing the disease to the child she nurses – while men were presented as victims.[57]

Skeletal changes suggesting treponemal infection – probably venereal syphilis – were identified in five category A individuals (/682: 0.7%), 1.0% of adults (5/503). Seven category B individuals were affected (/137: 5.1%), 6.9% of

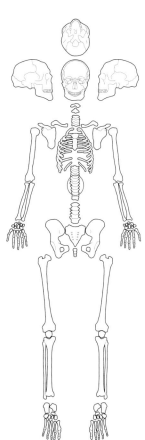

Fig 109 Adult female [8178], displaying the mid thoracic vertebrae showing evidence for Pott's disease (scale *c* 1:2)

adults (7/102). While there was an almost equal distribution between category A males and females, a higher crude prevalence was recorded in category B males (4/54: 7.4%) compared to females (1/32: 3.1%). A higher rate was recorded in individuals from phase 1 (10/368: 2.7%) compared to phase 2 (2/314: 0.6%), with a particular difference in the phase 1 males (6/149: 4.0%) compared to phase 2 (1/134: 0.7%).

A crude prevalence of 0.5% (25/5387) was recorded at medieval St Mary Spital with the highest rates recorded in *c* 1400–1539 (18/650: 2.8%).[58] Rates of 0.8% (2/239) were recorded at Bunhill Fields and 0.7% (5/705) at St Mary and St Michael.[59]

Adult [5383] displayed multifocal osteoblastic lesions throughout the appendicular skeleton, manifesting bilaterally in the tibiae and fibulae shafts (lower leg), the left ulna and radial shaft (lower arm). The lesions were a mixture of healed, healing and very active with localised bone swelling. The tibiae and fibulae in particular were expanded with healed bone growth and active porous bone overlaying the remodelled infection; the femur and smaller long bones were spared (Fig 110). The spread and appearance of the lesions reflected recurrent healing and infection characteristic of treponematosis.[60]

There were large areas of destruction and remodelling characteristic of caries sicca to the outer surfaces of the right parietal and occipital bones of the

Fig 110 Radiograph of adult [5383] displaying (left) the lower limbs and (right) right lower arm showing areas of bony thickening (arrowed), particularly on the tibiae, possibly resulting from venereal syphilis (scale *c* 1:4)

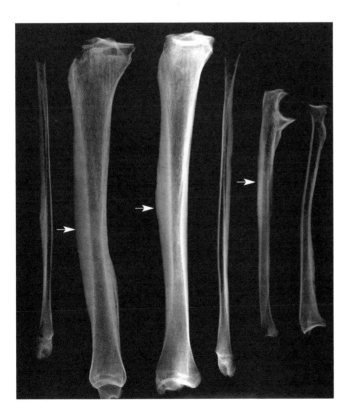

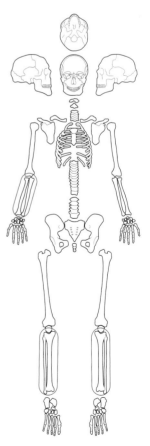

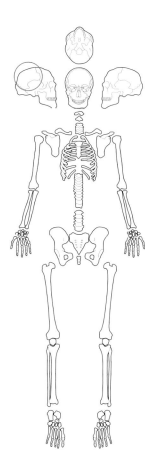

Fig 111 Adult male [7671], showing caries sicca lesions to the right parietal, indicative of venereal syphilis (scale *c* 1:2)

skull of adult male [7671], aged 18–25 years, suggesting venereal syphilis (Fig 111).[61] There was the beginning of rhinomaxillary destruction with lytic lesions eroding the medial (towards centre of body) surfaces of the maxillary facial bones and the mandible was slightly thickened with diffuse pitting. The long bones, including the humerii, ulnae and femora, were expanded through large areas of extensive remodelled bone with overlaying plaques of smooth and striated bone formation. The inferior (feet-facing) surfaces of the clavicles had pitted lesions.

Notes to Chapter 9

1   Aufderheide and Rodríguez-Martín 1998, 118

2   Török et al 2009, 3–5; Aufderheide and Rodríguez-Martín 1998, 118–19

3   Houston 1996, 148

4   Roberts and Cox 2003, 328–32

5   Hardy 1993, 67

6   Cox 1993, 76

7   Weston 2012, 492

8   Ibid, 493; Goodman et al 1984; Goodman and Armelagos 1988

9   Wood et al 1992

10 Redfern 2002, 157. Another possibility is that older females died before an infection became visible on their skeleton. Davenport et al (2010, 6) interpret low rates of TB in St Martin in the Fields females in the 1840s as suggesting they left London when they fell ill, returning to their families.

11 Lewis 2016, 139

12 Ibid, 158

13 Miles et al 2008, 125

14 Henderson et al 2013, 132–3

15 Roberts and Cox 2003, 344; also Start and Kirk 1998, 174

16 Henderson et al 2013, 132–3

17 Roberts and Cox 2003, 344; also Anderson 1991, 60

18 Henderson et al 2013, 132–3

19 Miles et al 2008, 125

20 Henderson et al 2013, 132–3

21 Ortner 2003, 206

22 Aufderheide and Rodríguez-Martín 1998, 179

23 Connell et al 2012, 109

24 Henderson et al 2013, 133–4

25 Roberts et al 1994

26 Santos and Roberts 2001; 2006

27 Miles et al 2008, 125; Henderson et al 2013, 134–5

28 Aufderheide and Rodríguez-Martín 1998, 257; Brimblecombe 1987, 3

29 Connell et al 2012, 110; Henderson et al 2013, 134

30 Bell et al 2011, 113–14

31 Aufderheide and Rodríguez-Martín 1998, 172

32 Ortner 2003, 181

33 Connell et al 2012, 109

34 Henderson et al 2013, 135–6

35 Resnick 2002, 4886; Kaufmann et al 1977

36 Lewis 2007, 144; Resnick 2002, 4888–91

37 Resnick 2002, 4886; Caffey 1952

38 Swerdloff et al 1970

39 Connell et al 2012, 109

40 Henderson et al 2013, 136

41 Roberts 2012, 434

42 Ibid, 435; Aufderheide and Rodríguez-Martín 1998, 118–20

43 Santos and Roberts 2001, 39

44 Morton 1720, cited in Wilbur et al 2008, 964

45 J Myers 1977 quoted in Santos and Roberts 2001, 38

46 Huizenga 1937, 175

47 Santos and Roberts 2001, 38; Cox 1993, 76–7; Roberts and Cox 2003, 338; Harding 2011, 38–40

48 Connell et al 2012, 114, 227, 233

49 Henderson et al 2013, 136–40

50 Ortner 2003, 230–1

51 Aufderheide and Rodríguez-Martín 1998, 158

52 Collins Cook and Lucas Powell 2012, 478–9

53 Stubblebine 1981

54 Cox 1993, 77; Siena 2004, 32

55 Roberts and Cox 2003, 341

56 Arrizabalaga et al 1997, 28

57 Siena 1998, 558

58 Connell et al 2012, 113

59 Connell and Miles 2010, 42; Henderson et al 2013, 140–2

60 Ortner 2003, 280–5; Walker 2012, 83

61 Ibid, 78–85

CHAPTER 10

DIET AND DENTAL HEALTH

Elizabeth L Knox

10.1   Introduction

In order to retain a healthy functioning body, a combination of amino acids, carbohydrates, minerals and certain vitamins are required that can only be obtained through a balanced diet.[1] By the late 16th and 17th centuries there were some major changes in the availability of domestic and imported foods, spices and beverages. These were minor at first with innovations in gardening and crop consumption, but by the early 18th century imports such as potatoes, sugars, tea, coffee and cocoa were a general part of the English diet that would impact the health of the population for years to come.[2] For the most part during the 17th century, these changes and the availability of new foods would have had more impact on the wealthier classes than the common city dweller. Food consumed by the poorer classes was unlikely to have changed from the 16th century, with bread being the main staple, with the occasional stick of butter and a rasher of bacon if they were lucky.[3] Garden vegetables, such as the onions, cabbages and legumes identified in DNA recovered from dental calculus in the New Churchyard (Metagenomic analysis, below, 10.8), would also have been eaten by the poor, as they had been throughout the medieval period, in the form of pottage. Consumption of fruit may initially have been limited to wild species such as blackberries and sloes, but would have increased in later periods, after the introduction of new species and varieties from north Europe made it more widely available.[4]

Several accounts refer to vegetables as a peasant food as the poor could afford very little meat, whereas the upper-class would dine on 'the flesh of all kinds'.[5] Recipes from the time, which describe the types of foods the middle to upper classes would prepare for a banquet, indicate meat-heavy menus, with few dishes containing vegetables or fruit unless in a sweet pudding.[6] Keeping up with the demand for meat was met in some cases by vendors heavily seasoning and washing rotting meats in the blood of fresh stock to hide the smell and trick the customers, potentially the cause of illness and intestinal parasites.[7] In 1632 King Charles I proclaimed that eating meat on church days was prohibited, partly in an attempt to help cattle farmers replenish their stocks; seafood was promoted as a substitute to be consumed on 'Fysshe dayes'.[8]

Many poorer households in London did not have a means of cooking hot food. Instead, when they could afford it, they would eat at the local public house or take their meats and offal to cookshops.[9] Water was barely drinkable and beer or ale was a safe alternative, with young children as well as adults consuming several pints a day.[10]

Isotope evidence on diet

Janet Montgomery, with Julia Beaumont, Nidia Lisic, Ruth Morley, Geoff Nowell, Chris Ottley, Joanne Peterkin

Several of the 20 individuals investigated using a range of isotopes and trace elements have unusually high strontium concentrations; these can arise due to a vegetarian diet, low dietary calcium, fertilisation of agricultural soils with seaweed, or residence in arid or coastal regions or unusual geological terrain. This is an admittedly small dataset and further research could clarify the causative factors and the link between high strontium and high lead concentrations (found in all 20 individuals) in relation to low dietary calcium uptake, nutritional stress and diseases such as rickets. While there was no difference in childhood diets between the mass pit [7482]/[8473] and attritional burials investigated, in later life the mass pit group (ten individuals) appears to be consuming a larger proportion of plants and thus less animal protein than the attritional group. This may suggest a shift to a poorer, less nutritious diet amongst the individuals in the mass pit in the last few years of life. Overall, the dietary isotopes of the New Churchyard population fit within the trend of increasing values from the medieval to the post-medieval periods, which documents the introduction of higher levels of fish (marine and freshwater) to the diet, particularly in urban populations such as York and London. Two migrants in particular (18–25 year old male [8216] and 26–35 year old male [8204]; Chapter 7.3) illustrate clearly the shift towards a diet typical for urban London.[11]

10.2 Adult stature

Variation in adult stature may relate to genetic and nutritional factors.[12] Disease, poor diet, inefficient absorption of nutrients and weakened immunity have all been shown to have an association with adult height.[13] The mean living stature for males from the category A sample of the New Churchyard was 169.1cm and for females was 160.9cm. No variation in stature was observed over the period of use of the burial ground or when compared to 15th- to 16th-century St Mary Spital, 17th- to 19th-century St Benet Sherehog and 19th-century St Mary and St Michael (Tables 4, 19).

10.3 Gout

A diet rich in meat and seafood can lead to many afflictions including constipation and gout, the latter potentially exacerbated by daily consumption of alcohol, especially amongst the wealthy classes as highlighted by Pepys.[14] Six category A adults from the New Churchyard had erosive lesions characteristic of gout (/682: 0.9%), 1.2% (6/503) of adults, 1.1% (3/283) of males and 1.0% (2/210) of females. This disorder is caused by an inflammatory

Site	Date	Male					Female				
		n	Mean (cm)	SD (cm)	Min (cm)	Max (cm)	n	Mean (cm)	SD (cm)	Min (cm)	Max (cm)
New Churchyard	1569–c 1670	83	169.1	5.5	155.9	182.1	48	161.3	5.3	153.0	170.2
	c 1670–1739	51	169.1	5.8	156.4	184.2	33	160.4	5.6	145.7	171.8
	Total	134	169.1	5.6	155.9	184.2	81	160.9	7.0	145.7	171.8
St Mary Spital	c 1400–1539 (period 17)	113	169.6	5.1	160.1	184.1	78	161.5	5.6	151.4	178.3
St Benet Sherehog	c 17th–19th century	12	169.4	6.3	158.8	177.1	9	160.2	3.3	155.7	165.2
St Mary and St Michael	1843–54	99	169.8	5.4	159.5	186.4	62	160.5	4.5	151.4	169.5

response to a build-up of uric acid crystals in the joints and has been associated with obesity, high alcohol consumption, kidney problems and high blood pressure.[15] It causes the joints to become swollen and painful with resulting limited mobility.[16] The head of the first metatarsal (big toe) is the most commonly affected site, although lesions may occur in the joints of the hand, wrist, elbow, knee and ankle.[17] Four individuals exhibited 'punched out' erosive lesions in the medial head of the big toe. Female [1553] had purely lytic (bone loss) scalloped erosions on the metacarpals and carpals of the left hand. Radiographs showed well-defined erosions with no evidence of reactive proliferative bone, consistent with a diagnosis of gout.[18] There were further well-defined sub-circular lesions on the greater tubercle, eminence to the anterolateral head of the right proximal humerus, the auricular surfaces of the ilia (articulation with the sacrum) and facet of the odontoid process (superior projection on the second cervical vertebrae of the neck). This individual also had bone changes suggestive of osteomalacia (Chapter 12.4). Multiple bilateral erosions in the hands and wrists of male [6028], aged 36–45 years at death, also suggested a case of gout (Fig 112).

Table 19 Adult stature (cm) calculated for the New Churchyard category A burials, and St Mary Spital, St Benet Sherehog and St Mary and St Michael

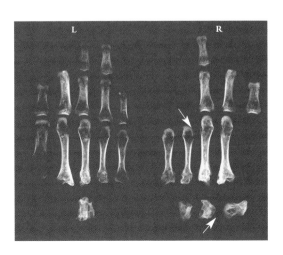

Fig 112 Anteroposterior radiograph of the hand and wrist bones of male [6028], showing well-defined erosions with no reactive bone (arrowed), consistent with gout (scale c 1:4)

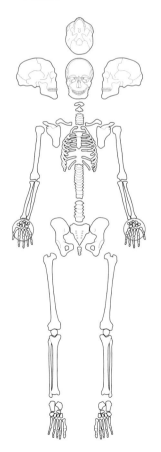

The low prevalence rates of gout in the New Churchyard assemblage suggest the majority could not afford much or any meat. Thomas Cogan in 1584 observed 'that poor men seldom suffered from gout and thus a peasant's diet of brown bread [should be] prescribed as a cure'.[19]

10.4 DISH

A rich and overindulgent diet with high calorie intake, lack of exercise and obesity may be a factor in the development of DISH (diffuse idiopathic skeletal hyperostosis).[20] This condition is characterised by an overgrowth of osteophytes on the margins of the vertebral bodies with an effect that resembles dripping candle wax, with fusion of the anterior longitudinal ligament along the right side of the spine. It results in spinal fusion and is diagnosed when at least four contiguous vertebrae become involved. The facet joints are not normally affected and the intervertebral disc spaces are maintained.[21] Extra spinal enthesopathies at tendon and ligament insertions may occur at joints and other sites around the skeleton.[22] All five individuals who exhibited bone changes diagnostic of DISH were adult males: four category A individuals (4/682: 0.6%; 4/503: 0.8% of adults; 4/283: 1.4% of males); one category B individual (1/137: 0.7%; 1/102: 1.0% of adults, 1/54: 1.9% of males). Category A adult male [3850] had smooth ossifications down the right side of the sixth thoracic to first lumbar vertebrae (Fig 113).

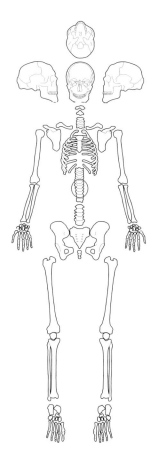

Fig 113 Sixth to 11th thoracic vertebrae of adult male [3850], showing characteristic 'dripping candle wax' osteophyte formation (arrowed) characteristic of DISH (scale *c* 1:2)

10.5 Iron deficiency

Although iron is present in foods other than meat, the iron in these foods is generally poorly absorbed by the body; thus the poorest classes who could not afford red meat may have been more vulnerable to the effects of iron deficiency. Conditions such as cribra orbitalia and porotic hyperostosis have been associated with dietary deficiency related to the body's attempt to stimulate more red blood cells to compensate for a lack of nutritional iron.[23] An insufficient diet can hinder the immune system, increasing vulnerability to infectious disease. Even for those with meat-rich diets, consumption of the spoiled meat commonly reported in London markets might have led to anaemia in those who picked up parasitic infections as a result. Chronic diarrhoea in children subsisting on meat-poor, wheat fibre-rich diets may also have led to iron deficiency anaemia.[24]

Cribra orbitalia

Cribra orbitalia is recognised as porous lesions in the orbital roofs of the skull (Fig 114). It results from thinning of the outer cranial table and expansion of the spongy bone that separates the inner and outer tables of the cranial bones, in order to boost the number of red blood cells during times of stress. The condition is predominantly observed in infants and young children.[25] While the exact aetiology remains unclear, the presence of cribra orbitalia has been linked to iron deficiency anaemia and increased pathogen loads.[26] This may relate to gastrointestinal infections, dietary deficiencies, genetic predisposition, lead poisoning and blood loss.[27]

The crude prevalence of cribra orbitalia in the category A burials where one or both orbits were affected was 14.5% (99/682). This included 14.7% of adults (74/503) and 14.0% of subadults (25/179). There was a slightly higher prevalence amongst males (47/283: 16.6%) compared to females (25/210: 11.9%). The true prevalence of cribra orbitalia in observable orbits was 19.3% (170/879). The majority of lesions (71/879: 8.1%) were recorded as comprising capillary-like impressions (grade 1).[28] Category A crude prevalence rates were similar in phase 1 (52/369: 14.1%) and phase 2 (47/314: 15.0%). There was a higher rate in the phase 1 attritional burials (OA105) (49/347: 14.1%) compared to mass pit burials (OA105E) and [7482]/[8473] (OA105A) (5/64: 7.8%). Just two individuals, both adult males aged 26–35 years from mass pit [7482]/[8473], displayed lesions (2/42: 4.8%, 2/26: 7.7% of adults). Nine category B burials had cribra orbitalia in at least one orbit (9/137: 6.6%, 9/102: 8.8% of adults, 8/54: 14.8% of males and 1/32: 3.1% of females). This affected 9.0% (13/145) of observable orbits, with the majority of lesions recorded as grade 1 (12/13: 92.3%).

Crude prevalence rates of cribra orbitalia at medieval St Mary Spital ranged from 17.2% to 27.8%, higher than other contemporary London sites.[29] The crude prevalence at 19th-century St Mary and St Michael was 35.5% (250/705).[30]

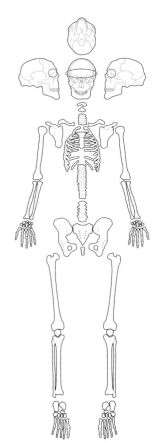

Fig 114 Female [5986] showing pitted lesions to the left and right orbits (arrowed) characteristic of cribra orbitalia (scale *c* 1:2)

Porotic hyperostosis

Porotic hyperostosis is manifest as pitting in the outer surface of the skull vault and has a similar, though not identical, aetiology to cribra orbitalia. They often co-exist, with cranial vault lesions perhaps representing more severe cases of anaemia.[31] The condition was identified in 5.4% of category A burials (37/682). This included 6.6% of adults (33/503), 7.8% of males (22/283), 4.8% of females (10/210) and 2.2% of subadults (4/179). Crude prevalence rates showed a peak in early adulthood with 9.5% (12/126) of those aged 18–25 years showing lesions. Lesions were most commonly observed in the left and right parietal bones (true prevalance – right: 33/519: 6.4%, left 33/513: 6.4%). Three category B individuals had porotic hyperostosis (3/137: 2.2%). This comprised 2.9% of adults (3/102), 3.7% of males (2/54) and 3.1% of females (1/32).

10.6 Vitamin C deficiency (scurvy)

Contemporary documents attribute much suffering and death, both on land and at sea during long voyages, to scurvy.[32] While texts outlining the symptoms and best remedies for sailors (oranges and lemons) were well known from the 16th century, these did not appear as preventatives or cures for city dwellers who were still prescribed medieval remedies related to humours or blood-letting (Chapter 11.2).[33] Old suspicions about fruit being the cause of fevers and illness lingered in the early 17th century, ensuring that a preventative cure remained elusive.[34]

Scurvy may result in painful symptoms including bleeding from the scalp and gums, loosening and eventual loss of teeth, swelling and bruising of the legs, red eyes and a putrid odour from the breath. If left untreated, it can also lead to changes in bone.[35] The effects of scurvy on dry bone are characterised by the osteological response to the haemorrhages and inflammation often seen as porous swollen bones, susceptible to fractures due to the weakened state of the skeleton.[36] Scurvy can be easily avoided or cured with a diet of fresh fruit and vegetables, specifically those high in vitamin C such as citrus fruits, but their consumption was not common practice at this time (above). The introduction of the potato, rich in vitamin C, in the 17th century was particularly important; its contribution to British diets coincided with a decline in deaths attributed to scurvy in the London Bills of Mortality by the 1720s.[37] It was not appreciated at that time, however, that fruit and vegetables needed to be eaten fresh, not cooked, and scurvy persisted into the late 18th century.[38]

During the late 16th and 17th centuries scurvy became a catch-all diagnosis for people presenting with listlessness, unnatural bleeding and skin lesions; later, scholars would suggest that many of these diseases were not scurvy, but rather venereal infections such as syphilis, which would not have been alleviated by dietary changes.[39]

Interestingly, there were few examples of scurvy identified in the New Churchyard. Less than 1% (6/682: 0.9%) of the category A sample exhibited skeletal lesions. All those affected were subadults (6/179: 3.4%) from the area of the deep ditch or to its west (OA105C) (ie phase 1, *c* 1607–70; Chapter 12.1, 'Illness and injury').

10.7 Vitamin D deficiency (rickets and osteomalacia)

London herbalist and physician Nicholas Culpeper, who was himself buried in the New Churchyard,[40] described the visual symptoms of children with rickets in the 17th century, but failed to understand the root cause. The people who went to see him were prescribed a list of vomit-inducing purges and ointments. This was a kinder remedy than scarification of the veins behind the ear that most physicians administered several times a week – not that Culpeper denounced this treatment, but he thought it had little effect.[41] Vitamin D metabolism is largely dependent on sufficient exposure to ultraviolet light from the sun, although a small proportion can be obtained from particular foods, such as eggs, fortified milk, liver and oily fish like salmon, tuna and mackerel. Vitamin D deficiency in adulthood is known as osteomalacia (Chapter 12.4).[42]

Fifty-two category A individuals (/682: 7.6%) displayed evidence of bone changes consistent with a diagnosis of rickets. This affected 11.7% of subadults (21/179) with 6.2% of adults (31/503) displaying residual effects of the disease. Twenty cases of rickets were recorded in the category B burials (20/137: 14.6%). This affected 34.3% of subadults (12/35) with 7.8% of adults (8/102) suffering residual effects (childhood rickets, Chapter 12.1).

10.8 Dental health

> Men dig their graves with their own teeth and die more by these fated instruments than by the weapons of their enemies[43]

Dental hygiene was rarely practiced in the 16th and 17th centuries and Britain seemed particularly slow when compared to France and Italy, where the upper classes were already using tooth brushes. The alternative was to rub salt on the teeth with a finger or vitriol (sulphuric acid) applied with a small piece of wood, the latter certainly whitening the teeth but of course weakening the enamel in the process. Wealthier individuals may have purchased a 'dentifrice' or 'tooth-powder', often manufactured in France, consisting of a soft clay mixed with crushed shellfish, coral, cream of tartar and powdered roses, an abrasive concoction which was probably not especially effective.[44]

The crude prevalence rates (by individual) and true prevalence rates (by tooth/tooth socket) for the category A sample are presented in Tables 20 and 21.

Enamel hypoplasia

Enamel hypoplasia presents as linear grooves or pitting on the enamel surfaces of teeth and results from temporary periods of delayed growth while the

Dental pathology	Subadult			Adult			Total		
	n	No. of individuals affected	%	n	No. of individuals affected	%	n	No. of individuals affected	%
	179			503			682		
Caries		65	36.3		320	63.6		385	56.5
Calculus		80	44.7		365	72.6		445	65.2
Enamel hypoplasia		59	33.0		200	39.8		259	38.0
Periapical abscess		13	7.3		148	29.4		161	23.6
Periodontal disease		6	3.4		187	37.2		193	28.3
Ante-mortem loss		16	8.9		295	58.6		311	45.6

Dental pathology	Deciduous			Permanent			Total		
	n	No. affected	%	n	No. affected	%	n	No. affected	%
	716			8598			9314		
Caries		83	11.6		1531	17.8		1614	17.3
Calculus		103	14.4		5610	65.2		5713	61.3
Enamel hypoplasia		34	4.7		1406	16.4		1440	15.5
	1142			12212			13354		
Periapical abscess		3	0.3		301	2.5		304	2.3
Periodontal disease		4	0.4		1294	10.6		1298	9.7
Ante-mortem loss		9	0.8		1868	15.3		1877	14.1

dentition is still developing.[45] It can also appear as deep linear furrows with exposed dentin or as localised circular defects. In the early 18th century pioneering dentists were beginning to identify such defects. Pierre Fauchard in his *Le Chirurgien dentiste* described a disease which resembled dental caries but was not formed by decay; he believed that enamel hypoplasia was caused by some form of corrosive substance, but did not proffer an opinion as to what it might be.[46] Enamel hypoplasia has been associated with several different disorders including syphilis, fever, low birth weight and nutritional imbalances including vitamin D deficiency (above, 10.7).[47] Modern studies have shown that a compromised immune system during dental development is a key cause of dental hypoplasia and that the defects are most pronounced when there is a combination of disease and vitamin D deficiency.[48] Crude prevalence of enamel hypoplasia at the New Churchyard was 38.0% (259/682), affecting a total of 1440 teeth. The true prevalence rate for subadults was 14.3% (328/2288) and for adults 15.8% (1112/ 7026). This was nearly double the amount of adult teeth affected at the 19th-century City

Bunhill burial ground (153/1861: 8.2%), indicating that people in the New Churchyard suffered more stress during development and/or that more of those affected survived these stresses into adulthood when compared with the City Bunhill population.[49]

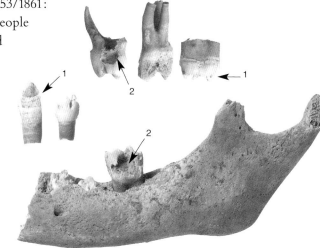

Fig 115 Linear enamel hypoplasia (arrow 1) and caries (arrow 2) of subadult [380] (scale *c* 1:1)

Subadult [380] aged 6–11 years had severe linear enamel hypoplasia affecting all developing and erupted teeth. It is possible that the child did not receive adequate nutrients from the mother before birth and also during weaning (Fig 115).

Periodontal disease

Periodontal disease (or periodontitis) is a condition that results in inflammation of the bone surrounding the tooth socket in response to gingivitis (gum disease). The weakened bone recedes away from the crowns of the teeth exposing the roots and eventually resulting in tooth loss.[50] Periodontal disease affected 193 individuals from the category A sample (/682: 28.3%), including six subadults (/179: 3.4%). When divided into age groups, half the adults in each category over 36 years of age were affected by periodontitis, reflecting an increased prevalence with age (Fig 116).

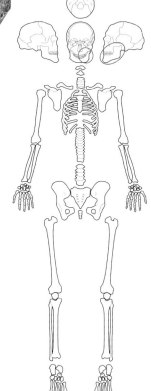

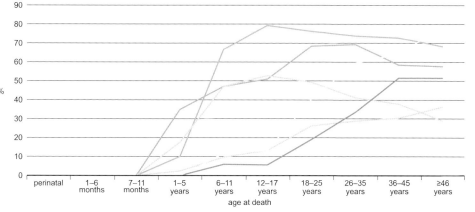

caries
calculus
hypoplasia
periapical lesion
periodontis
ante-mortem tooth loss

Fig 116 Crude prevalence of dental disease by age for category A burials (n=385)

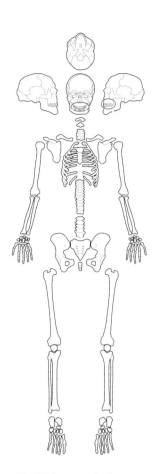

Fig 117 Severe calculus deposits (arrowed) of male [819] (scale *c* 1:2)

Fig 118 Crude prevalence of dental calculus by phase for category A burials (phase 1, n=344; phase 2, n=277)

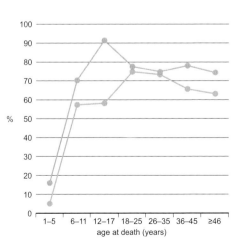

Dental calculus

Dental calculus consists of hardened deposits of plaque that form on the surface of the teeth, trapping bacteria, bodily fluids and food debris in the mouth.[51] The mouth is full of a complex bacterial colony of plaque which coats the teeth; depending on the foods consumed, oral plaque will either metabolise food into an alkaline or acidic waste product. A balanced diet is required to maintain healthy oral hygiene and to ensure the mouth is never too alkaline or acidic. Carbohydrates produce lactic acid when metabolised weakening the enamel of teeth. Conversely proteins produce an alkaline environment when metabolised, prompting mineralisation of oral plaques and strengthening enamel.[52] A high protein diet could produce an almost entirely alkaline environment. This would stimulate a high degree of plaque mineralisation in the mouth and result in thickened calculus deposits.

Woolley reminded her readers in 1682 not to pick at their teeth at or after meals with a knife (or other) as it was uncivil. Many did so, however, with all manner of utensils. Allen wrote in 1686 of the need to remove the 'scales' or 'scurf', a 'stone-like substance' adhered to the tooth surfaces; he recommended a regular professional scaling and the frequent use of toothpicks.[53]

Calculus affected 72.6% (365/503) of adults in the New Churchyard and just under half the subadult sample (80/179: 44.7%). Male [819], aged 36–45 years, had severe deposits of calculus on the left mandible and maxillary dentition. This may be the result of a lack of oral hygiene, but the minor deposits on the right dentition suggest there was some underlying pathological condition that discouraged chewing on the left side, allowing rapid build-up of plaque (Fig 117). Rates of calculus were similar in both periods of use of the burial ground (phase 1 and phase 2), with the exception of a relatively high rate in 12–17 year olds in phase 1 (Fig 118).

Analyses of dental calculus

Dental calculus can provide evidence of a variety of debris of both dietary and non-dietary origin to which individuals were exposed during life. Three different analytical techniques were applied to the New Churchyard population.

MICROSCOPIC ANALYSIS

Anita Radini

Dental calculus microscopy studies are increasingly popular in the discipline of archaeology, for their potential to provide information about the consumption of plant foods.[54] Although diet has been the main focus of recent dental calculus research, a small number of studies have demonstrated that a range of micro-debris of non-dietary origin and chemical compounds can become entrapped in the calculus. For instance, smoke, occupational dust generated by pottery making and plant fibres, such as cotton (*Gossypium* spp), have been recovered from the calculus matrix of past populations.[55]

Micro-remains retrieved and identified during the study of 20 samples from the New Churchyard showed that staple food plants such as oats, wheat and legumes were consumed across the population (cf below, 'Metagenomic analysis'). A number of pollen grains from potential medicinal plants, such as borage *(Borago officinalis)*, mugwort (*Artemisia* spp) and mallow (*Malva* spp) were also found. Five individuals had the remains of feather barbules, thought to be chicken, probably present in dust in the environment as the result of consumption or plucking of such birds. Non-dietary evidence consisted mainly of fibres of plant origin, likely flax (*Linum usitatissimum*) or hemp (*Cannabis sativa*), and of animal origin such as wool. These finds could be the result of exposure to occupational dust. Evidence of exposure to smoke and soot were also scattered across the population with female [175] showing a very high concentration of micro-charcoal.

CHEMICAL ANALYSIS

Stephen Buckley

Ten samples of dental calculus taken from ten individuals were analysed by sequential thermal desorption-gas chromatography-mass spectrometry (TD-GC-MS) and pyrolysis-gas chromatography-mass spectrometry (Py-GC-MS). The results revealed not only evidence of bacterially derived components, as one might expect from material taken from the microbially active human mouth, but also evidence for food-based fats and proteins, although notably there was no chemical evidence for smoke inhalation, tobacco use or cooking.

METAGENOMIC ANALYSIS

Jessica Hendy and Camilla Speller

PUTATIVE DIETARY DNA SEQUENCES

Previous metagenomic studies of dental calculus identified the presence of dietary DNA sequences, albeit at an extremely low frequency.[56] Here, a total of 140 putative dietary sequences were recovered from the 20 individuals studied. The most common food product identified was cereals (specifically the genus *Triticum*), accounting for 80% of the dietary sequences. Due to the similarities in the nuclear genomes of *T aestivum* (common wheat or bread wheat), *T monococcum* (einkorn wheat), *T durum* (durum wheat) and *Aegilops tauschii* (goatgrass), it is difficult to assign the obtained cereal sequences to particular species within the Triticeae tribe. Thus, the obtained *Triticum* and *Aegilops* species sequences should not be considered 'species specific', but instead indicative of the consumption of *Triticum* cereals in general. However, archaeological finds of charred grain and chaff from this period are almost all of bread wheat (*T aestivum* sl), suggesting that this is the most likely wheat to have been consumed.[57] DNA sequences assigned to Brassicaceae (cabbage or mustard family) and onion were identified in two individuals, respectively. DNA evidence of herbs (parsley (*Petroselinum crispum*), rosemary (*Rosmarinus officinalis*) and *Artemisia* sp) was identified in two individuals, and DNA sequences specific to grapes (*Vitis vinifera*), the cucurbit family (which includes gourds, melons and squash) and the legume family were identified in one individual each. Seeds of grapes, as well as brassicas, parsley, legumes and various cucurbits have been identified on archaeological sites from the 16th to the 18th century, including Spitalfields.[58]

DNA sequences matching to animal products were found in seven individuals, with the most common sequences matching cattle (*Bos taurus*) and domestic pig/wild boar (*Sus scrofa*), as well as DNA sequences matching chicken (*Gallus gallus*) and goose (*Anser anser domesticus*) in one individual each. The fact that no putative dietary sequences were identified within the bone samples or the laboratory controls suggests that the dietary DNA sequences within the dental calculus are not a result of systematic laboratory contamination, lending authenticity to the obtained dietary data. Although the DNA evidence for dietary sources is extremely limited, it provides new complementary evidence for the use of vegetative material such as herbs and leafy greens, which survive in the archaeological record mainly as seeds and pollen.

INFECTIOUS DISEASE

The DNA within the dental calculus samples was dominated by bacteria (average of 97.3% across all 20 samples) with relatively lower percentages of archaeal (0.99%), eukaryotic (1.4%) and viral DNA (0.004%). The metagenomic analysis of the dental calculus sample displayed a microbial composition consistent with an oral microbiome, indicating that the samples were generally well preserved and not systematically contaminated with exogenous DNA from the burial environment. The composition of microbial sequences from the dental calculus was distinct from that recovered from the bone samples, which displayed a microbial composition consistent with soil contamination (as expected).

Within the eukaryotic DNA isolated from the dental calculus, evidence for endogenous host DNA as well as dietary sources was recovered. Percentages of human DNA within the dental calculus ranged from 0.07% to 0.81% of the obtained sequences, and within the range expected from previous analyses of dental calculus.[59] Based on the number of sequences matching to the sex chromosomes, the quantity of human DNA was sufficient to predict the biological sex of the individual for 18 of the 20 skeletons; the sex predicted through genetic analysis corresponded with the osteological analysis in 17 of the 18 cases.

Overall, the metagenomic screening indicated that the biomolecules within the samples were well preserved with a high potential for further, in-depth analysis.

Dental caries

Carbohydrates, including sugars, grains and potatoes, produce lactic acid when broken down; this can weaken tooth enamel leading to the formation of caries (cavities). The consumption of sucrose in particular carries a high risk so the importation of sugar into Britain in the 17th century is significant in any consideration of dental health in London. During the 16th century, sugar was a luxury food item consumed by the elite. A popular ingredient in fruit tarts and puddings, it had fallen in price by the 17th century, although it still lay beyond the means of most commoners.[60] The introduction of tea, coffee and cocoa from Turkey and the West Indies popularised the consumption of sugar and made it available to more people by the mid 1650s. Coffee shops sprang up all over London, as a place to meet socially and to talk of politics and world affairs. With this increase in both social non-alcoholic drinking and in bitter beverages in need of sweetening, sugar consumption in Britain soared from 10,000 tons (c 10,160 metric tonnes) in 1700 to 150,000 (c 152,407 metric tonnes) by 1800.[61]

Sugars have long been associated with dental decay. Observations by Johannes Arculanus in the 15th century suggested that rich, sweet and sticky foods like figs and honey be avoided for the same reason.[62] By adding the sugar to tea and coffee it was believed that the decay would be lessened, a theory that has received support in recent years.[63] Nevertheless, through a variety of foods and recipes, sugar consumption increased.

Many other foods can also weaken tooth enamel by increasing oral cavity acidity. The high starch carbohydrate content of potatoes may also have been responsible for increased vulnerability to the condition.[64] Toothaches were blamed on dental 'worms' burrowing into the enamel of a tooth. Pepys described the dentistry charlatans of London's markets who claimed they could cure toothaches by extracting the 'worm' from the tooth. The desperate sufferer made payment whereupon the amateur dentist put their unwashed hands into the individual's mouth and produced a 'worm' fashioned from paper or some other common material.[65] Even supposedly learned physicians would treat toothaches with spells or charms, a throwback to medieval practices. By the late 17th and early 18th centuries tooth extraction was no longer fashionable in medical circles. To avoid the procedure sulphuric acid was applied to an infected tooth in order to dissolve it.[66]

In the New Churchyard, more than half of adults (320/ 503: 63.6%) and over a third of subadults (65/179: 36.3%) were affected by at least one cavity. Caries affected 19.8% of adult teeth and 9.7% of subadult teeth.

The loss of teeth prior to death (ante-mortem) was strongly correlated with advancing age (Fig 119). However, these lost teeth may mask indicators of dental disease such as caries. When the corrected caries rate was calculated, assuming that the rate of carious lesions

Fig 119 Crude prevalence of ante-mortem tooth loss by age group for category A adult males (n=273) and females (n=199)

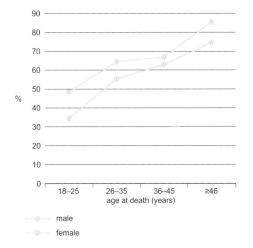

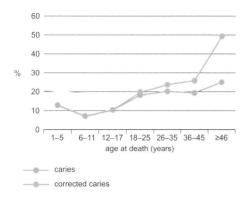

Fig 120 Corrected caries true prevalence by age group for category A (n=9134)

would have been the same if the teeth had not been lost, the results revealed a strong association with older age (Fig 120).

These results for adult caries can be compared with later, 18th- to 19th-century London burials. The results are similar to those from St Mary and St Michael with 20.2% (987/4890)[67] and slightly lower than those from wealthy St Marylebone with 23.1% (510/2211).[68] However, the true prevalence rate of caries in the New Churchyard is higher than Sheen's burial ground, with 12.8% (207/1617) and City Bunhill, with only 12.3% (228/1861) of adult teeth affected by caries.[69] This suggests that people from the New Churchyard had a diet comparable to those of St Mary and St Michael, but possibly with less sugar and delicacies available than those of St Marylebone. Interestingly, if we look at the medieval London site St Mary Spital, *c* 1400–1539 (period 17), 13.3% of adult teeth had caries.[70] These results show a great leap in dental caries in the 17th century, probably a result of introduced sugars and additional carbohydrates.

Periapical lesions

If left untreated, dental caries may lead to a more severe infection involving the tooth socket. A dental abscess (periapical lesions) is usually painful and can spread to neighbouring teeth in the mouth. Sometimes the infection results in pus which migrates through small gaps in the bone; this liquid can become encapsulated by a thin bone wall which become cysts. These cysts rarely survive in the archaeological record but leave open abscesses in their place.[71] Periodontal lesions affected almost a quarter (161/682: 23.6%) of category A individuals, 29.4% of adults (148/503) and 7.3% of subadults (13/179). There was a slightly higher rate amongst males (87/283: 30.7%) than females (58/210: 27.6%). There was an increased rate of periodontal lesions in the older age categories of phase 1 compared to phase 2 (Fig 121).

Fig 121 Crude prevalence of periapical lesions by phase for category A burials (phase 1, n=344; phase 2, n=277)

Male [5820], aged 25–36 years, had a large abscess at the sockets for the left maxillary first and second molars that had been lost ante-mortem, probably through carious erosion. The abscess has destroyed the bone of the maxilla and spread into the left sinus with active bone destruction to the external bone surfaces and inferior left orbit (eye socket) (Fig 122).

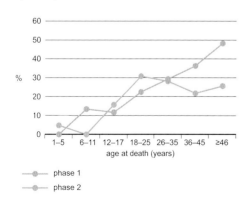

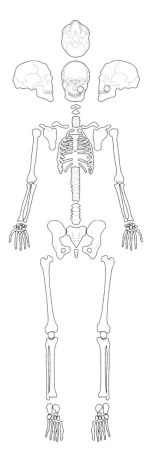

Fig 122 Severe periapical lesion (arrowed) of the left maxillary tooth sockets of skeleton [5820] (scale *c* 1:2)

Notes to Chapter 10

1   Mushrif 2000–1, 367

2   Newman 1946; Lanfranco and Eggers 2012, 7–18; Schneider 1926; Anderson et al 2009; Austen and Smith 1990

3   Drummond and Wilbraham 1991, 48

4   Brears 1985

5   W Harrison, *A description of England* (1577), cited in Drummond and Wilbraham 1991, 49

6   Woolley 1675, 167–220; see the 17th-century cesspit groups from the relatively affluent properties in the new suburb of Spitalfields: Harward et al 2015, 127–38

7   Drummond and Wilbraham 1991, 35–6, 63

8   Gregg 1981, 231

9   Drummond and Wilbraham 1991, 105

10   L Magalotti quoted in Picard 2003, 157; Drummond and Wilbraham 1991, 114

11   Montgomery et al 2016

12   Roberts and Cox 2003, 308

13   Roberts and Manchester 2012, 39

14   *Pepys diary*

15   Rogers 2000, 172

16   Duckworth 1995, 319

17   Rogers and Waldron 1995, 78

18   Resnick 2002, 1763

19   Drummond and Wilbraham 1991, 74

20   Roberts and Manchester 2012, 226–35

21   Rogers 2000, 170–1

22   Rogers and Waldron 1995, 48–51

23   Roberts and Manchester 2012, 226–34

24   Mushrif 2000–1, 367; Stuart-Macadam 2006, 132; Picard 2003, 153; Drummond and Wilbraham 1991, 35

25   Aufderheide and Rodríguez-Martín 1998, 349

26   Stuart-Macadam 1992

27   Roberts and Cox 2003, 234; Roberts and Manchester 2012, 226–34

28   Stuart-Macadam 1991

29   Connell et al 2012, 240

30   Henderson et al 2013, 199

31   Stuart-Macadam 1992, 39; Roberts and Manchester 2012, 229–30

32   Lorenz 1954, 666; Drummond and Wilbraham 1991, 135; Manchester 1998, 167–8; Baron 2009, 316–18; Glouberman 2009; Magiorkinis et al 2011, 147–8; Allgaier et al 2012; Mays 2014

33   Clowes 1596, 40–3; Kirkup 1978, 185; Magiorkinis et al 2011, 148

34   Drummond and Wilbraham 1991, 125

35   Magiorkinis et al 2011, 147

36   Ortner 2003, 384–5; Mays 2014

37   Roberts and Cox 2003, 306

38   Ortner 2003, 384

39   Baron 2009, 319

40   Poynter 1962, 155; Farthing 2013

41   Culpeper 1814, 228–9, 237, 297; Sibly 1802, 236–7; Picard 2003, 95–6

42   Roberts and Manchester 2012, 237–40

43   Thomas Moffet 1600 quoted in Newman 1946, 39

44   Woolley 1675, 10; L Magalotti quoted in Picard 2003, 130–1

45   Aufderheide and Rodríguez-Martín 1998, 405; Hillson 2005, 168

46   Fauchard 1728

47   Hillson 2014, 184–5; 1979, 148–9; Roberts and Manchester 2012, 75

48   Hillson 2014, 190–1

49   Connell and Miles 2010, 39

50   Hillson 2005, 304–5; Walker 2012, 244

51   Hillson 2005, 288–9

52   König 2000, 163–4; Lanfranco and Eggers 2012, 13–16; Hillson 1979, 150

53   Woolley 1682, 108; Allen 1687; Picard 2003, 131

54   Power et al 2015

55   Blatt et al 2011; Blondiaux and Charlier 2008; Hendy et al 2013; Radini et al 2016

56   Warinner et al 2014

57   A Davis, pers comm 2016

58   Harward et al 2015, 268–70

59   Warinner et al 2014

60   Drummond and Wilbraham 1991, 112

61   Schneider 1926, 312; Pincus 1995

62   Newbrun 1982

63   Lanfranco and Eggers 2012, 15; Touger-Decker and van Loveren 2003, 889

64   König 2000, 168–70; Lanfranco and Eggers 2012, 12

65   *Pepys diary*; Smith 1958, 26, 32; Anderson 2004

66   Smith 1958, 32; Picard 2003, 105

67   Henderson et al 2013, 116–17

68   Miles et al 2008, 112–13

69   Connell and Miles 2010, 38–9; Henderson et al 2013, 116–17

70   Connell et al 2012, 42–3

71   Hillson 2005, 307–10

CHAPTER 11

INJURY, DISABILITY AND CARE

Michael Henderson

11.1 Trauma

Evidence of injury in the form of traumatic lesions to the skeleton (fractures, soft tissue injuries and dislocations) were recorded in approximately a quarter of category A burials (165/682: 24.2%), 31.6% of adults (159/503) and 3.4% (6/179) of subadults. No subadults under the age of five years showed evidence of trauma. Crude prevalence showed an increase with age, with those aged ≥46 years showing the highest frequency of injury. Males had a higher injury rate than females in all adult age categories. Males aged 18–35 years suffered a much higher trauma frequency than females the same age (Fig 123).

Forty-two category B individuals (the 'special cases': Chapter 6.2) had evidence of injury (/137: 30.7%), 37.3% of adults (38/102) and 11.4% of subadults (4/35).

Fig 123 Crude prevalence of trauma by age for category A males (n=273) and females (n=199)

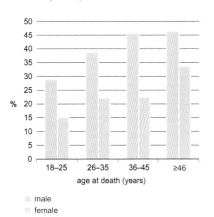

male
female

Fractures

Fractures were the most common form of trauma in the New Churchyard with a crude prevalence of 20.2% (138/682) for the category A burials, 26.4% of adults (133/503) and 2.8% (5/179) of subadults. Fracture rates increased with age and males showed a higher frequency in each age category than females (Fig 124). Thirty-three category B burials had fractures (/137: 24.1%), 28.4% of adults (29/102) and 11.4% of subadults (4/35). Seven individuals from mass burial pit [7482]/[8473] had evidence of fracture (/42: 16.7%), 15.4% of adults (4/26) and 18.8% (3/16) of subadults.

Skull fractures

Fourteen category A individuals had suffered fractures to the bones of the skull (/682: 2.1%), 2.8% of adults (14/503) affecting 3.5% (10/283) of males and 1.9% (4/210) of females. The majority of fractures occurred in the bones of the cranial vault (frontals, parietals, temporals) and the facial bones (nasal,

Fig 124 Crude prevalence of fractures by age for category A males (n=273) and females (n=199)

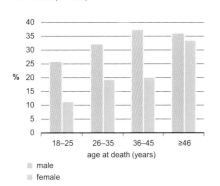

male
female

zygomatic). Males were more likely to suffer injuries to both of these regions than females. True prevalence showed the nasal bones to be the most frequently fractured bone of the skull (right 4/180: 2.2%, left 4/182: 2.2%) accounting for 42.1% of all skull fractures (8/19). Facial fractures were present in 47.4% of all skull fractures (9/19). This type of injury may occur from direct or indirect trauma, and fractures to the nose may indicate interpersonal violence from a blow or punch to the face.[1]

Nine category B burials displayed skull fractures (9/137: 6.6%), 7.8% of adults (8/102), 14.8% of males (8/54) and 2.9% of subadults (1/35). The majority of injuries occurred in the cranial vault (10/11: 91.0%).

Blunt force injuries

The majority of cranial fractures were caused by blunt force injuries affecting eight category A individuals (/682: 1.2%), 1.6% of adults (8/503), 1.8% of males (5/283) and 1.4% of females (3/210). Healed depressions were observed on the surfaces of 0.6% of frontal bones (6/1005) and 0.3% of parietal bones (3/1033).

Seven category B burials displayed evidence of blunt force trauma (7/137: 5.1%), 5.9% of adults (6/102), 11.1% of males (6/54) and one subadult (/35: 2.9%). True prevalence showed the left frontal (3/156: 1.9%) and left parietal (4/79: 5.1%) to be the most injured. Adult male [1256] displayed a large, oval-shaped depression (pond fracture) measuring c 50mm by c 30mm to the left parietal bone with radiating fissures running from the lesion. The internal (endocranial) surfaces of the skull revealed corresponding regions of smooth, rounded displaced bone. The injury was well healed and the individual had survived this trauma. A similar injury was recorded in male [5348], aged 36–45 years, who had a large oval-shaped depression c 76mm by c 24mm to the left frontal and parietal bones with a raised area of bone on the internal cranial surface (Fig 125).

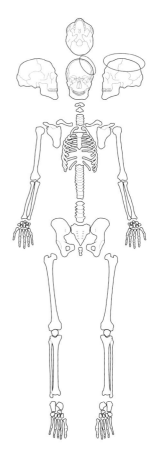

Fig 125 Cranium of male [5348] with blunt force injury (arrowed) (scale c 1:2)

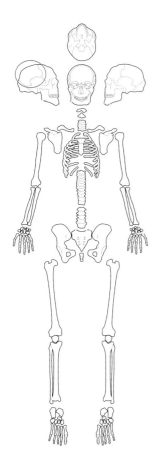

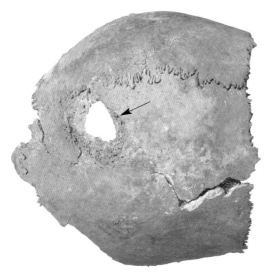

The lesion had healed, smooth and rounded margins indicating survival. Such injuries may occur from a low velocity impact to the side of the head, such as a blow from a rounded object or hitting the head during a fall.[2]

Sharp force injuries

There was little evidence of sharp force injuries in the New Churchyard assemblage. Category A adult male [1123], aged 36–45 years (1/682: 0.1%, 1/503: 0.2% of adults, 1/283: 0.4% of males), had an injury to the right parietal bone where a sub-oval slice of bone 51.3mm by 34.0mm had been removed from the back of the skull, exposing the inner bone surfaces. Smooth, polished and straight edges to the lesion suggested that this may have been inflicted by a blow from a sharp-edged weapon. Evidence of slight new bone growth and of small bone fragments which had adhered to the internal edges of the wound suggested that the victim had survived the initial trauma (Fig 126).

Two category B males had evidence of sharp force injuries (2/137: 1.5%, 2/102: 2.0% of adults, 2/54: 3.7% of males). There was a large lesion on the left skull of male [608], aged 26–35 years. This was located on the frontal bone just behind the orbit, measuring 32.6mm by 20.2mm. The posterior aspect of the lesion was linear and flattened with a fragmented flap of dislodged bone projecting internally into the cranial vault leaving an open wound. The lesion appeared well healed with some remodelling of the margins. This may represent a blade injury (or blunt force) that was survived and possibly treated (Fig 127). Male [6245] aged 18–25 years had a deep linear depression to the right parietal directly next to the sagittal suture. The lesion measured 48mm by 9mm in width and 4mm in depth. The margins were smooth and remodelled with steep sides and a thin straightened base. The nature of this wound, with defined clean edges, suggested an impact from a long, sharp-bladed object, probably a weapon.[3] A healed flap of bone adhered to the inferior margin suggesting that the victim survived this attack. Additional fissures ran diagonally upwards, across the suture and into the left parietal. The angle of the injury suggested a blow to the back of the head from the right side (Fig 128).

Fig 126 Right parietal of male [1123], showing that a sharp force injury had removed a slice of bone (scale *c* 1:2)

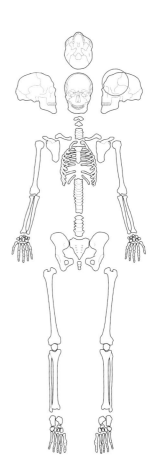

Fig 127 Skull of male [608] showing large semi-circular-shaped lesion (arrowed), from an injury which had healed (scale *c* 1:2)

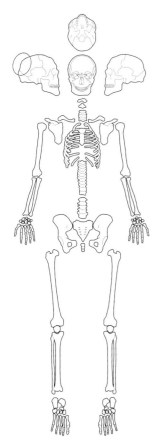

Fig 128 Skull of male [6245] with sharp force injury, probably from a blade, to the right parietal (arrowed) (scale *c* 1:2)

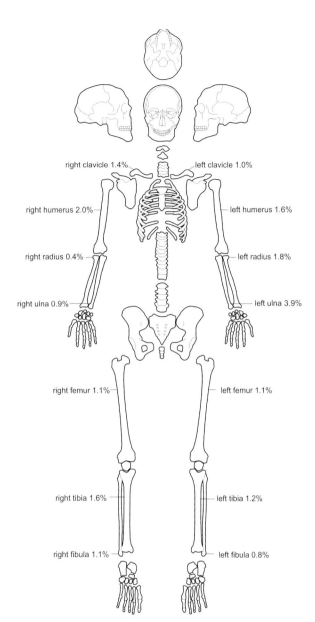

right clavicle 1.4% left clavicle 1.0%

right humerus 2.0% left humerus 1.6%

right radius 0.4% left radius 1.8%

right ulna 0.9% left ulna 3.9%

right femur 1.1% left femur 1.1%

right tibia 1.6% left tibia 1.2%

right fibula 1.1% left fibula 0.8%

Fig 129 True prevalence of long bone fractures by side, for all category A individuals

Only 0.5% of all individuals (27/5387) from St Mary Spital displayed sharp force injuries to the cranium, possibly reflecting that this was a less typical form of attack than blunt force.[4]

Long bone fractures

Long bone fractures were present in 45 category A individuals (/682: 6.6%), 8.2% (41/503) of adults, 10.2% (29/283) of males, 5.2% (11/210) of females and 2.2% (4/179) of subadults. The total long bone true prevalence rate (clavicle, humerus, radius, ulna, femur, tibia and fibula) was 1.4% (59/4324), with a slightly higher rate in the bones of the upper limb (including clavicle) (30/1832: 1.6%) compared to those of the lower limb (29/2492: 1.2%) (Fig 129). The ulna was the most frequently fractured long bone (11/463: 2.4%) with the left side (9/228: 3.9%) more affected than the right (2/233: 0.9%). The left ulna was also the most fractured long bone in males (6/244: 2.5%) and females (3/94: 3.2%) (Fig 130). All other long bones had a fracture true prevalence of ≤2.0%. Just under half of all long bone fractures were recorded in the distal (end farthest away from the body) segments of the bone (32/59: 54.2%), 30.5% at the midshaft

Fig 130 True prevalence of category A long bone fractures for all individuals, adults and subadults, adult males and females, by side (total long bone numbers: subadult n=1924, male n=3233, female n=1569, adult n=3467, all individuals n=4324)

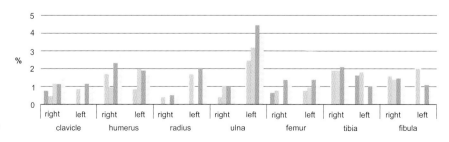

(18/59) and 23.7% (14/59) in the proximal segment (end nearest the body midline).

Twelve category B individuals had fractured long bones (/137: 8.8%), 10.8% (11/102) of adults, 13.0% (7/54) of males, 6.3% (2/32) of females and 2.9% (1/35) of subadults. True prevalence of long bone fracture prevalence was 1.4% (16/1178) with 0.6% (4/666) occurring in the upper limb and 2.3% (12/512) in the lower limb. The fibula was the most fractured bone (6/158: 3.8%, left 4/82: 4.9%, right 2/76: 2.6%).

Vertebral fractures

Fifty-five category A individuals had vertebral fractures (/682: 8.1%), 10.7% of adults (54/503), 12.7% (36/283) of males, 8.6% (18/210) of females and 0.6% (1/179) of subadults (Fig 131). This affected 0.9% of observable vertebrae (145/15,349). The lower thoracic load-bearing region of the spine had the highest true prevalence with the eighth thoracic vertebrae the most affected (21/585: 3.6%). The majority of these fractures involved compression injuries that often involve the collapse and anterior wedging of a vertebral body. These can result from a fall on to the feet or base of the spine. Avulsion injuries affecting vertebral endplates were also common; these may result from hyperflexion injuries to the spine.[5]

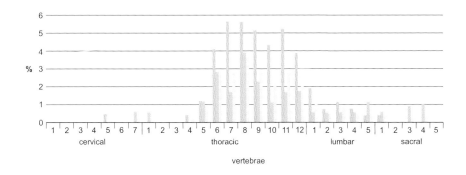

Fig 131 Vertebral fractures by location for all category A individuals (total vertebrae n=15,349), adult males (n=6664) and females (n=4651)

▪ male
▪ female
  total

A severe compression fracture to the third lumbar vertebra was recorded in male [6244], aged 26–35 years (Fig 132). There was anterior wedging of the body and a deep fissure that almost separated the vertebral body into two aspects. Further injuries included a dislocation of the right shoulder, a soft tissue injury to the medial right clavicle and healed fractures in the right tibia and ribs. This pattern of injuries, with a focus on the right side of the body, suggested a major trauma, or a fall on to the right side of the body.

Seven category B burials had vertebral fractures (/137: 5.1%), 5.9% (6/102) of adults, 5.6% (3/54) of males, 9.4% (3/32) of females and 2.9% (1/35) of

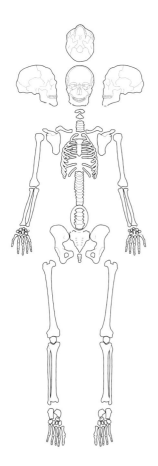

Fig 132 Severe compression fracture of the third lumbar vertebra (arrowed) of male [6244]: top – anterior view of the first to fifth lumbar vertebrae; bottom – inferior view of third lumbar vertebra (scale *c* 1:2)

subadults. This affected 0.9% (21/2292) of observable vertebrae. The sixth thoracic vertebrae had the highest true prevalence (4/90: 4.4%).

Other fracture locations

Twenty-eight category A individuals had evidence of fractured ribs (/682: 4.1%), 5.6% (28/503) of adults, 7.4% (21/283) of males and 3.3% (7/210) of females. There was an even number of rib fractures occurring in the right (17/646: 2.6%) and left rib cages (16/629: 2.5%). Five category B individuals had rib fractures (/137: 3.6%), 3.9% (4/102) of adults and 2.9% (1/35) of subadults. The majority of rib fractures reflected direct trauma from a blow or a fall on to the back or chest, although these can also occur from occupational habits, violent coughing or vomiting.[6]

Sixteen category A adults had fractures located in the bones of the hands (/503: 3.2%). In four cases these represented Bennett's fractures/subluxation of the first carpometacarpal joint at the base of the thumb (/503: 0.8%). This injury results from a force applied along the long axis of the thumb, a forced movement away from the hand or punch.[7] Two females, [1575] and [1667] (Fig 133), both aged ≥46 years, had bilateral Bennett's fractures with secondary osteoarthritis.

Three category B burials had fractures in the bones of the hand (/137: 2.2%).

Eight category A adults had fractures in the bones of the feet (/503: 1.6%) and foot fractures were present in four category B individuals (/137: 2.9%). Category B male [3238], aged ≥46 years, had multiple healed transverse fractures in the left foot with severe deformity and bony cross-union between the second to fifth metatarsals (toe bones) and between the shaft of the first metatarsal and head of second metatarsal (Fig 134). The first proximal phalanx was fused to the head of the first metatarsal, probably secondary to the fractures in the other toes. Such injuries can result from a crushing accident such as dropping a heavy object on to the foot.

Fig 133 Female [1667] showing Bennett's fractures (arrow 1) to the right and left first metacarpals (thumb bones) with secondary osteoarthritis of the right and left trapezium (wrist bones) (arrow 2) (scale *c* 1:1)

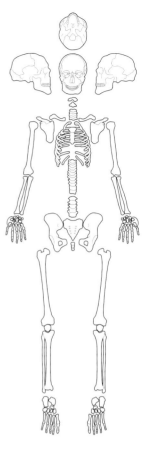

Fig 134 Male [3238] with multiple healed fractures and cross-union of left foot (arrowed) (scale *c* 1:2)

INJURY, DISABILITY AND CARE

Soft tissue trauma

Soft tissue injuries were present in 5.6% of category A individuals (38/682), 7.4% (37/503) of adults, 10.6% (30/283) of males, 1.0% (2/210) of females and one subadult (/179: 0.6%). The highest crude prevalence was recorded in adults aged 36–45 years (13/132: 9.8%). The majority of soft tissue injuries were enthesophytes affecting 5.4% of adults (27/503). These represent modifications to the attachment sites of tendons and ligaments expressed as new bone or excavations into a bone surface. They can result from activity-related changes to the musculature or traumatic injury as well as other pathological conditions that cause bone formation such as DISH (Chapter 10.4). Eighteen individuals (/682: 2.6%), 3.6% (18/503) of adults, displayed a myostitis ossificans, a localised soft tissue bone growth in the muscle tissue, often formed in association with hematoma in response to trauma.[8]

Bone changes resulting from soft tissue trauma were recorded in 8.8% (12/137) of category B individuals with a higher crude prevalence recorded amongst males (7/54: 13.0%) than females (1/32: 3.1%).

Dislocation

Dislocation or subluxation injuries were present in ten category A individuals (/682: 1.5%), 1.8% (9/503) of adults and one subadult (1/179: 0.6%). There was an almost even crude prevalence between males (5/283: 1.8%) and females (3/210: 1.4%). The majority of these injuries occurred in the sternoclavicular joint of the clavicle (4/10: 40.0%). Such injuries commonly follow a fall or blow to the front of the shoulder or a fall on to an outstretched hand. In modern contexts this can leave an individual with a recurring dislocation.[9]

Female [1716], aged 26–35 years, had a subluxation injury between the first (atlas) and second (axis) cervical vertebrae in the neck (Fig 135). This had resulted in secondary bony union between the two bones and degenerative joint disease. This may well be a case of atlantoaxial rotatory fixation which can be caused by a variety of different mechanisms such as minor or moderate trauma or inflammatory disease and may lead to a painful, twisted neck with reduced movement of the head.[10]

Three category B adults displayed subluxation injuries (/137: 2.2%), 2.9% (3/102) of adults and 3.7% (2/54) of males. Adult [7700], aged ≥46 years, had a possible dislocation of the left elbow secondary to Madelung's deformity (Chapter 12.4, 'Skeletal dysplasia').

Severe bone changes were recorded in the right elbow of male [5228], aged ≥46 years, resulting from an intercondylar fracture with secondary dislocation (Fig 136). The distal humeral shaft was thickened and the radial facet

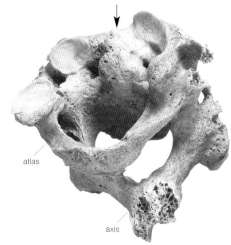

Fig 135 Atlas and axis vertebrae of female [1716], showing subluxation and secondary bony union (arrowed) (scale *c* 1:1)

atlas

axis

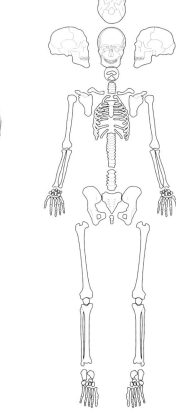

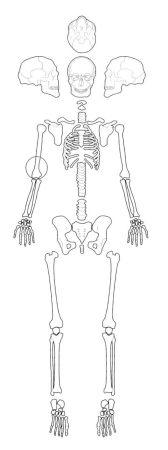

Fig 136 Right humerus of male [5228], showing severe intercondylar fracture of the elbow resulting in dislocation (scale *c* 1:2)

expanded and concave. The medial condyle was expanded and a new joint surface had formed that articulated with the ulnar notch. The right radial head was enlarged and the ulnar olecranon had a reduced height with an irregular joint surface. This would have resulted from a violent direct force such as a blow to the elbow.[11] Secondary degenerative osteoarthritis indicated that the joint was still moveable. At excavation, the right elbow was found flexed and pronated at a 45° degree angle, possibly reflecting how the limb was held in life following the trauma. This individual also had a healed Bennett's fracture of the left thumb.

Risk of injury

The very nature of a rapidly growing city such as London must have increased the chances of suffering some forms of trauma, whether from accidental injury or interpersonal violence, particularly in more crowded, poorer areas (Chapter 7.1). Disadvantaged groups living in urban centres may have a higher risk of recurring injury and death. This is particularly the case for young adult males and is often related to interpersonal violence.[12] Clinical evidence, however, indicates that the majority of injuries are incurred through daily activities rather than interpersonal violence, though this may be indistinguishable from observations of traumatic lesions in a skeleton. Most fractures occur in the home or are related to high risk occupations such as mining, forestry, construction and agriculture where close proximity to livestock may carry an increased risk of injury.[13]

In the 16th to 18th centuries accidents in the home involving burns and scalds from candles or open fires may have been frequent but would not leave a trace on the skeleton. Traffic accidents, falls from a horse as well as injuries incurred in the workplace may all have resulted in injury. Graunt's analysis of the Bills of Mortality revealed few deaths from accidents, violence or suicide. Falls from scaffolds, or being run over by a cart were among the more common causes. The number of murders listed by Graunt for the years 1629 to 1636 and 1647 to 1660 rarely rose above single figures. These rates could increase during times of disorder and political turmoil.[14]

Men aged between 16 and 60 could be forcibly recruited to serve as soldiers, with the poor most at risk of impressment. Between 1582 and 1602 London sent 9515 men to fight in various military campaigns, roughly 11% of England's soldiers. This also brought with it a high risk of death, injury and disease. In the aftermath of wars fought at home and overseas in the late 16th to early 18th centuries there was much anxiety about the potential for disorder from demobilised soldiers who had been poorly paid and had few job prospects.[15]

The large concentration of young male apprentices living in London in the 16th and 17th centuries led to opportunities for both personal violent dispute and to more widespread disorder (Chapter 7.4). Throughout the period of the New Churchyard the population rioted over various scandals, the price of bread, working conditions and unpaid wages, as well as xenophobic, religious and political causes. The Bawdy House riots in 1668 involved perhaps 40,000 people over the course of five days. The 17th-century expansion of public meeting places – coffee houses, alehouses, taverns and spirit shops – allowed people to escape cramped home life, but also encouraged interaction and, to an extent, drinking and disorder. Public displays of drunkenness only increased as the gin craze took hold of London's streets in the first half of the 18th century (Chapter 10.3).[16]

Only 0.3–0.5% of deaths attributed to fractures were recorded in the London Bills of Mortality between the 1620s and 1690s; after this there was an overall drop until the 19th century. Overall rates of adult trauma in the New Churchyard showed an increase with age with both males and females demonstrating the highest prevalence in the ≥46 years age category. A reduced trauma rate in individuals aged 18–25 years (24/126: 19.0%) was higher than the same age range from St Mary Spital in *c* 1400–1539 (period 17) (5/127: 3.9%). These rates suggested a reduced injury risk in young adulthood when compared to 19th-century St Mary and St Michael (9/33: 27.3%). Many injuries such as soft tissue lesions, cuts and abrasions would not be identifiable in the skeleton and therefore trauma rates in archaeological assemblages may represent underestimations.[17]

Most fractures in the New Churchyard category A burials were compression (77/298: 25.8%) or avulsion fractures (66/298: 22.1%) affecting the vertebrae. These injuries would result from indirect forces following a fall or stresses placed on the spine, possibly through occupation-related activities such as lifting heavy loads. The most common long bone fractures were oblique (9/298: 3.0%), transverse (8/298: 2.7%), intra-articular (6/298: 2.0%) and avulsion (4/298 1.3%). Where possible to determine, these fractures resulted from indirect forces (69/298: 23.2%) and direct forces (40/298: 13.4%).

Eight category A individuals suffered ankle fractures involving the distal tibia and/or fibula (8/682: 1.2%), 1.4% (7/503) of adults, 1.8% (5/283) of males, 1.0% (2/210) of females and one adolescent (1/179: 0.6%). Male [436], aged ≥46 years, had a severe oblique fracture of the distal right tibia and fibula. The fractures were well healed but with severe lateral (to the side) and posterior

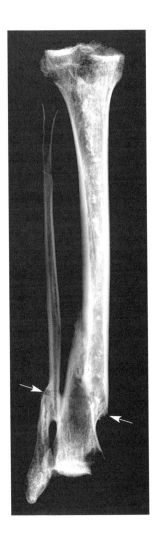

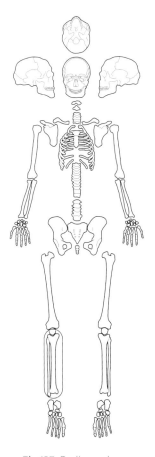

Fig 137 Radiograph showing severe healed fractures (arrowed) with marked displacement to the right ankle of male [436] (scale *c* 1:3)

displacement of the distal tibia and fibula. The right leg showed *c* 90mm shortening compared to the left limb. Remodelling had resulted in bony union between the tibia and fibula shaft (Fig 137). These injuries probably resulted from a direct blow to the leg or possibly an indirect violent force transmitted through the feet such as a fall from a height, an occupational hazard in building work. A further fracture was present in the acetabulum of his right hip joint, suggesting a force transmitted through the femoral head.[18] Five category B burials had ankle fractures (/137: 3.6%).

Analysis of the New Churchyard fracture rates showed a significant increase in crude prevalence between periods of use (1569–*c* 1670, phase 1, 62/368: 16.8%; *c* 1670–1739, phase 2, 76/314: 24.2%; χ^2=5.6802, df=1, p≤0.5). This was true for male and female adults and subadults. At St Mary Spital there was a comparable overall crude fracture prevalence (1125/5387: 20.9%); fracture rates increased through each period of cemetery use with the highest frequency recorded in *c* 1400–1539 (163/650: 25.1%). This was suggested as indicating that London had become a more dangerous place to live throughout the medieval period with a significant risk of fracture in the 15th century. In the New Churchyard a higher rate of fractures recorded for those aged 18–25 years perhaps reflected increased numbers of young migrants moving to London (Fig 138). However, there was a greater fracture crude prevalence among those aged 26–45 years at St Mary Spital (*c* 1400–1539). A much higher fracture rate was recorded at the later, 19th-century, St Mary and St Michael (111/705: 15.7%), affecting 40.3% of adults (108/268) and 0.7% (1/78: 1.3%) of subadults. This suggests an increase in risk of fracture from the medieval period and throughout the post-medieval period.[19]

When each fracture site was counted as unique, half of all category A individuals with fractures had multiple broken bones (68/138: 49.3%). This comprised 10.0% of all category A individuals (68/682), 13.5% of adults (68/503). Most of those with multiple fractures were male (48/283: 17.0%) compared to females (20/210: 9.5%). Thirty-six with fractures had injuries at three or more locations (/138: 26.1%) and four had more than eight individual

Fig 138 Crude prevalence of fractures by age for New Churchyard category A (n=656), St Mary Spital *c* 1400–1539 (n=159) and 19th-century St Mary and St Michael (n=665)

——— New Churchyard

·········· St Mary Spital, *c* 1400–1539

——— St Mary and St Michael, 19th-century

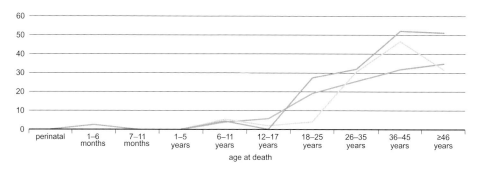

fractures (/138: 2.9%). Multiple fractures were recorded in 15 category B individuals (/137: 10.9%), 14.7% (15/102) of adults, 22.2% (12/54) of males and 6.3% (2/32) of females.

The head and face are particularly vulnerable areas and may be targeted in interpersonal violence. In modern populations the nose, cheek bones (zygomatic) and mandible are often focal points of attack. In the New Churchyard, males were more likely to show evidence of injuries to the skull and this included a higher true prevalence of fractures to the facial bones than females. Fractures to bones of the hands and feet can also indicate trauma related to violence from punching or kicking. Category A males presented a higher number of hand bone fractures (10/283: 3.5%) compared to females (5/210: 2.4%); this included 14 fractured metacarpals (finger bones) that may indicate a direct blow or punch. Twenty-one category A males had evidence of rib fractures (/283: 7.4%) resulting from a direct blow or a fall, compared to seven females (/210: 3.3%).[20]

Injuries predominantly occurring on the left side of the skull are common in interpersonal violence where a right-handed attacker strikes the left side of the opponent they are facing. Blows to other areas of the skull may indicate a victim in retreat or having fallen.[21] Male [1123], aged 36–45 years, had a sharp force wound to the right parietal (above, 'Fractures'; Fig 126). There was also a non-united fracture to the right clavicle and a healed left rib injury. The first left metacarpal had a compression fracture to the distal joint surface (knuckle). Healed oblique fractures were also present on the shafts of the third and fourth metacarpals of this individual, possibly resulting from a punch. Male [6202], aged ≥46 years, had a healed blunt force injury to the left parietal bone following a blow to the head. Healed fractures were also present in the nasal bones, and in the seventh thoracic vertebra resulting in anteroposterior curvature of the spine; a further unhealed fracture affected the fifth cervical vertebra.

The ulna of the lower arm was the most commonly fractured long bone in the New Churchyard affecting ten category A individuals (/682: 1.5%). In six cases these comprised transverse fractures to the mid or distal ulna shaft of category A individuals (/682: 0.9%), 1.2% (6/503) of adults, 1.1% (3/283) of males and 1.4% (3/210) of females. These fractures can be caused by a direct blow to the forearm, often interpreted as defensive injuries resulting from raising the arm to protect the head from a blow (parry fractures). However, the ulna and radius are amongst the most commonly fractured bones and injury can also result from other indirect mechanisms including a fall. In the New Churchyard these fractures only occurred in the left limb (true prevalence rate 6/228: 2.6%), a pattern that was also recorded at medieval St Mary Spital, suggesting that forearm injuries were more likely to occur in the non-dominant limb, to parry a blow or possibly while carrying an object in

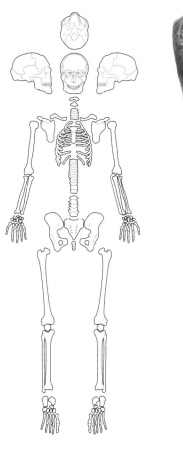

Fig 139 Male [6104] with a healed possible parry fracture (arrowed) to the left ulna midshaft (scale *c* 1:2)

the dominant arm.[22] Male [6104], aged 36–45 years, had a healed possible parry fracture to the shaft of the left ulna. The left radius was not affected and may have acted as a splint to the ulna. Further injuries were present in the left tibia with a depressed intra-articular fracture into the left knee joint and healed fractures in several left ribs. All injuries occurred on the left side of the body possibly relating to a single traumatic event (Fig 139).

Only one example of a transverse mid or distal ulna shaft fracture was found associated with an injury to the skull. Male [4111], aged 26–35 years, had a small healed depressed fracture to the left frontal bone above the eye socket and left ulna fracture.

11.2 Care, treatment and post-mortem intervention

Hospitals and public health services in England differed from other European cities where funding for medical services and facilities for professional education and training were more highly developed. However, London did have a large variety of medical and surgical practitioners able to cater for the needs of all sections of the population. These were largely controlled by the powerful guilds that supervised the numerous, partially regulated practitioners, including healers, surgeons, barbers and apothecaries.[23]

Increased concerns over public health following repeated outbreaks of epidemic disease led to the foundation of the College of Physicians in 1518, similar in type to those common throughout Italy. Surgery was taught by apprenticeships and organised guilds with the mystery or guild of the Barbers of London receiving its first charter in 1462. In 1540 the guild of Surgeons merged with the Barbers to form the Barber-Surgeons of London. Surgeons were more numerous than physicians and provided services for people from most social backgrounds. Their work was largely routine and restricted to the body's surface, setting fractures, treating burns and wounds, tumours, swellings, ulcers and skin diseases. The Barber-Surgeons of London also supplied recruits for military service, and surgical advances were often picked up through experiences in battle where surgeons witnessed horrifying wounds, particularly those inflicted by the growing use of gunpowder.[24]

The majority of Londoners, however, would rarely have encountered a physician or Master Surgeon, turning elsewhere for assistance. This may have come from family members, priests or from the numerous unlicensed practitioners, including herbalists, charmers and bonesetters with no formal authorisation to practice medicine. Women were recognised as apothecaries, surgeons, nurses and midwives, undertaking public health duties during epidemics, collecting data for the Bills of Mortality and occupying important roles in hospitals (Chapter 6.1; 12.3, 'Marriage').[25]

With the rise of the hospital movement in the 18th century, the infirmary became the site of accident and emergency cases, treated by surgeons who could control admissions and also the supply of unclaimed dead bodies to dissect (Chapter 5.7).[26]

Fracture healing and deformity

Skeletal injuries can potentially have severe consequences and may lead to impairment and secondary joint disease. Examination of the fracture type, rate of healing and any complications associated with the injury can help determine possible causes and if any treatment was sought.[27]

Long bone fractures in the New Churchyard were examined for evidence of deformity. These fractures may have had a debilitating impact on an individual who may therefore have been more likely to seek treatment rather than for injuries to the hands or feet. Evidence of severe shortening, overlap of the fractured bone ends and deformities in the positioning of the bone may indicate ineffective fracture treatment or that none had been attempted.[28]

There were 59 long bone fractures recorded in the New Churchyard category A assemblage affecting 6.6% of individuals (45/682). The majority were well healed suggesting long-term survival following the injuries and that treatment may have been sought to reduce the fractures. Fourteen individuals displayed evidence of poorly aligned fractures (/682: 2.1%), comprising 18 individual broken bones. Three had failed to unite and eight showed evidence of secondary infection. Seven fractures were associated with secondary osteoarthritic joint degeneration and in two cases the bones had fused together.

There were 16 category B long bone fractures affecting 3.6% (5/137) of individuals. Eight fractures had evidence of deformity or complications including four fractures with secondary infection, two with associated soft tissue injuries and two fused bones.

There was a malaligned, oblique fracture to the left femoral midshaft of category A adult male [5556], aged 26–35 years. This had probably resulted from a violent direct or indirect force such as a fall from a height or blow to the thigh.[29] The fracture was well healed but the knee end of the bone had been pushed upwards, overlapping the upper half and resulting in shortening of the bone by c 90–100mm. This injury may have resulted in severe pain, and

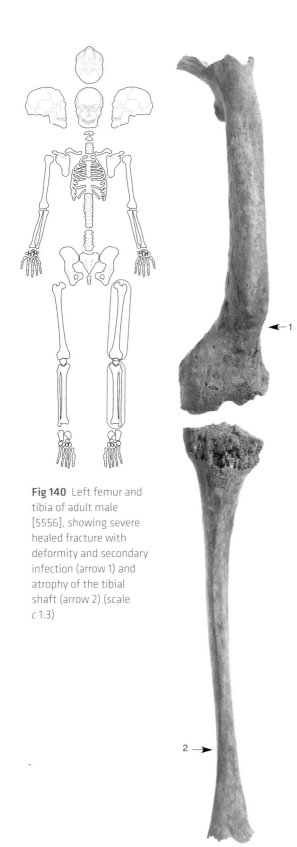

Fig 140 Left femur and tibia of adult male [5556], showing severe healed fracture with deformity and secondary infection (arrow 1) and atrophy of the tibial shaft (arrow 2) (scale *c* 1:3)

possible blood loss. Plaques of dense remodelled bone covered the distal shaft and two small sinus openings (hollows) indicated a long-standing osteomyelitis infection. The joint surfaces of the knee were flattened with marginal new bone growth. The left tibia was thinned compared to the right side suggesting atrophy or wasting of the bone, probably due to a lack of use following the trauma (Fig 140). Survival of this injury may indicate that a level of treatment and care was provided but that any attempts at traction or reduction were unsuccessful.

Category B male [4375], aged 36–45 years, had a well-healed oblique fracture to the distal third of the right tibia shaft with a second fracture to the proximal right fibula (Fig 141). Both fractures showed evidence of marked deformity. Overlap of the broken segments of *c* 50mm had resulted in 14mm of shortening compared to the left leg. A direct blow to the lower leg can cause fractures in both the tibia and fibula; a violent force transmitted through the feet from a fall from a height may also cause such injuries. These fractures can be unstable and would require reduction and internal fixation. Displacement, therefore, may indicate ineffective treatment. This individual also displayed supracondylar processes, bony spur-like projections above the medial condyle (elbow) of the humeri, with additional bone growths located on the lateral surface of the right distal first metacarpal (thumb) and the palm-facing surfaces of the right-hand phalanges (finger bones) (Fig 141). The margins of the glenoid fossa of the shoulder joints had pitted and irregular bone formation. Together these bone changes may indicate the use of a crutch to compensate for the impaired use of the lower right leg; the transverse rest of a crutch held under the arm would help support the weight of the body by the arms.[30]

Injuries to the skull can cause epilepsy, chronic headache, memory loss, problems with sight and mobility as well as other, psychological, problems. Severe penetrating wounds may also result in injury to the meninges protecting the brain, the blood vessels and associated structures, resulting in bleeding and possible loss of consciousness due to the impact. Death may

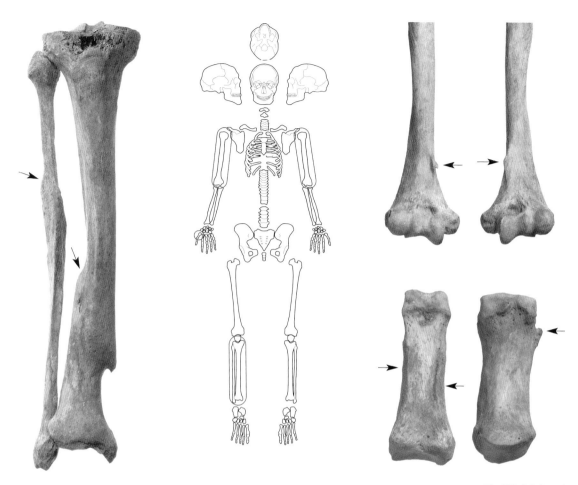

Fig 141 Adult male [4375]: left – tibia and fibula with healed fracture (scale *c* 1:3); top right – bone changes to the arms possibly resulting from crutch use – bilateral humeral supracondylar bone spurs (scale *c* 1:3); bottom right – right hand – first metacarpal bone spur and ridges to palmar surface of proximal hand phalanx (scale *c* 1:1)

follow almost immediately from shock to the sensory nervous system and blood loss. The healed nature of the cranial injuries encountered in the New Churchyard suggested the survival of interpersonal violence or even warfare and possibility that surgical intervention and care was sought (above, 11.1). At medieval St Mary Spital, a male had also survived a severe sharp force trauma some years prior to death.[31]

Congenital and developmental disorders

A range of minor to more severe developmental and congenital abnormalities can affect the soft tissues and skeleton. These conditions cannot be attributed to a single cause and pathological changes during foetal development, hereditary and genetic factors may all play a role. Viral infections affecting a mother during pregnancy such as maternal measles, mumps, chicken pox and shingles may also have caused malformations. Excessive alcohol consumption and possibly the use of herbal remedies to treat illness may also have damaged a developing foetus. Congenital disorders were little understood in the 16th century. In 1570 the French surgeon Ambroise Paré listed possible causes that included God's wrath, the mother's imagination, indecent posture during pregnancy, injury to the womb and hereditary or accidental illness.[32]

The majority of disorders identified in the New Churchyard population represented minor disorders and vertebral border shifts that would have been asymptomatic or produced only slight symptoms.[33]

Certain identified congenital conditions, however, may have affected an individual's mobility and quality of life. Eight individuals from category A (/682: 1.2%) had scoliosis, the lateral curvature of the spine. While mild forms may be unnoticeable, more severe cases can produce visible deformities, such as a hunchback, and lead to mobility disabilities, loss of balance, pain and compromised heart and lung function.[34]

Scoliosis was observed in four category B individuals (/137: 2.9%). Severe deformities were present in the thoracic and lumbar vertebrae of female [4049], aged 18–25 years (Fig 142). The fourth to seventh and eighth to 12th thoracic vertebral bodies were wedged to the left and right sides respectively. This caused severe left lateral curvature of approximately 80° from the fourth to seventh vertebrae and approximately 90° from the eighth to the 12th. The severity of the scoliosis had also caused thin and irregularly shaped ribs.

Fig 142 Burial of female [4049] showing severe scoliosis, curvature of the spine, with spine of a different individual visible to the side, looking north (0.2m scale)

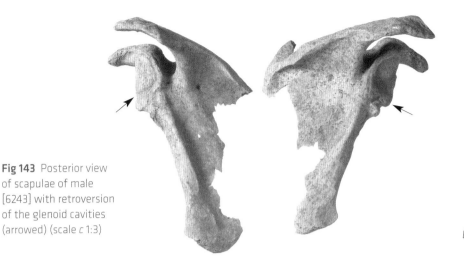

Fig 143 Posterior view of scapulae of male [6243] with retroversion of the glenoid cavities (arrowed) (scale *c* 1:3)

Congenital kyphosis, the anteroposterior curvature of the spine, was observed in four individuals from category A (/682: 0.6%) and three from category B (/137: 2.2%).

Male [6243], aged 18–25 years, had abnormalities in the shoulder joints of the upper limb (Fig 143). There was bilateral excessive retroversion of the glenoid cavities of the scapulae with the articular surfaces angled posteriorly (*c* 40° in this case). This would have increased shoulder joint instability and risk of dislocation.[35]

Category B male [8184], aged 26–35 years, had bilateral talipea equinus, a variation of club foot where the talus is malformed and the tarsals point vertically downward (Fig 144). The left talus had osteophytes along the anterior trochlea locking the ankle with very limited movement. The right talus was also affected but

Fig 144 Calcanei and tali of male [8184] with club foot (scale *c* 1:2)

to a lesser degree. The distal ends of the fibulae were flat and wide, probably a secondary effect of the club foot. These deformities may have compromised mobility.[36]

Surgery

The work of early surgeons may not have been entirely crude or lethal. The notes of London surgeon Joseph Binns dated 1633 to 1663 record treatment for a variety of conditions including wounds from battles and fights. Out of 402 outcomes, 265 were cured, 62 improved, 22 showed no improvement and 53 died. Surgeons did not routinely involve themselves in high risk operations: the dangers of blood loss and sepsis were well known and internal complaints were treated instead by medicine.[37]

One exception was the treatment of compound limb fractures where the bone is exposed. These can interrupt blood circulation and infection may spread that can contaminate a wound. Prior to advances in arterial repair in the 20th century, these injuries would have resulted in an almost routine amputation. Attempts to straighten and tightly bind fractures with splints and tourniquets may have resulted in complications if applied incorrectly, leading to infection and gangrene. Many lives were lost on the operating table due to poor surgery, or shortly after from pain, shock, blood loss, exhaustion and later infection. Severe haemorrhage was a particular risk for above the knee procedures where the main arteries could be damaged. Before the discovery of effective anaesthesia (chloroform) in the mid 18th century and the first antiseptics (carbolic acid spray) in the 1870s, mortality rates were high and surgeons had to rely on the speed in which they carried out the operation.[38]

There were two examples of surgery in the New Churchyard, both from category B individuals (/137: 1.5%), 2.0% (2/102) of adults. There was a clean saw cut to the right femoral midshaft of female [4171], aged 18–25 years, probably representing an above knee amputation. There was no evidence of remodelling or new bone indicating that this individual died during or shortly after the procedure. Diffuse plaques of healed periosteal bone throughout the shaft indicated the presence of a long-standing infection, and erosive lesions in the sixth to eighth thoracic vertebrae suggested that this individual may have suffered from tuberculosis (TB) (Chapter 9.3).

The heavily truncated and disturbed burial of male [7004], aged 26–35 years, had a sawn right femoral midshaft. Three additional cut marks to the medial surface of the bone indicated where the saw had skipped or the cut restarted. A lip of bone on the posterior margin of the shaft indicated the break-off point. There was no evidence of healing to suggest that this individual survived the operation. New periosteal bone growth along the remaining femoral shaft indicated the presence of a long-standing infection.

Interestingly, two additional bones with saw cuts were excavated, lying directly beneath the femur. A right fibula and tibia had been sawn at the midshaft with only the lower portion of the bones present (Fig 145). It is possible that these represented the lower 'amputated' leg of [7004]. Alternatively, the absence of the distal femur and proximal tibia and fibula (knee) elements may suggest that the lower leg of this individual was not included in burial and perhaps was retained for further study if there was a significant associated pathology. Excavations at the Royal London Hospital revealed evidence of disarticulated bone representing prosections or teaching specimens. This unwanted material was sometimes disposed of and formally buried within coffins in a burial ground.[39]

Fig 145 Cross section of a sawn right tibia found with male [7004] who had undergone an amputation of the right lower leg (scale *c* 2:1)

Autopsy/dissection

There were two examples of surgical intervention at the New Churchyard: both individuals were buried in coffins, with saw cuts limited to the skull, and both probably represent a craniotomy. While it cannot be assumed that the thoracic cavity had not been opened, it is possible that autopsy, rather than dissection, was the prime reason for intervention in both cases. Category A female [5986] (OA105C), aged 18–25 years, displayed a single straight saw cut running horizontally through the cranium (Fig 146). Several fine horizontal incisions above and below the saw cut may indicate points where the soft tissues were reflected. There was evidence of at least three restarts and skip marks, and a small notch above the left eye socket may indicate the point where the calvarium was levered off. This individual had evidence of cribra orbitalia in both orbits perhaps indicating an underlying illness; there was also a fracture to the left radial head.[40]

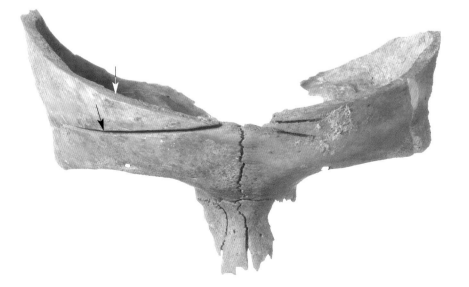

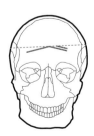

Fig 146 Craniotomy of adult female [5986]: below – location of saw cut marks to cranium; left – frontal bone showing saw cuts to the skull (anterior view) (scale *c* 1:1)

Fig 147 Craniotomy of male [5328]: top – location of saw cut marks to left lateral cranium; bottom – sawn left frontal bone (anterior view) (scale *c* 1:1)

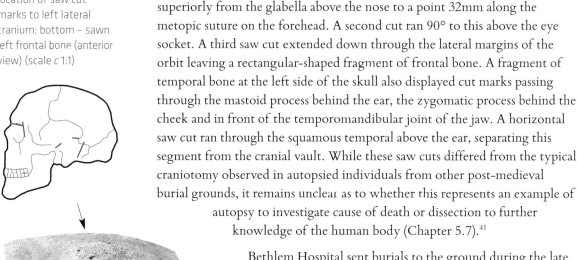

Several fragments of skull from category B male [5328] (OA105A), aged 36–45 years, had been sawn (Fig 147). A clean cut on the left frontal bone ran superiorly from the glabella above the nose to a point 32mm along the metopic suture on the forehead. A second cut ran 90° to this above the eye socket. A third saw cut extended down through the lateral margins of the orbit leaving a rectangular-shaped fragment of frontal bone. A fragment of temporal bone at the left side of the skull also displayed cut marks passing through the mastoid process behind the ear, the zygomatic process behind the cheek and in front of the temporomandibular joint of the jaw. A horizontal saw cut ran through the squamous temporal above the ear, separating this segment from the cranial vault. While these saw cuts differed from the typical craniotomy observed in autopsied individuals from other post-medieval burial grounds, it remains unclear as to whether this represents an example of autopsy to investigate cause of death or dissection to further knowledge of the human body (Chapter 5.7).[41]

Bethlem Hospital sent burials to the ground during the late 17th and early 18th centuries (Chapter 6.1, 'Burying the dead of Bethlem Hospital') and is known to have carried out autopsies on patients, including craniotomies, from as early as 1676.[42] Both New Churchyard cases were from phase 1, 1569–*c* 1670.

Notes to Chapter 11

1   Lovell 1997, 155–6

2   Ibid, 149, 156

3   Wenham 1989, 127

4   Connell et al 2012, 181

5   Dandy and Edwards 1998, 255; Galloway 1999, 96; Maat and Mastwijk 2000, 148

6   Lovell 1997, 159; Galloway 1999, 107

7   Dandy and Edwards 1998, 225; McRae 1999, 338

8   Knüsel 2000, 387; Resnick 2002, 4643, 4727; Ortner 2003, 134

9   McRae 1999, 262; Dandy and Edwards 1998, 185

10   Resnick 2002, 2955–7

11   McRae 1999, 293

12   Connell et al 2012, 156, 186; Judd 2002, 90–1

13   Judd and Roberts 1998, 54; 1999, 240–2; Lovell 1997, 166–7

14   Picard 2003, 103; Porter 2011, 183–202; J Graunt, *Natural and political observations*, cited in Porter 2012b, 106; Spence 2016, 95–124

15   Porter 2011, 202–4; Bucholz and Ward 2012, 242

16   Shoemaker 2004, 7–8, 155; Bucholz and Ward 2012, 268–95

17   Roberts and Cox 2003, 302; Connell et al 2012, 88; Henderson et al 2013, 146

18   McRae 1999, 387, 440, 448; Lovell 1997, 164

19   Connell et al 2012, 89; Henderson et al 2013, 144

20   Larsen 1997, 156; Waller 2000; Lovell 1997, 159, 166

21   Novak 2000, 96–7; Wenham 1989

22   Mann and Hunt 2005, 153; Lovell 1997, 165–6; Connell et al 2012, 182

23   Pelling and Webster 1979, 167–8, 180, 192; Rawcliffe 2013, 295

24   Pelling and Webster 1979, 173–4; Pelling 1986, 85; Porter 1997, 187

25   Pelling and Webster 1979, 186–7, 192; Rawcliffe 2013, 293

26   Porter 1997, 280

27   Larsen 1997, 110; Grauer and Roberts 1996, 531

28   Grauer and Roberts 1996, 533, 535

29   Lovell 1997, 162

30   McRae 1999, 440, 448; Knüsel and Göggel 1993

31   Wenham 1989, 128, 131; Powers 2005, 12

32   Roberts and Manchester 2012, 44–7; Aufderheide and Rodríguez-Martín 1998, 51

33   Powers 2008, 64–8 (after Barnes 1994); Roberts and Cox 2003, 275

34   Dandy and Edwards 1998, 351–2

35   Brewer et al 1986; Hurley et al 1992; Nyffeler et al 2006

36   Resnick 2002, 4614–16

37   Porter 1997, 188, 277

38   Kirkup 2007, 26, 43, 50; Richardson 1988, 40; Hempel 2007, 84–5

39   Fowler and Powers 2012, 189–91

40   Cherryson et al 2012, 135

41   Ibid, 137

42   Andrews et al 1997, 271

208   THE NEW CHURCHYARD

CHAPTER 12

FROM THE CRADLE TO THE GRAVE

Michael Henderson

12.1 Childhood

Health and mortality

Mortality was higher in 16th- and 17th-century Britain than in the 19th and 20th centuries and a greater percentage of all deaths occurred in the young. Infant and child mortality rates varied between different communities and between rural and urban populations. In London, life expectancy could differ between those from wealthy and less affluent parishes. Poorer children were more likely to die young.[1]

Infant mortality figures recorded in the London Bills of Mortality and other contemporary sources may suffer from reliability problems and inconsistencies with the ways in which still births and neonatal deaths were reported. Infants sent by parishes out to baby farms or wealthy families sending children away to wet nurses in the countryside may have led to many burials away from home.[2]

There was a reduction in life expectancy over the course of the 17th century; perhaps half of London-born children did not survive into adulthood. In poorer parishes perhaps 500 children per 1000 survived until their 15th birthday compared to about 600 in wealthier parishes. Writing in 1662 Graunt estimated that a little over a third of deaths (36%) were of children under six years of age. In the 18th and 19th centuries, death rates as recorded in the London Bills of Mortality show that *c* 25–30% of children did not survive their second birthday and 40% of deaths were of children aged five years and below.[3]

The age at death profile of subadults can provide important information regarding maternal health and disease, birthing and infant feeding practices, how a population has adapted to the environment and social attitudes towards children. In the New Churchyard assemblage there was an overall under-representation of subadults (Chapter 6.3). Subadult mortality rates indicated a period of risk in early life. The mortality rate of perinates was higher than those aged one month and those aged 1–11 months (Fig 72).

These suggested genetic, maternal and childbirth factors may have presented a greater mortality risk than external hazards and the general living environment. Infants under one year are particularly vulnerable to disease and death, but after the first year of life the chances of survival increase.[4] A degree of immunity to bacteria and disease is acquired through the placenta and the colostrum that precedes their mother's milk.[5] Breast milk supplies the nutrients and passive immunity needed to grow and survive. Children are less likely to become infected by water- and food-borne gastric diseases than those fed artificially.[6] If a child fails to adapt to the new environment into which it is born, it will die. Infants whose mothers had died soon after birth were deprived of breast milk and were three times more likely to die in their first year. Those sent to wet nurses would also not have benefited from the purpose-made immunisation.[7]

Growth and indicators of stress

At two years of age, children have reached a critical stage of development and are vulnerable to inadequate weaning methods or environments unfavourable to health. A multitude of childhood diseases – measles, mumps, whooping cough, scarlet fever, German measles, diphtheria, meningitis, erysipelas and miscellaneous 'fevers' including typhus – would have been responsible for many deaths. Children can be especially vulnerable, not just in a virgin population but also where a disease immunises those that survive where subsequent outbreaks may only affect children or newcomers.[8] Moreover, one in three may have died of gastroenteric disorders before the age of five. London's location along an increasingly foul river, together with overcrowding and environmental pollution, helped the spread of many diseases (Chapter 7.1, 7.2).[9]

Analysis of subadult growth can provide information about the health and well-being of a population as well as indirect evidence of developmental stresses and disease. Studies have shown a link between stunted growth and impoverished environmental conditions.[10] The development of teeth in the first two decades of life can be an accurate indicator of the biological age of an individual.[11] Rates of subadult growth for the category A individuals were measured by comparing ages estimated from diaphyseal bone length measurements (growth) with those obtained from dental development. In the majority of cases this showed the dental age to be older than that calculated from long bone growth (90/113: 79.6%).[12] This suggested that children within this population failed to obtain their full growth potential. These differences appeared more marked from the age of four years with a discrepancy of up to five years for some individuals. There was no evidence of catch-up growth in the teenage years. This pattern has commonly been observed in archaeological skeletal remains and from burial grounds of differing status. Studies have shown poor growth to be related to poverty. During periods of stress, the growth rate of a child slows until normal nourishment is resumed. However, once a child's health is restored, it has the ability to resume growth at an increased rate.[13]

THE NEW CHURCHYARD

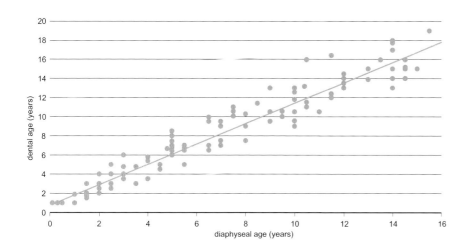

Fig 148 Subadult age at death calculated from diaphyseal length and dental age for category A (n=113)

Certain non-specific bone changes and pathological lesions occurring in the skeleton and teeth described as 'indicators of stress' may also show an individual's ability to adapt to certain stresses placed on the body during growth. The extent to which these bone responses manifest themselves can depend on a variety of factors including immune status, genetic predisposition, environmental constraints and cultural systems.[14] The occurrence of these lesions also requires survival long enough for bone changes to occur and normal growth to resume. A skeleton showing no markers of stress could therefore indicate a healthy individual or alternatively someone with a weakened immune system unable to survive an illness. A high prevalence of stress indicators may suggest a population more able to adapt to disease and malnutrition (Table 22).[15]

Site	Date	Cribra orbitalia %	Porotic hyperostosis %	Enamel hypoplasia %
New Churchyard category A burials	1569–1739	14.0	2.2	33.0
St Mary Spital	c 1400–1539 (period 17)	33.1	8.1	43.5
Bow Baptist	1763–1853	29.7	5.0	13.4
St Mary and St Michael	1843–54	41.0	3.9	8.5

Table 22 Summary of the crude prevalence rate of indicators of stress (cribra orbitalia, porotic hyperostosis and enamel hypoplasia) for subadults at the New Churchyard, St Mary Spital, Bow Baptist and St Mary and St Michael

Cribra orbitalia

The category A subadult crude prevalence rate for cribra orbitalia in the New Churchyard was 14.0% (25/179) (where one or both orbits were affected) (Table 22). When analysed by age, lesions were present in the orbits of 4.3% of perinates (1/23) with an almost equal frequency between those aged 1–5 years (6/40: 15.0%) and those aged 6–11 years (8/51: 15.7%). There was a peak in those aged 12–17 years (10/53: 18.9%), possibly reflecting individuals that survived later childhood but were particularly vulnerable to social and environmental stresses in adolescence (Chapter 10.5; below, 12.2).[16]

A higher rate of subadult cribra orbitalia was recorded in phase 1 (1569–c 1670) (16/99: 16.2%) compared to phase 2 (c 1670–1739) (9/80: 11.3%), with those aged 12–17 years showing the highest rates in both periods. A higher rate was also recorded in the attritional burial sample (14/89: 15.7%) compared to those from mass burial pit [7482]/[8473] (2/26: 7.7%). This may reflect a weaker immune response amongst those buried in the mass pit, possibly at times of increased disease.

The crude prevalence rates in the New Churchyard appeared low when compared to those from St Mary Spital (17.2–27.8%), where in c 1400–1539 rates for 6–11 year olds were c 50–54% and in 12–17 year olds c 33–46%. At 19th-century Bow Baptist, cribra orbitalia affected 29.7% of subadults (60/202) (1–5 years: 38.4%, 6–11 years: 39.1%, 12–17 years: 35.3%), and at 19th-century St Mary and St Michael (1843–54), 41.0% of subadults (179/437) were affected, with high rates recorded in the subadult age ranges (1–5 years: 45.8%, 6–11 years: 82.2%, 12–17 years: 56.3%).[17]

Porotic hyperostosis

Porotic hyperostosis was identified in 2.2% of category A subadults (4/179) with the highest rates recorded in the 6–11 years age range (2/51: 3.9%) (Chapter 10.5; Table 22).

At St Mary Spital in c 1400–1539 only subadults aged 6–11 (1/37: 2.7%) and 12–17 years (9/49: 18.4%) were affected. At Bow Baptist there was a subadult crude prevalence of 5.0% (10/202), again with high rates recorded in those aged 7–11 months (2/15: 13.3%) and young adults (3/25: 12.0%). At St Mary and St Michael, subadult crude prevalence was 3.9% (17/437) with the highest rates recorded in those aged 7–11 months (3/30: 10.0%) and 12–17 year olds (1/16: 6.3%), with the highest overall rate recorded in early adulthood 18–25 years (12/33: 36.4%).[18]

Enamel hypoplasia

Enamel hypoplastic defects were observed in the teeth of 33.0% (59/179) of category A subadults (Table 22). This may relate to a range of conditions including dietary deficiency, childhood fever and infection.[19] The highest rates were recorded in those aged 6–11 years (24/51: 47.1%) and 12–17 year olds (28/53: 52.8%). There was a slight decline in crude prevalence with increasing adult age, potentially suggesting a lower life expectancy for those affected (Chapter 10.8).

In the category B burials, enamel defects were recorded in 31.4% of subadults (11/35). Again the highest frequencies were recorded in subadults aged 6–11 years (3/6: 50.0%) and 12–17 year olds (6/13: 46.2%), and young adults aged 18–25 years (19/27: 70.4%).

A higher proportion of subadults from phase 1 (1569–*c* 1670) (38/99: 38.4%) were affected compared to phase 2 (*c* 1670–1739) (21/80: 26.3%). In mass pit [7482]/[8473], 31.3% of subadults (5/16) were affected. The highest prevalence rates were recorded in those aged 6–11 years (2/3: 66.7%) and young adults 18–25 years (6/9: 66.7%), although the small numbers in each age group may have distorted these results.

These rates were lower than those recorded at St Mary Spital in *c* 1400–1539, where there was no evidence of enamel hypoplastic defects in those aged 1–5 years and the highest rates were recorded for 6–11 year olds (22/37: 59.5%) and 12–17 year olds (32/49: 65.3%). At Bow Baptist 13.4% of subadults had evidence of hypoplastic defects (27/202), with a sharp rise from 6–11 years (12/23: 52.2%) and 12–17 years (9/17: 52.9%). At St Mary and St Michael, 8.5% of subadults were affected (37/437), with high rates recorded for 6–11 year olds (12/45: 26.7%) and those aged 12–17 years (11/16: 68.8%).[20] This may indicate that affected subadults buried in the New Churchyard had a greater survival rate than seen in later periods.

Periostitis

Periostitis was recorded in 10.1% (18/179) of category A subadults. Analysis of subadult age ranges showed a peak in those aged 6–11 years (10/51: 19.6%) and 12–17 year olds (7/53: 13.2%), although these rates were lower than those recorded in adults who would have been exposed to infections for longer (Chapter 9.2).

Periostitis affected 2.9% of category B subadults (1/35). There was a higher rate in phase 1 (1569–*c* 1670) subadults (14/99: 14.1%) compared to phase 2 (*c* 1670–1739) (6/80: 7.5%).

At St Mary Spital, periostitis had the lowest rate of all stress indicators in all periods. In *c* 1400–1539 this affected 2.7% of 6–11 year olds (1/37) and 10.2% of 12–17 year olds (5/49). At St Mary and St Michael, 11.2% of subadults (49/437) were affected; this included 10.8% of 1–5 year olds (27/249), 22.2% of 6–11 year olds (10/45) and 56.3% of 12–17 year olds (9/16).[21]

Rickets

Rickets is a disease of early childhood but does not directly result in death, although it can cause an increased susceptibility to infections and other illnesses. In particular, rickets can lead to increased respiratory and gastrointestinal infections and therefore may cause an increased mortality risk.[22] It is a metabolic disease caused by a lack of vitamin D, necessary for the absorption of calcium and phosphorus, important in developing strong and healthy bones. While some vitamin D can be obtained through eating certain foods, the majority of the body's requirements come through exposure to sunlight (Chapter 10.7).[23] Deficiencies occurring during childhood growth can result in softened and weakened bones which can no longer support the body's weight and become bowed. As well as skeletal lesions, rickets may also result in muscular weakness, retarded growth and anaemia. For women in labour, deformities resulting in the narrowing of the pelvis may result in obstruction during birth.[24]

Rickets was rarely seen in medieval England. Eight cases of active rickets were identified in the infant population from the medieval rural population at Wharram Percy (Yorkshire East Riding). This population might be expected to have led a largely outdoor life with adequate sunlight exposure. The presence of rickets, therefore, may indicate that this was secondary to another underlying illness that kept children indoors and away from sunlight. No individuals who survived childhood had evidence of residual rickets, where bone deformities may remain into adulthood.[25]

By the post-medieval period rickets had become a significant disease and during the 17th and 18th centuries was known as the English disease. While there are possible depictions of the disease dating from the 15th and 16th centuries, the first accurate clinical descriptions were reported in the 17th century where it was described as a new disease, and rickets is first mentioned in the London Bills of Mortality in 1634. Graunt's analysis of the Bills of Mortality shows the number of deaths attributed to rickets increased between 1634 and 1660. Contemporary physicians believed it to be a consequence of malnourishment, exposure to cold air, drinking cold fluids or eating coarse foods. The disease was not confined to urban areas but was also observed in rural communities. Children from wealthy backgrounds also did not escape the disease and in some cases were more affected, possibly because they coddled and pampered their children indoors whereas those from a lower social order, for example, working as farm labourers, may have spent more time outside. Seasonal changes may also have resulted in rickets being more common in the winter months.[26]

Urbanisation and growing population levels together with increasing industrialisation and climatic change may all have contributed to a reduction in sunlight exposure for those living in towns and cities like London. For the urban poor, crammed in overcrowded tenements, with narrow, dark alleyways this may have had a more dramatic impact in the rise of rickets (Chapter 7.1, 7.2).[27]

Fifty-two category A individuals in the New Churchyard presented evidence of bone changes consistent with a diagnosis of vitamin D deficiency rickets (/682: 7.6%). This affected 11.7% of subadults (21/179) and 6.2% of adults (31/503). Only one infant ≤1 years had diagnostic bone changes (1/35: 2.9%).

Rickets rarely affects young infants as vitamin D passes from the mother to her baby through the placenta, although undernourished mothers may have insufficient levels to pass on. If the child survived birth, deficiencies in the quality of breast milk from a chronically underfed mother would further endanger her infant's health. A poor diet, with an inadequate level of vitamin D in infant foods used during and after weaning, and the onset of many illnesses leading to diarrhoeal disease, gastrointestinal, kidney and liver conditions may also cause a reduction in the absorption of calcium and vitamin D thereby exacerbating ill health (Chapter 10.7).[28]

There was a peak in children aged 1–5 years (14/40: 35.0%) with five aged 6–11 years (/51: 9.8%) and one aged 12–17 years affected by the disease (/53: 1.9%). Ten subadults (/21: 47.6%) had died while the disease was still active.

A comparatively high rate of rickets was recorded in the category B burials (20/137: 14.6%). This affected 34.3% of subadults (12/35) and 7.8% of adults (8/102). All affected subadults were aged ≥1 year at death with 66.7% (8/12) aged 1–5 years. Half of category B subadults had active changes at the time of death (6/12: 50.0%).

There was a large increase in the crude prevalence of rickets over time from phase 1 (1569–c 1670) (18/368: 4.9%) to phase 2 (c 1670–1739) (34/314: 10.8%) (χ^2=8.49, df=1, p≤0.5) (Fig 149). In the subadult sample, 20.0% (16/80) from phase 2 had evidence of rickety bone changes compared to 5.1% (5/99) from phase 1 (χ^2=9.55, df=1, p≤0.5). When the different burial types were examined, 4.9% of individuals (17/347) from the pre-c 1670 attritional burials had rickets (13/258: 5.0% of adults, 7/141: 5.0% of males, 4/110: 3.6% of females and 4/89: 4.5% of subadults). This contrasted with the mass graves

Fig 149 Crude prevalence of rickets by age for all category A burials (n=656), phase 1 (n=353), phase 2 (n=303), attritional burials (n=332) and burials from mass graves (n=59)

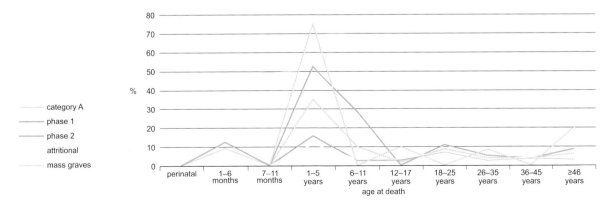

(pits – OA105E – and mass pit [7482]/[8473] – OA105A) where there was a much higher presence of the disease (9/64: 14.1%) (χ^2=7.67, df=1, p≤0.5). This affected 5.3% of adults (2/38) and over a quarter of subadults (7/26: 26.9%).

Analysis of mass pit [7482]/ [8473] showed a particularly high rate of rickets (8/42: 19.0%). This affected two of the adults (/26: 7.7%) and six of the subadult burials (/16: 37.5%). Five subadults buried in the mass pit aged 1–5 years at death showed bowed limb deformities suggesting they had suffered from rickets (/6: 83.3%). This high rate of rickets amongst subadults in the mass pit may suggest it included individuals with an increased risk of and/or susceptibility to plague and a weakened prospect of survival. Alternatively, and more generally, the use of the mass pit may have been contemporary with a period of increased risk of vitamin D deficiency and/or that these people lived in densely occupied areas of the city where exposure to sunlight was limited.

This appears to show an increase in prevalence from the medieval period. Eight of all individuals from St Mary Spital had rickets (/5387: 0.1%). This was recorded in only one individual aged 1–5 years from the *c* 1400–1539 sample (/650: 0.2%). Five subadults in total from St Mary Spital had evidence of rickets, all were buried during *c* 1250–1539 during which time episodes of famine occurred.[29]

By the 19th century, as pollution worsened during the Industrial Revolution, rickets reached epidemic proportions in England and was predominantly a disease of the urban poor.[30] At Sheen's burial ground 5.5% (14/254) were affected with 12.5% of subadults (11/88). A high rate was also found at Bow Baptist (32/416: 7.7%) where 13.9% of children were affected (28/202) and at St Mary and St Michael with 11.1% (78/705), all subadults. At the higher-status St Marylebone's Paddington Street north burial ground 10.7% (31/291) had rickets, with 23.0% (14/61) of subadults affected, indicating that rickets was still a disease that affected all classes.[31]

Many individuals who suffered from vitamin D deficiency during infancy and childhood would have survived into adulthood.[32] A high rate of healed or resolved bone changes was seen in the subadult and adult population (Fig 150). Residual rickets was identified in 6.2% of category A burials (42/682), 6.2% of adults (31/503) and 6.1% of subadults (11/179). Similar changes were identified in the category B sample (14/137: 10.2%), 7.8% of adults (8/102) and 17.1% of subadults (6/35).

Remodelled changes were observed in three adults and one subadult aged 6–11 years at St Mary Spital (4/5387: 0.1%). At Bow Baptist residual rickets affected only adult males and there were no cases of resolved rickets at St Mary and St Michael.[33]

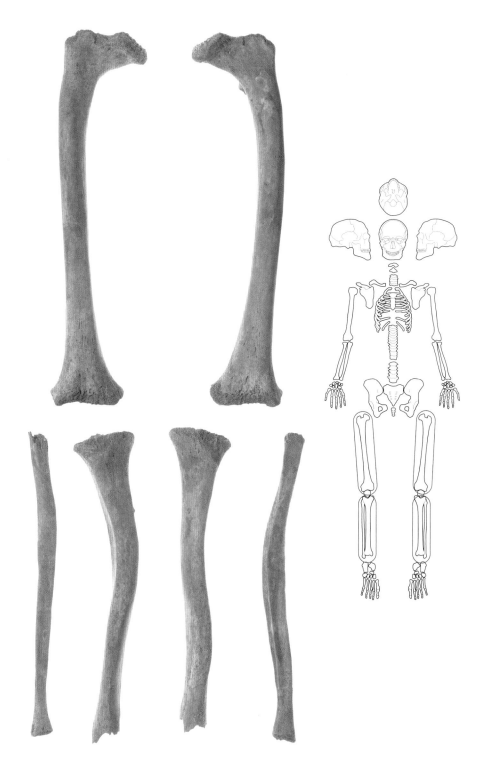

This suggests that those buried in the New Churchyard may have been more likely to have survived recurring episodes of vitamin D deficiency. The deformities incurred during childhood would have remained present into adulthood and clothing may have concealed the bowed limbs. Evidence suggests that such deformities may have been relatively common and did not cause significant problems for the affected individuals.[34]

Endocranial lesions

Reactive new bone to the endocranial (internal) bone surfaces of the skull may reflect inflammation and/or haemorrhage of the meninges. This can be linked to trauma, infection and metabolic disorders.[35]

These lesions were present in 1.8% (12/682) of category A individuals, 1.4% of adults (7/503), 0.7% of males (2/283), 2.4% of females (5/210) and 2.8% (5/179) of subadults. The highest frequencies occurred in perinates (2/23: 8.7%) with 5.0% of those aged 1–5 years (2/40) and 2.0% of those aged 6–11 years (1/51) showing lesions.

Eight individuals from phase 1 (1569–c 1670) (/368: 2.2%, 5/296: 1.7% of adults and 3/99: 3.0% of subadults) displayed endocranial lesions compared to four individuals from phase 2 (c 1670–1739) (/314: 1.3%, 2/234: 0.9% of adults and 2/80: 2.5% of subadults).

Three category B individuals displayed endocranial lesions (3/137: 2.2%), 2.0% of adults (2/102), 3.7% of males (2/54) and 2.9% of subadults (1/35).

Ten individuals with endocranial lesions also displayed evidence of other pathological conditions (/15: 66.7%). This included three individuals with evidence of vitamin D deficiency rickets: subadults [777], [3413] and adult male [3912]. Female [3323], aged ≥46 years, had healed fractures to several ribs as well as cribra orbitalia and periosteal lesions. Male [3850] had bilateral enthesosophytes in the patellae (kneecaps) (Table 23).

Comparisons between assemblages are problematic as only the internal surfaces of broken crania can be observed and therefore assemblages with a high number of intact crania may underestimate prevalence rates. At medieval St Mary Spital, endocranial lesions affected 1.5% of all individuals (80/5387), 1.0% of males (22/2237), 0.7% of females (13/1883) and 3.3% of subadults (34/1027). Thirteen individuals, c 1400–1539, were affected (/650: 2.0%) with a higher proportion of males (5/290: 1.7%) than females (2/203: 1.0%). The highest frequencies were recorded in subadults aged 1–5 years (2/11: 18.2%). At Bow Baptist endocranial lesions affected 3.6% individuals (15/416), 6.9% of subadults (14/202), and at St Mary and St Michael 8.9% of individuals (63/705), including 14.2% of subadults (62/437), had lesions.[36]

Illness and injury

Non-specific bone infectious changes were identified in 10.6% of subadult category A burials and 11.4% of category B burials. This largely comprised

Context	Age (years)	Sex	Burial category	Cribra orbitalia	Periostitis	Porotic hyperostosis	Rickets	Trauma	Enamel hypoplasia
[167]	36–45	female	A						
[777]	1–5	subadult	A	y			y		
[786]	1–5	subadult	A	y		y			
[787]	18–25	female	A						
[1922]	6–11	subadult	A						y
[3063]	26–35	male	B		y				y
[3323]	≥46	female	A	y	y			y	
[3413]	6–11	subadult	B	y			y		
[3850]	adult	male	A					y	y
[3869]	perinatal	subadult	A						
[3912]	18–25	male	B		y		y		y
[4133]	≥46	female	A						
[4205]	perinatal	subadult	A						
[4379]	26–35	male	A		y				
[5462]	18–25	female	A	y	y				y

Table 23 Endocranial lesion co-morbidities for 15 individuals with endocranial lesions from the New Churchyard

evidence of periosteal new bone lesions including those present on the ribs and in the maxillary sinus cavities. Specific bone changes diagnostic of tuberculosis (TB) were identified in 1.7% of the category A subadults (3/179) including one individual aged 6–11 years (1/51: 2.0%). Subadult [5193] aged approximately ten years at death presented extensive bone lesions throughout the skeleton with active osteomyelitis affecting the bones of the left elbow and lesions to the skull, mandible, upper spine, scapulae and ribs reflecting possible Caffey's disease (infantile cortical hyperostosis; Chapter 9.2, 'Osteomyelitis').

Six category A subadults had lesions indicative of vitamin C deficiency scurvy (/179: 3.4%). This affected 9.1% of those aged 1–6 months (1/11), one individual aged 7–11 months and 7.5% (3/40) of those aged 1–5 years. None were affected aged 6–11 years. Two category B subadults, both aged 1–5 years also displayed evidence of scurvy (/35: 5.7%; 2/12: 16.7%) (Chapter 10.6).

Evidence of traumatic injury was recorded in 3.4% of category A subadults (6/179) including 5.9% of those aged 6–11 years (3/51). There was no evidence of trauma in those aged <6 years. Trauma was identified in 11.4% of category B burials (4/35), 16.7% of those aged 1–5 years (2/12). Category A subadult [6303], aged 6–11 years, had a healed transverse fracture to the left proximal (end nearest the knee) tibia, probably resulting from a direct blow to the lower leg. Subadult [1978], also 6–11 years, had a compression fracture in the third lumbar vertebra, probably occurring from a fall. Two individuals displayed greenstick fractures to limbs, possibly secondary to underlying bone weakening through rickets. Category A subadult [380], aged 6–11 years, had

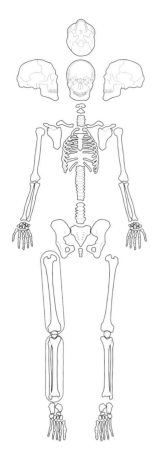

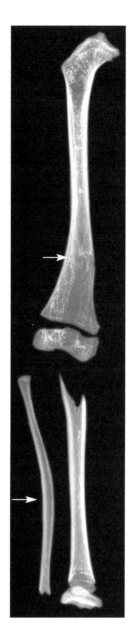

a possible healed right femoral fracture (Fig 151), and category B subadult [8210], aged 1–5 years, had a left humeral fracture. Category A subadult [6169], aged 6–11 years, had a possible dislocation injury to the right shoulder at the sternoclavicular joint.

Childhood was short-lived. Those that survived to five years of age could have contributed to the household with minor chores. In a home-working environment, simple tasks could be given to children – tying silk threads, picking up buttons and pins. Older boys might have been sent to school, but girls were likely to be at home and available to look after their siblings while their parents worked. In many families, a boy would eventually leave the family home (urban or rural), for example for an apprenticeship, to work in a shop or in a craft (Chapter 7.3, 7.4). They would rarely see their parents again, especially if they travelled from the provinces into London. Orphaned children taken in by a parish might begin their apprenticeships as early as 11.[37]

12.2 Adolescence

Health and mortality

A high number of teenagers were recorded amongst the New Churchyard burials and this pattern was present in each burial category and type (Chapter 6.3). Some of these individuals may represent migrants moving to London whose urban environment may have had a detrimental effect on health, but young teenagers (and children) are more likely to be London-born (Chapter 7.2, 7.3, 7.4). There were certainly a large number of adolescents and young adults aged c 15–25 years in the London population.

There were 53 category A burials aged 12–17 years (/682: 7.8%) comprising 29.6% of subadults (53/179). This pattern was also seen in the category B sample (13/137: 9.5%; 13/35: 37.1% of subadults). There was a higher number of teenagers in the phase 1 (1569–c 1670) assemblage (34/99: 34.3%) compared to phase 2 (c 1670–1739) (19/80: 23.8%). There was also a slightly higher rate of 12–17 year olds in the mass graves (pits – OA105E – and mass pit

Fig 151 Radiograph of subadult [380] with bowing deformities of rickets and a possible secondary healed greenstick fracture in the right femur (arrowed) (scale c 1:3)

[7482]/[8473] – OA105A) (10/26: 38.5%) compared to the attritional burial sample (30/89: 33.7%). Six teenagers (/16: 37.5%) were excavated from mass pit [7482]/[8473]. This was in contrast to standard attritional models that show a low rate of adolescent deaths with a gradual rise in mortality through adulthood.[38]

Evidence of non-specific infectious disease was recorded in 13.2% of category A (7/53) and 30.8% (4/13) of category B 12–17 year olds. This compared to 28.8% of category A and 11.1% of category B 18–25 year olds. Seven had inflammatory periosteal new bone lesions (/53: 13.2%) and two category B adolescents had evidence of osteomyelitis infection (/13: 15.4%). Subadult [5954] had expansive changes to the distal (end farthest away from the body)

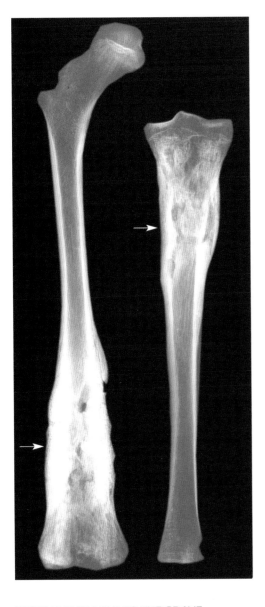

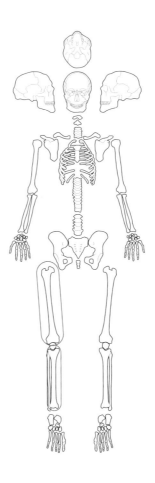

Fig 152 Radiograph of the right femur and tibia of subadult [5954], showing osteomyelitis (scale *c* 1:3)

right femur and proximal right tibia resulting from slowly remodelled bone indicating a long-standing infection. Four large sinuses were present on the shaft of the femur and four on the tibia. Radiographs showed extensive disorganisation with layers of new bone and areas of dead bone indicating osteomyelitis infection (Fig 152; Chapter 9.2).

Specific infectious bone changes were recorded in two category A adolescents (/53: 3.8%) and two from the category B sample (/13: 15.4%). All had a distribution of bone lesions diagnostic of TB (Chapter 9.3). Subadult [4000] had destructive lesions in the second and third thoracic vertebrae of the spine. Pitted lesions of new bone were present on the anterior surfaces of the scapulae wings and necks of several ribs and in the bones of the upper and lower limbs. Erosions in the joints of the left hip had completely destroyed the femoral head. Plaques of florid and pitted remodelled new bone were present on the anterior and posterior surfaces of the left ilia. There was evidence of TB osteomyelitis infection in the long bones with bulbous expansion of new cortical bone to the shafts and multiple cloacal perforations in the left ulna and fibula. This form of TB is especially common in children (Fig 153).[39] The unfused epiphyseal joint surfaces were not affected. This individual also had a shallow, smooth depression to the posterior right parietal bone, possibly reflecting a healed blunt force trauma injury.

Subadult [4615], aged approximately 17 years at death, had severe bilateral erosive bone changes at the metatarsophalangeal joints of the toes and lesions of active inflammatory periostitis located in the lower legs, left femur and distal humeri. These bony changes may be a result of a number of seronegative or erosive arthropathies such as psoriatic arthritis or Reiter's syndrome, or possibly rheumatoid arthritis. Septic or viral arthritis may result in the spread of an infection into a joint and can be associated with TB and also leprosy where an individual injures their extremities and introduces bacteria into the joint spaces.[40]

Several individuals presented bone lesions reflecting non-fatal stresses and strains placed on the body at a young age. Schmorl's nodes represent the herniation of the intervertebral disc that lies between two vertebral bodies. This fibrous capsule contains a gelatinous substance that can exert pressure resulting in indentations on the superior and inferior surfaces of a vertebral body.[41] Schmorl's nodes affected 63.4% of category A adults (319/503) and displayed the highest crude prevalence rate for category A adult males (210/283: 74.2%). This affected 17.0% of observable adult vertebrae (1901/11192) with a distribution in the weight-bearing regions of the mid to lower thoracic and lumbar spine.

Analysis of spinal joint disease occurring in the subadult sample showed high rates of Schmorl's nodes recorded in the 12–17 years age category only.

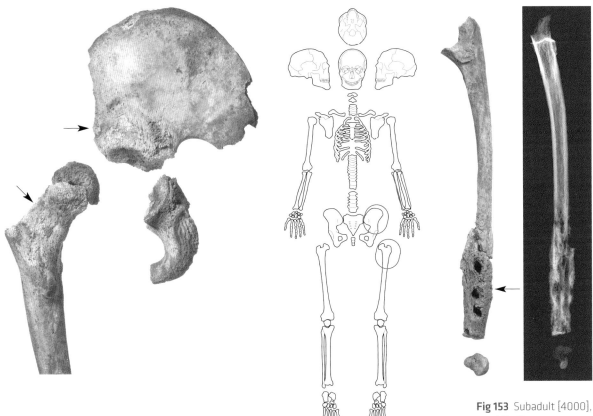

Fig 153 Subadult [4000], aged 12–17 years, showing (left) destruction of the left hip (posterior) consistent with tuberculous arthritis and (right) extensive remodelling to the left ulna indicating tuberculous osteomyelitis (photo posterior view; radiograph anteroposterior view) (scale *c* 1:3)

Osteoarthritis reflecting degeneration of the synovial joints of the apophyseal facets was also present in this age range with lower rates of intervertebral disc disease (pitting), osteophytes (new bone formation) and vertebral fusion also observed. Together this evidence may suggest higher stresses placed on the spine, possibly through activity from a young age, perhaps though manual work such as carrying heavy loads.[42]

As well as Schmorl's nodes in the lower spine, the left femoral head of subadult [5198], aged approximately 17 years, was in an abnormal posterior and inferior position and the neck was severely shortened in length; eburnation (polishing) to the hip joint indicated secondary osteoarthritis and that the joint continued to move (Fig 154). This represented a slipped femoral head caused by a stress fracture of the metaphyseal growth plate. This may result from a shearing stress during the adolescent growth spurt commonly occurring between the ages of nine and 16 years and has been linked to obesity and increased physical activity.[43] There was also healed intra-articular fracture in the left ankle joint of the left tibia probably resulting from a jump or a fall.

There was a rounded notch between the left maxillary lateral incisor and canine of subadult [8145], aged 15 years. Black staining to the occlusal and

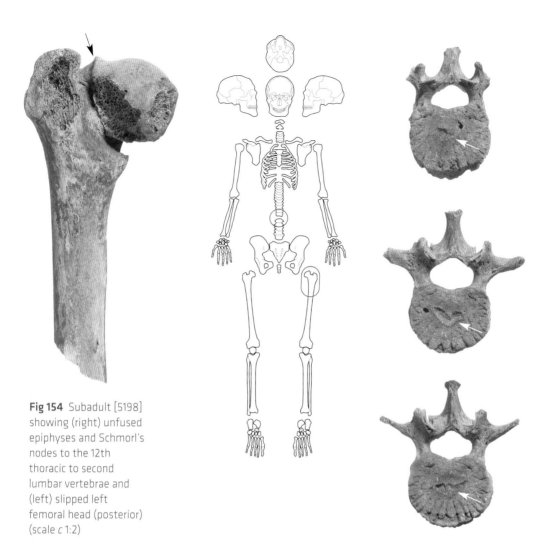

Fig 154 Subadult [5198] showing (right) unfused epiphyses and Schmorl's nodes to the 12th thoracic to second lumbar vertebrae and (left) slipped left femoral head (posterior) (scale *c* 1:2)

lingual surfaces of the teeth suggested habitual clay tobacco pipe smoking (below, 12.3).

Osteochondritis dissecans was recorded in 3.2% of category A burials (22/682) including 4.0% of adults (20/503) and 1.1% of subadults (2/179); the highest frequency was recorded in adults aged 36–45 years. Teenager [6215], aged *c* 16 years, had bilateral healed sub-circular, well-defined pits to the medial femoral condyles of the knee joints. This benign, non-inflammatory condition results from the detachment of a focal area of joint surface with associated bone necrosis. This condition has been described as idiopathic but may also result from trauma. The common age of onset is between ten and 25 years.[44]

Bone changes suggesting a diagnosis of Scheuermann's disease were identified in 1.0% of category A burials (7/682), 1.2% of adults (6/503) and 0.6% of subadults (1/179). Subadult [6228], aged 12–17 years, displayed anterior wedging of the sixth to eighth thoracic vertebrae and irregular margins to the apophyseal rings of the vertebral bodies. All exhibited osteophytes and severe Schmorl's nodes. This had resulted in an anterior curvature of the mid spine. Scheuermann's disease or juvenile kyphosis is commonly found in individuals aged 12–18 years. There may be a genetic predisposition, but trauma may also result in its onset. This may be unnoticeable or may cause aching pain following physical exertion.[45]

Spondylolysis, the separation of the neural arch and pars articularis of the posterior vertebra, may relate to a stress fracture following lower back injury or repeated trauma. A congenital predisposition may also increase some individuals' predisposition to the condition.[46] Twenty-seven category A individuals (/682: 4.0%) were affected, 6.0% of males (17/283) and 4.3% of females (9/210), and one subadult aged 12–17 years (/179: 0.6%). In 21 individuals the separation was bilateral, in three cases only the right side of the neural arch was affected and in three cases only the left. Two of these individuals from category A, male [516] aged ≥46 and female [1245] aged 36–45 years, also displayed mild spondylolisthesis, where the fourth lumbar vertebra had slipped anteriorly relative to the fifth vertebra.

Overall rates of trauma for the 12–17 years age category were low with three individuals from category A (/53: 5.7%) and two from category B (/13: 15.4%) showing injuries. Two adolescents had healed fractures located in the spine: [1978], aged 13 years, had a compression fracture to the third lumbar vertebrae probably resulting from a fall or jump; [8145], aged 15 years, had slight anterior wedging to the first lumbar vertebra with a large depression extending anteriorly into the epiphyseal ring suggesting an avulsion injury, probably resulting from hyperflexion of the spine. Subadult [1675], aged 15 years, had an oblique fracture to the medial right clavicle. This type of injury may be caused by a blow to the shoulder or fall on to an outstretched hand.

Subadult [8219], aged *c* 12 years, from mass pit [7482]/[8473], displayed diffuse nodular bony exostoses (growths) distributed in areas of enchondral (cartilaginous) ossification (Fig 155). These were located on the proximal and medial shaft of the left humerus, medial clavicles, right proximal femur, the proximal and medial shafts of the fibulae, the sternal end of the first right rib as well as the shafts of the surviving metacarpals. The femora and radii were bowed. These changes were consistent with a diagnosis of diaphyseal aclasis or hereditary multiple exostoses. This hereditary condition is caused by an autosomal dominant disorder leading to cartilaginous exostoses. While this example reflects the first stages of the disease, the abnormal bone formation may have led to some restriction of movement and abnormal posture.[47]

Adolescent/young adult male [4770], aged *c* 19–20 years, displayed multiple

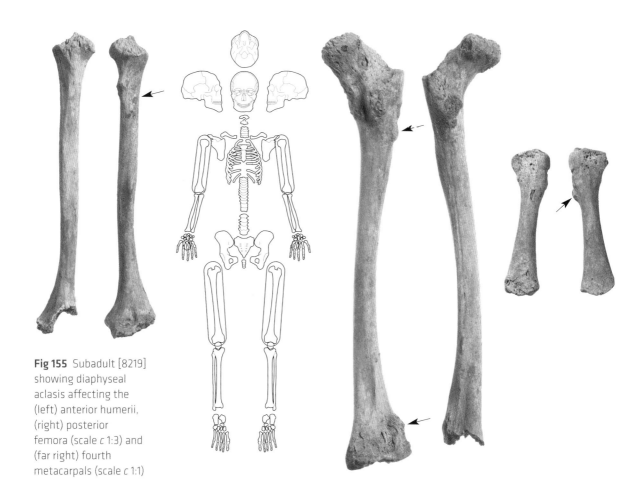

Fig 155 Subadult [8219] showing diaphyseal aclasis affecting the (left) anterior humerii, (right) posterior femora (scale *c* 1:3) and (far right) fourth metacarpals (scale *c* 1:1)

widespread erosive lesions throughout the skeleton (Fig 156). A large 'punched out' sub-circular lytic lesion penetrated the tables of the right frontal bone. This was surrounded by white, porous 'hair on end' periosteal new bone on the endocranial (internal) surface. A second lesion was present on the left frontal above the left orbit, possibly involving the eye. There was a small erosive lesion to the endocranial and ectocranial surface of the right parietal bone that had not penetrated all the way through the skull. A large lesion to the inner surface of the right mandible had destroyed much of the alveolar bone from the ramus to the first molar. The lesion had scalloped edges and was remodelled with the diplöe (the inner spongy bone structure) obscured by new healed bone. There was widespread destruction to the joints of the right elbow, particularly at the distal humeral lateral epicondyle, ulna olecranon and radial head. The right distal radial shaft and joints of the wrist also presented destructive lesions. The proximal joint surfaces of the first to second metacarpals of the hand were also eroded. Similar changes were present in the joints of the left arm. In the legs, there were further erosive lesions to the anterior surfaces of the right and left tibia. Radiographs

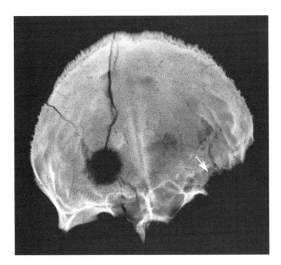

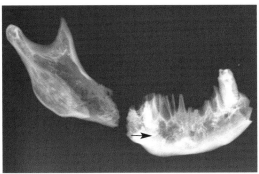

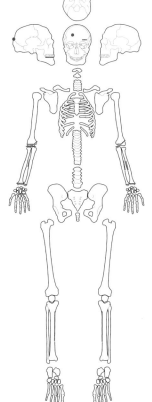

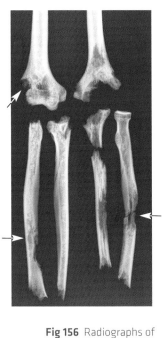

Fig 156 Radiographs of adolescent/young adult male [4770] showing multiple destructive lesions of (top left) the frontal skull, (bottom left) mandible (scale *c* 1:2) and (right) arm bones (scale *c* 1:4), and (centre) diagram showing distribution of lesions consistent with a diagnosis of Langerhans cell histiocytosis (not to scale)

confirmed the presence of multiple destructive lesions (Fig 156). This individual also suffered deformities to the ribs with a well-healed right rib fracture, severe dental enamel hypoplasia and cribra orbitalia.

The distribution and type of lesions suggested a possible diagnosis of Langerhans cell histiocytosis. This condition includes several, age-specific conditions affecting children. It is caused by a pathological disturbance to the reticuloendothelial system within the immune system and is characterised by a proliferation of histiocytes (Langerhans cells). Bone changes in children with this disease can be similar to those seen in adults with multiple myeloma cancer. Single or multiple skeletal lesions commonly affect the skull, mandible, spine, ribs, pelvis and long bones, particularly the femur and humerus.[48] The average age of onset is ten to 14 years. This rare disease has a reported incidence of 0.2–2.0 cases per 100,000 children under 15 years old with a higher prevalence in men than in women. Clinical manifestations include local pain, tenderness and swelling related to adjacent skeletal lesions. Fever and leucocytosis (high white cell count) may also be apparent. Prognosis for an individual can be unfavourable due to the location of lesions near major organs and the brain. A differential diagnosis of meloma multiplex and lytic metastatic carcinoma were considered but discounted due to the nature of the lesions and the age profile of the individual affected.[49]

12.3 Adulthood

Health and mortality

Once a person had survived the risks of infancy, childhood and adolescence, they might expect to live through several decades of adult life. However, the exact age at death of relatively few adults is known and estimates of average life expectancy reflect a complex relationship between adult and high infant and child mortality rates. Mortality in all decades of life was higher in London than elsewhere in England and the expectation of life at birth was lower. In wealthy central London, life expectancy for those aged 1–14 years was 30–35 years, compared to 20–25 years in poorer areas. Men who became London freemen in the mid 16th century at an average age of 26 years might live a further 28 years, with the majority surviving into their 50s; some lived into their 70s or 80s. A woman's life expectancy was almost the same.[50]

Males outnumbered females (Chapter 6.3). This pattern was consistent through the phases of burial ground use and is comparable to evidence from contemporary Christian post-medieval burial grounds where a male bias is often encountered.[51]

For those adults where age could be estimated, a slightly higher number of category A females died aged 18–25 years (54/199: 27.1%) compared to males (70/273: 25.6%) and female mortality peaked in the 26–35 years age category (73/199: 36.7%) compared to males (78/273: 28.6%). By comparison, male mortality peaked between 36 and 45 years (86/273: 31.5%). There was an almost equal distribution of males (39/273: 14.3%) and females (27/199:13.6%) in the older ≥46 years age category.

At St Mary Spital, in c 1400–1539, there were more 18–25 year old females as a proportion of total aged females (49/162: 30.2%) compared to the male equivalent (51/232: 22.0%). A higher proportion of 36–45 year old males (67/232: 28.9%) compared to females (35/162: 21.6%) was also recorded. A similar pattern was identified at St Mary and St Michael where both males and females showed the highest mortality rates in early and middle adulthood. A higher relative female mortality in the third and fourth decade of life within archaeological samples has often been linked to death in pregnancy or childbirth.[52]

Marriage

For ordinary people marriage was mostly deferred until their mid 20s, or later. By this time, working men may have saved sufficient funds to support a wife and set up an independent household.[53] Apprentices were forbidden to marry and those who did complete their apprenticeships were not necessarily immediately economically able to marry; they joined the lowest rank of freemen and became journeymen. Many men married older women, often widows with some financial security. A second husband could expect to succeed to the first husband's position and apprentices could jump the remaining years of service by marrying their master's widow. Few widowers remained unattached for long and it has been estimated that in the late 16th century 25–30% of all marriages were remarriages. Remarriage was, however, less common amongst the poor women and widows who dominated the older female population.[54]

London-born females were more likely to marry younger than their migrant peers who often delayed marriage.[55] Through marriage some women may have acquired status and income/earning power. However, a high proportion of women were wholly or partially dependent on what they could earn themselves. Wives of the less skilled and poorly paid often needed their own earnings to help support a family and work undertaken by mothers such as needlework and catering could be combined with childcare in the home.[56] Women had traditionally worked alongside men in the fields or in industry and some were apprenticed into trades (Chapter 7.4). Few women were employed in the same occupation throughout their working lives. The majority of London-born younger women, as well as migrants, would have undertaken a period of domestic service, often as a first job. Following marriage, many women engaged in catering or shopkeeping, or the needle trades where women played a major role in the city's manufacturing sector. Some provided personal services in alternative medicine as well as in a variety of other industries and roles. Older age groups in particular may have been confined to lower-status occupations such as nursing, charring, washing and hawking, although a few may have found higher-status roles as midwives and school teachers. While some businesses may have been inherited after a husband's (or father's) death, few widows carried on the husband's trade. There was probably little in the way of shared occupation in life between husband and wife, who probably saw little of each other during the long working day.[57]

Not everyone married. Emigration was at its highest in the mid 16th century with most representing young adults who would have married and reproduced in the colonies, thus impacting upon fertility among the remaining population. The 17th century was a peak time for young single men to leave England for the colonies or as part of military service. Approximately 5% of those born in 1566 did not marry during their childbearing years and 22% of those born in 1616 remained celibate. A high rate of celibacy, together with an overall delayed age of first marriage, may have had an impact on total fertility.[58]

Fertility and childbirth and maternal mortality

Family size could be regulated by delayed marriage, sexual restraint and other practices such as delayed weaning that may have hindered fertility. Contraceptive devices were used to protect men from disease and not to prevent conception. The strongest influence on marital fertility was infant feeding practices; mothers who breastfed tended to wait longer before conceiving another child.[59]

The risks of childbirth would have been well known but had little effect on attitudes. Death during childbirth accounted for around 20% of all female deaths between the ages of 25 and 34, 11–14% of those aged 20–24 and 35–44. The death rate at this period from maternal mortality was probably about 5 in 1000 births. Working women from urban areas, with reduced stature, weight and possibly deformed pelves from childhood rickets, may have faced an increased risk of premature birth and infant death. Prior to aseptic conditions, there was a high risk of infection within days following birth. Up until the 20th century, puerperal fever, haemorrhage and toxaemia accounted for about three quarters of maternal deaths.[60]

In the 16th and 17th centuries the female midwife played an important role in childbirth. Most were respectable married women or widows with years of practical experience. Midwives were licensed by the Church and may have had to perform baptisms on sickly children if there was a danger of death before a properly qualified person could arrive. It was only later in the 18th and 19th centuries that physicians and surgeons began to take more of an interest.[61]

In the analysed sample, mortality rates for both sexes peaked in the 26–45 years category, although a slightly higher number of females died younger compared to men (Chapter 6.3). One adult female, [739], was found associated with the skeletal remains of a child, [736], aged one month to six years. At site A, a neonate, A[532], was buried with an adult female, A[525], possibly a mother and baby (Fig 157).

Tobacco smoking

Elizabeth L Knox

Tobacco was first introduced into Europe from the Americas in the middle of the 16th century, with the earliest account of the dried leaves being smoked in a pipe in England dating to the 1570s.[62] London was the initial focus of the pipe-making industry, which rapidly expanded to other centres around the country during the 17th century as smoking became ever more popular and tobacco from the colonies more widely available. The Charter of Incorporation of the Tobacco Pipe-Makers of Westminster was signed in

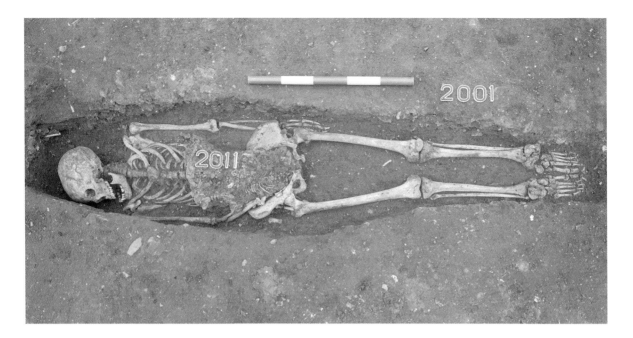

1619, and pipes of this period have been recorded in excavated material from Spitalfields and other sites in London.[63] By 1634, when a new charter was signed, smoking had become firmly and inextricably embedded within London society, with all the inevitable eventual consequences for public health.

Poorer members of society are unlikely to have been able to afford tobacco in the late 16th century; over the course of the 17th century, however, the quantities imported increased hugely while the cost fell.[64] By 1650 there were over 1000 pipe-makers working in London alone. This was described as a harsh industry with many workers coming from the poorest quarters on the margins of the city. Pipe-makers battled against publicans cleaning and reusing spent pipes left in the pubs and inferior homemade versions. By the time that tobacco became more affordable for the majority in the late 18th century, wealthy smokers moved on to cigars and the clay pipe became synonymous with the working class.[65]

Some 17th-century women took up smoking (Fig 158) and this was reflected in the osteological evidence. Women were not permitted to be pipe-makers but maintained important roles within the trade. Widows of pipe-maker masters would take over the apprentices of their late husbands, teaching them the trade and often being responsible for their lodging (above, 'Marriage').[66]

Evidence of clay tobacco pipe smoking in the form of rounded notches to the biting surfaces of the teeth (Fig 159) was recorded in 51 category A individuals (/682: 7.5%), 10.1% of adults (51/503), with a higher rate in males (41/283: 14.5%) than females (10/210: 4.8%). There was a peak in male

Fig 158 'A woman smoking a [clay] pipe at a table', oil painting by Dutch artist Edward Collier, 1679
(Christie's Images/Bridgeman Images)

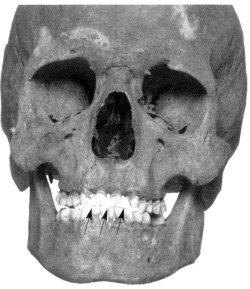

Fig 159 Male [5218], showing three large pipe notches in the anterior dentition between the central incisors and canines (the lateral incisors were congenitally absent) (scale c 1:2)

smokers aged 26–35 years (15/78: 19.2%) (Fig 160). There was a slight increase in crude prevalence from phase 1 (26/368: 7.1%) to phase 2 (25/314: 8.0%); while this remained true for males (phase 1: 18/149: 12.1%; phase 2: 23/134: 17.2%), there were more female smokers in the earlier period (phase 1: 8/113: 7.1%) than later (phase 2: 2/97: 2.1%). This may reflect a growing

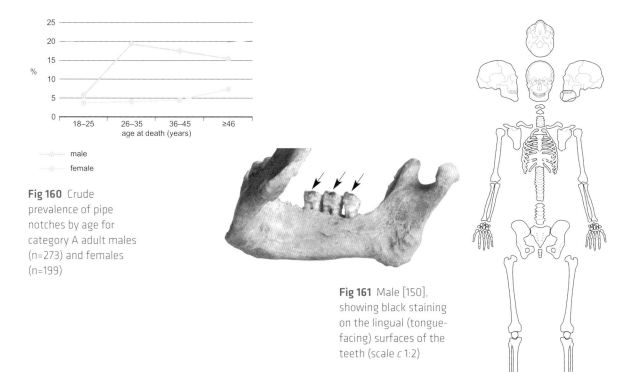

Fig 160 Crude prevalence of pipe notches by age for category A adult males (n=273) and females (n=199)

Fig 161 Male [150], showing black staining on the lingual (tongue-facing) surfaces of the teeth (scale *c* 1:2)

gender bias, with higher rates of male smokers recorded in the 19th century.[67]

Black staining on the inside, lingual (tongue-facing) surfaces of the teeth may reflect staining from tobacco products and is often found associated with pipe notches (Fig 161). Nine individuals had evidence of dental stains and pipe notches (/682: 1.3%), 1.8% of adults (9/503) and 1.0% of females (2/210).

The rates recorded in the New Churchyard population were lower than in the population from 19th-century St Mary and St Michael (58/248: 23.4% of adults). Here, 54 males (54/143: 37.8%) had pipe notches and only three females (3/105: 2.9%), reflecting the increase in the availability of tobacco after the 17th century, the decline of female smokers and the shift towards clay pipe smoking as a lower-status habit.[68]

Health issues related to smoking are well documented; modern studies into the effects of smoking and diseases including TB and cancer indicate that smokers are at a higher risk than non-smokers.[69] Cancers which begin in the soft tissue such as the lungs can produce bone lesions (metastases), but no individuals from the New Churchyard had evidence of both cancerous lesions and pipe notches (Chapter 7.2).[70] Inflammation of the lungs can lead to periosteal lesions on the visceral (inner) surfaces of the ribs (Chapter 9.2, 'Rib lesions'). Two adult males aged over 26 years had both rib lesions and pipe notches; male [5218], aged 36–45 years, had multiple pipe notches (Fig 159) and thick deposits of active new bone to the visceral surfaces of six right and two left ribs.

Clothing and fashion

Elizabeth L Knox

Certain restrictive clothing and fashions during the time of the New Churchyard could leave their mark on the skeleton. Two category A adults (2/503: 0.4%), one male (/283: 0.4%) and one female (/210: 0.5%) displayed abnormal deformities to the ribs, including tapering and angulation of the rib shafts, which may reflect the wearing of a corset.[71] Similar changes were seen in the rib cage of category B female [6436] (1/102: 1.0% of adults, 1/32: 3.1% of females). 'The evil effects of the corset', published in 1903, described these rib deformities and advised women against wearing corsetry that caused a noticeable shortness of breath and restricted movement, warning that the habitual wearer may permanently deform by the age of 24 and be crippled by 30 years of age.[72] Corsets or stays (stiffened, boned attire; Fig 162) were worn in the 15th to 18th centuries by the wealthy elite – by men, women and young girls – inspired by fashions in France and Italy.[73]

The left and right ribs of male [6244], aged 26–35 years, displayed *c* 90° abnormal curvature at the rib angles with flattening of the midshafts and tapering towards the sternal ends; this individual had also suffered a severe spinal injury. In this case, a corset may have been worn for medical reasons rather than fashion. The use of the corset in orthopaedic treatment for spinal injuries preceded the modern back brace (vertebral fractures, Chapter 11.1).[74]

Fig 162 17th-century wool, silk and linen corset (stays) (left, front view; right, back view) (not to scale)
(Museum of London)

Valgus deformity of the proximal phalanx of the big toe, known as hallux valgus, is when the big toe points towards and sometimes crosses over the other toes. This is commonly associated in modern populations with the wearing of restrictive, ill-fitting shoes.[75] Prior to the Industrial Revolution and mechanised production, shoes were often made symmetrically for both the left and right foot with pointed toes that could contribute to the condition.[76] In category A, hallux valgus was observed in 1.3% of individuals (9/682), 1.8% of adults (9/503), 1.8% of males (5/283) and 1.9% of females (4/210). Although only adult individuals were affected, there was no variation in prevalence between different age categories. Hallux valgus affected 2.9% of individuals (4/137) from category B.

12.4 Old age

Health and mortality

Long apprenticeships and economic factors meant that financial stability and independence might be achieved rather late, if at all. While wealthier individuals may have aimed to accumulate sufficient money to retire, poorer Londoners had to work until they no longer could. There was no retirement or insurance for old age; for those incapable of work, the only alternative was to seek aid from the parish. Help for the aged and infirm could be sought from the community rather than family members and there was no guarantee that parents could rely on the support of their offspring.[77]

Between 1541 and 1751 in England, the proportion of those aged ≥60 years changed little (7–10%). The London Bills of Mortality show that throughout the post-medieval period approximately 6–11% of people survived past 70 years, although these records may exclude those with a recognisable cause of death who would be classified elsewhere.[78] Parish registers might suggest a small proportion survived past 50 years, but the partial nature of many entries means that there was a high number for whom age was not recorded and/or may have been unknown (Chapter 6.1). The coffin plate of Sarah Williams records that she died at the age of 60 and Ann Halford is recorded to have reached the age of 81 (Chapter 5.6). In the New Churchyard, 66 category A burials were recorded in the ≥46 years age category (/682: 9.7%), comprising 13.1% of adults where age could be estimated (66/503). Sixteen category B burials were recorded in the older age category (16/137: 11.7%; 16/102: 15.7% of aged adults). While this indicated survivorship into old age for at least some of the population, inherent problems with osteological ageing methods may mean that these rates actually represent an underestimation.[79]

In phase 1 (1569–c 1670) 8.4% (31/368) of individuals (31/269: 11.5% of aged adults) survived into the older age category with a slight rise in phase 2 (c 1670–1739) (35/314: 11.1%, 35/234: 15.0% of aged adults). When broken down by sex, a slightly higher number of category A adult males were aged ≥46 (39/273: 14.3%) compared to females (27/199: 13.6%), a pattern that was mirrored in the category B males (10/50: 20.0%) and females (5/31: 16.1%). A higher number of females from phase 1 (1569–*c* 1670) were in this age category (16/113: 14.2%) compared to males (15/149: 10.1%), but this was reversed in phase 2 (*c* 1670–1739) where there was a higher number of males (24/134: 17.9%) to females (11/97: 11.3%), perhaps indicating improved life expectancy for men (Chapter 6.3).

In the New Churchyard, rates of dental disease, including ante-mortem tooth loss, periodontal disease and corrected caries, as well as rates of traumatic injuries showed a strong correlation with increased age. Survivorship into old age was supported by the presence of certain bone and joint conditions that become more prevalent with advancing age (Chapter 10.8).

Joint disease

Joint disease is one of the more frequently recorded types of pathology in archaeological skeletons. While a main factor behind the development of joint disease is advancing age, biomechanical factors resulting from trauma and activity may also contribute (Chapter 11.2).[80]

Spinal joint disease

In the absence of other pathological conditions, the occurrence of spinal joint disease may reflect a normal aspect of ageing.[81] In the category A burials, adult spinal joint disease showed an increased prevalence with advancing age, and this pattern continued when the sexes were separated (Fig 163). This included evidence of new bone growth at the margins of vertebral bodies as a compensatory reaction to stresses placed on the spine (osteophytosis), pitted lesions to the superior and inferior surfaces of the vertebral bodies reflecting degeneration of the cartilaginous joints (intervertebral disc disease), degeneration of the synovial joints of the posterior apophyseal vertebral

Fig 163 True prevalence rate of spinal joint disease by age and sex for category A burials (male n=1565; female n=1181)

- 18–25 years
- 26–35 years
- 36–45 years
- ≥ 46 years

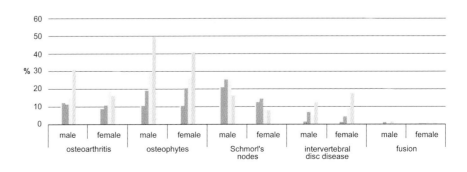

facets resulting in eburnation or polishing of the joint surfaces (osteoarthritis) and extensive new marginal bone growth between contiguous vertebrae resulting in localised fusion of one or more spinal segments.[82] The only exception to this was the presence of Schmorl's nodes that showed the highest frequencies in the male and female 26–35 years age group and female osteoarthritis with a peak in the 36–45 years age category (above, 12.2). A similar pattern was observed in the category B burial sample.

Extra-spinal joint disease

Osteoarthritis affects the synovial joints where there is a loss of the articular cartilage and remodelling of the surrounding bone tissue. Changes to the mechanics of a joint through injury or activity, advancing age and a systemic and genetic predisposition are all probable factors in the development of the disease.[83]

Osteoarthritis at extra-spinal joint locations affected 12.5% (85/682) of category A individuals: 16.9% (85/503) of adults, 16.6% (47/283%) of males and 16.7% (35/210) of females. Crude prevalence rates showed an increase with advancing age for both males and females with just under half of category A adults (32/66: 48.5%): 48.7% (19/39) of males and 48.1% (13/27) of females aged ≥46 years showing at least one osteoarthritic joint. Joint disease secondary to other pathological conditions such as fractures affected 2.0% (10/503) of category A adults. When secondary osteoarthritis was removed from the overall crude prevalence rates a similar pattern remained, although there was a slight reduction in the younger adult age ranges.

Osteoarthritic changes were present in the joints of 10.9% (15/137) of category B individuals: 14.7% (15/102) of adults, 16.7% (9/54) of males and 9.4% (3/32) of females. While there was an overall increase with older age, category B males showed the highest prevalence in the 36–45 years age category.

When adult true prevalence rates were calculated for each observable joint, the greatest frequency of osteoarthritis in the category A burials was recorded in the temporomandibular joint (jaw) (14/964: 1.5%), with a higher rate in the right side (8/484: 1.7%) compared to the left (6/480: 1.3%). When the sexes were separated, males demonstrated the highest prevalence in the left coxal joint (hip) (6/264: 2.3%), right hip (5/264: 1.9%), left acromioclavicular joint (shoulder) (4/213: 1.9%) and left jaw (4/215: 1.9%). Females had the highest rate in the right jaw (6/158: 3.8%), followed by the left femoropatellar joint (knee) (3/164: 1.8%).

When the true prevalence of all extra-spinal joint osteoarthritis in category A burials was shown as a proportion of the body, the small joints of the hand displayed the highest prevalence (30/169: 17.8%), followed by the costovertebral

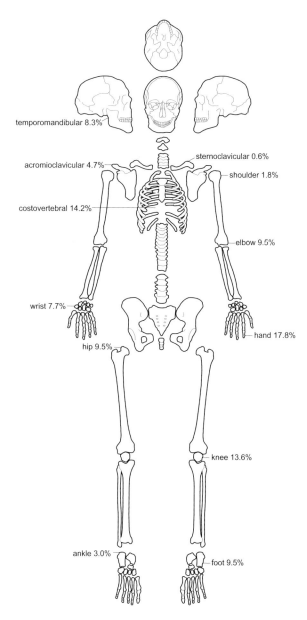

temporomandibular 8.3%

acromioclavicular 4.7%

sternoclavicular 0.6%

shoulder 1.8%

costovertebral 14.2%

elbow 9.5%

wrist 7.7%

hand 17.8%

hip 9.5%

knee 13.6%

ankle 3.0%

foot 9.5%

Fig 164 Distribution of category A adult extra-spinal osteoarthritis

joints (ribs) (24/169: 14.2%) and knee (23/169: 13.6%) (Fig 164).

The highest overall frequency of extra-spinal osteoarthritis in the category B burials was seen in the left distal radioulnar joint (wrist) (3/61: 4.9%) and right acromioclavicular joint (1/66: 1.5%). Male osteoarthritis was most common in the right lateral femorotibial joint (knee) (1/31: 3.2%), while females displayed the highest prevalence in the right hip 1/25: 4.0%). True prevalence shown as parts of the body affected showed appendages of the hands (5/19: 26.3%) and feet (6/19: 31.6%) to be the most affected.

Male [1698], aged 36–45 years, displayed extensive erosive and bone forming changes to the bones of the right foot with fusion between the navicular and cuneiform bones and the second to third metatarsals (Fig 165). Infectious bone changes were also present in the tibiae and fibulae of the lower leg. The distribution of the lesions suggested a seronegative spondylarthropathy. Reiter's syndrome has an asymmetric distribution pattern in the lower limb and extremities, with marginal erosions commonly affecting the small joints of the feet, ankle and knee.[84]

Two category A adults (/682: 0.3%), 0.4% (2/503) of adults, 0.4% (1/283) of males and 0.5% (1/210) of females, displayed evidence of degeneration to the muscles and tendons of the rotator cuff of the shoulder. This condition affected 0.6% of observable category A humeri (3/505). Rotator cuff disease often shows an increased prevalence with age and can cause pain, stiffness and weakening in the shoulder.[85]

Three adults aged ≥46 years displayed bony bridging to the margins of the sacroiliac joints of the pelvis. These changes may result from age-related degeneration, injury or occupational stresses.[86]

Male [7806], aged ≥46 years, had fusion of the seventh to 11th thoracic vertebrae along the anterior longitudinal ligament characteristic of DISH. The disease is more common in males and is rarely detected before the age of 40 years; the condition may cause pain, stiffness and restricted motion (Chapter 10.4).[87]

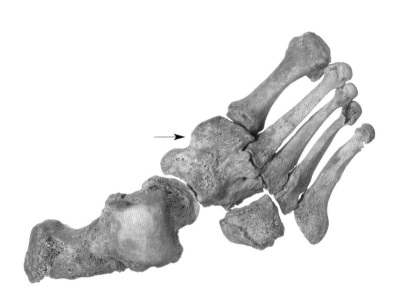

Paget's disease of bone

Paget's disease is a commonly symptomless condition that results in increased rates of bone remodelling, deformity and enlargement and is most commonly seen in the skull, leg bones and pelvis. Today, over 90% of cases are seen in those aged over 40 years and males are more affected than females. While the cause of the condition is not fully understood, inflammatory, vascular infectious, autoimmune disorders, diseases of the connective tissue and viral disease have been suggested as possible causes.[88]

Two category A individuals displayed bone changes diagnostic of Paget's disease (/682: 0.3%), 0.4% (2/503) of adults, 0.4% (1/283) of males and 0.5% (1/210) of females. The cranial bones of female [3417], aged 26–35 years, were thickened with abnormal porosity to the outer surfaces and pronounced vascular impressions on the internal aspects. Radiographs showed dense and thickened bone, and a post-mortem break revealed a cross section of disorganised spongy bone with poor definition of the cranial bone tables. Similar thickening of the cranial bones was observed in male [4048], aged ≥46 years.

Widespread bone changes were recorded in category B male [6100], aged 36–45 years (Fig 166). The right scapula, sternum, right ribs, sacrum and os coxa were all enlarged. The vertebral bodies were reduced in height and showed slight anterior wedging in the mid thoracic spine. There was marked thickening and deformity of the right proximal and distal femoral shaft with enlargement of the distal right tibia. These bone changes suggested polyostotic Paget's disease of the bone with multiple involvement of the skeleton.[89]

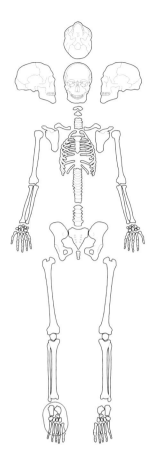

Fig 165 Right foot of male [1698] showing seronegative spondyloarthropathy (scale *c* 1:2)

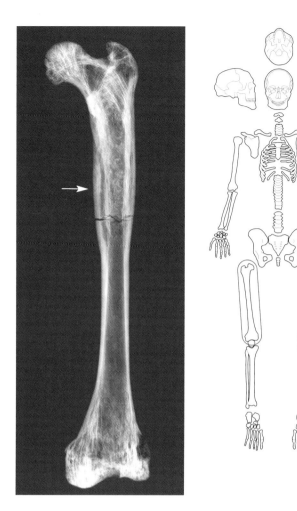

Fig 166 Anteroposterior radiograph of adult male [6100], showing severe bone thickening (arrowed) in the right femoral proximal shaft suggestive of Paget's disease (scale *c* 1:4)

Osteomalacia

Osteomalacia represents the adult counterpart to rickets (Chapter 10.7; above 12.1). Softening of the bones may occur as a result of dietary calcium deficiencies or as a result of the abnormal loss of calcium in the body through kidney or intestinal disease. This may result in stress fractures and deformities in the vertebrae and pelvis. Category A female [1553] (1/682: 0.1% of individuals, 1/503: 0.2% of adults, 1/210: 0.5% of females) displayed slight bowing of the femoral midshafts and abnormal curvature in the sacrum with a *c* 70° angle at the third sacral element, possibly a healed stress fracture. Radiographs confirmed the marked sacral angulation and new bone formation on the dorsal surfaces. Scalloped lesions to the metacarpals and carpals of the left hand suggested this individual had also suffered from gout. At St Mary Spital, in *c* 1400–1539, a single case of osteomalacia was identified in a ≥46 year old female (1/203: 0.5%).[90]

Hyperostosis frontalis interna

Observations of the internal structures of the cranium revealed 1.5% (10/682) of category A burials to be affected by hyperostosis frontalis interna (HFI). This included 2.0% of adults (10/503), with a higher crude prevalence amongst females (7/210: 3.3%) compared to males (1/283: 0.4%). Two adults were aged 26–35 years (2/153: 1.3%), one individual was aged 36–45 years (1/132: 0.8%), but the majority were aged ≥46 years (7/66:10.6%). The true prevalence of lesions affected 1.8% (9/504) of right and 2.0% (10/501) of left frontal bones. Five adults were from phase 1 (/368: 1.4%, 5/296: 1.7% of adults) and three individuals (/314: 1.0%, 3/234: 1.3% of adults) were from phase 2.

A single category B adult (/137: 0.7%, 1/102: 1.0% of adults) had HFI. Female [5613], aged ≥46 years, had bilateral, nodular cortical thickening to the endocranial (internal) surfaces of the frontals. True prevalence affected 1.8% (1/56) of right and 1.3% (1/76) of left frontal bones.

This condition is more frequently associated with women and increasing age. It has an unknown cause but may relate to disorders of the pituitary gland, particularly in post-menopausal women.[91] Twenty-two adults from St Mary Spital had HFI (22/5387: 0.4%), with females more affected than males. At St Mary and St Michael this was recorded in 0.6% of individuals (4/705) and 1.5% of adults (4/268); the low prevalence observed here may have been a result of the high number of intact crania.[92]

Skeletal dysplasia

The partial remains of adult [7700], aged ≥46 years, showed severe deformities to the bones of the upper limbs (Fig 167). The left humeral shaft was slender and there was a large y-shaped hiatus between the humeral capitulum and trochlea (elbow joint) with the surviving joint surfaces rugged and irregular. The ulnae were thickened and abnormally shortened and the left ulna had an enlarged and irregular proximal joint surface and a distal end that tilted forwards and laterally. The radii were short compared to the ulnae and displayed lateral bowing. The radial heads were enlarged and flattened and the distal joint surfaces at the wrists were flared and tilted in an ulnar and volar (palm-facing) direction. The left radial wrist joint surface was abnormally formed with a large hiatus between the scaphoid and lunate (wrist bones) articular surfaces. There was a large depression in the lateral left elbow that may have articulated with the head of the radius that had slipped inferiorly, possibly a result of dislocation of the joint. A small region of eburnation (osteoarthritis) on the joint surfaces of the left elbow indicated that there was still movement. Degenerative joint disease was also present

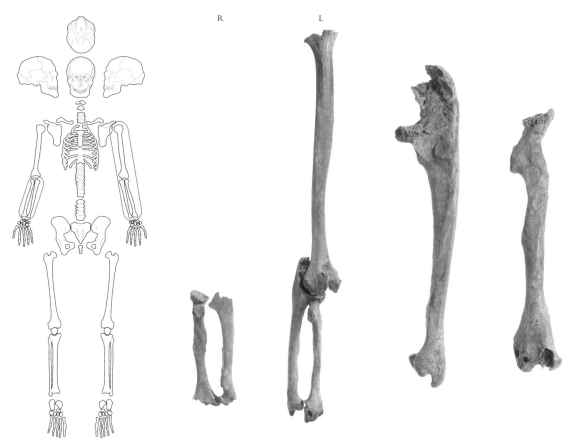

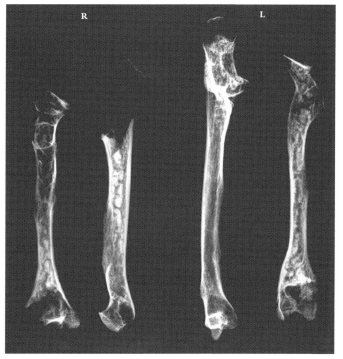

Fig 167 Adult [7700] showing deformities to the bones of the lower arms consistent with a skeletal dysplasia or dyschondroplasia such as Madelung's deformity: top left – anteroposterior view of arm bones (scale *c* 1:4); top right – right radius and ulna (scale *c* 1:2); and bottom – anteroposterior radiograph of lower arm bones (scale *c* 1:2)

throughout the spine and the ribs appeared tapered with marked medial curvature at the rib angles.

The incomplete nature of the skeleton hindered a diagnosis, although the marked deformities suggested a skeletal dysplasia or dyschondrosteosis (abnormal bone development) such as Madelung's deformity. This condition is characterised by shortening of the bones of the lower legs and forearms, and abnormalities in the bones of the wrist present from birth. Stunted growth and premature fusion of epiphyseal growth plates result in abnormal angulation of the distal radial joint surfaces and may result in compensatory wedging and volar (palm-facing) dislocation of the proximal carpal (wrist) bones. Clinical cases are usually evident in adolescents or young adults who may exhibit visible deformity, pain, fatigue and limited motion at the affected joints. Carpal tunnel syndrome may also be present. It may occur with other syndromes such as diaphyseal aclasis and nail patella syndrome. The condition may also feature increased muscle size and elbow abnormalities, scoliosis and exostoses. The aetiology is unknown but may relate to inheritance or a mutilated gene during development. Differential diagnoses considered congenital or acquired growth plate disturbances and trauma, although the symmetrical and bilateral nature of the deformities made injury an unlikely cause.[93]

Notes to Chapter 12

1 Houston 1996, 138, 141–4

2 Finlay 1981, 146; Harding 1990, 111; Lewis 2007, 33, 82

3 Finlay 1981, 16, 109, 100; J Graunt cited in Porter 2012b, 105; Roberts and Cox 2003, 303–4

4 Connell et al 2012, 171; Lewis 2007, 6

5 Lewis 2007, 98; Newton 2011, 261

6 Evidence from combined isotope and trace element analysis (Chapter 7.3) for breastfeeding is limited and suggests that if individuals were breastfed it was not for a sustained period (Montgomery et al 2016).

7 Picard 2003, 95; Houston 1996, 168; Lewis 2007, 81

8 Cox 1993, 77

9 Lewis 2007, 6; Picard 2003, 95; Porter 1991,

10 Humphrey 2000, 29

11 Whittaker 2000, 95

12 Fig 148 following Moorrees et al 1963a; 1963b; with Smith 1991 recalibration from Buikstra and Ubelaker 1994, fig 23

13 Lewis 2007, 67

14 Roberts and Manchester 2012, 222

15 Lewis 2007, 103; Wood et al 1992

16 Connell et al 2012, 175

17 Ibid, 240; Henderson et al 2013, 201

18 Connell et al 2012, 124; Henderson et al 2013, 201

19 Hillson 2000, 250

20 Connell et al 2012, 126; Henderson et al 2013, 123

21 Connell et al 2012, 126; Henderson et al 2013, 133

22 Ortner 2003, 393; Mays 2003, 145; Brickley and Ives 2008, 113

13; Bucholz and Ward 2012, 64–5

23 Roberts and Manchester 2012, 237–9

24 Brickley and Ives 2008, 75–90; Roberts and Manchester 2012, 238; Mays 2003, 145

25 Mays 2003, 149; Brickley and Ives 2008, 95

26 Graunt 1662; Mays 2003, 147–9, 151; 1999, 332; Picard 2003, 95; Brickley and Ives 2008, 92; Roberts and Manchester 2012, 238–9

27 Mays 2003, 148

28 Ortner 2003, 393; Brickley and Ives 2008, 85, 93; Roberts and Manchester 2012, 238–9

29 Connell et al 2012, 118, 174

30 Brickley and Ives 2008, 95; Mays 2003, 144, 148, 151

31 Henderson et al 2013, 201; 2015, 115

32 Brickley et al 2010, 54

33 Connell et al 2012, 119; Henderson et al 2013, 201

34 Brickley et al 2010, 64–6

35 Lewis 2004, 93

36 Connell et al 2012, 147–8, 257; Henderson et al 2013, 207

37 Lewis 2007, 6; Picard 2003, 172–3; 2004, 99, 209; Porter 1991, 146

38 Gowland and Chamberlain 2005, 146

39 Resnick 2002, 2537; Ortner 2003, 246

40 Waldron 2009, 46–65; Burt et al 2013, 29, 54

41 Rogers 2000, 169; Roberts and Manchester 2012, 140–1

42 Stirland 2000, 135; Rogers and Waldron 1995, 27

43 Ortner and Putshar 1981, 241–2; Resnick 2002, 2729–30

44 Aufderheide and Rodríguez-Martín 1998, 81–2; Ortner 2003, 351

45 Aufderheide and Rodríguez-Martín 1998, 87; Resnick 2002, 3725, 3728; Walker 2012, 231

46 Merbs 1983, 35, 39; Waldron 1991, 64

47 Walker 2012, 263–4; Stieber and Dormans 2005

48 Resnick 2002, 2258–9

49 Aufderheide and Rodríguez-Martín 1998, 354; Khung et al 2013, 569; Song et al 2011, 1422; D'Ambrosio et al 2008, 589; Resnick 2002, 2258; Ortner 2003, 362

50 Houston 1996, 142; Finlay 1981, 83–4, 100; Rappaport 1989, 69

51 Henderson et al 2013, 282

52 Connell et al 2012, 34; Henderson et al 2013, 285

53 Bucholz and Ward 2012, 79–80; Porter 1991, 143–7; Houston 1996, 169

54 Houston 1996, 129; Picard 2003, 2000; Earle 1994, 162–3

55 Houston 1996, 125–30; Earle 1994,160–1

56 Earle 1994, 114–15

57 Ibid, 116–18, 122; Porter 1991, 31

58 Houston 1996, 126, 154–5; Picard 2003, 96

59 Porter 1991, 147; Picard 2004, 203; Houston 1996, 130

60 Houston 1996, 147; Roberts and Cox 2003, 316–18; Loudon 1986, 607

61 Roberts and Cox 2003, 316; Picard 2003, 94

62 Oswald 1960, 40

63 Pearce 2015, 286; Atkinson and Oswald 1969, 2–3

64 Goodman 1993, 62

65 Atkinson and Oswald 1969, 1–5; Walker and Henderson 2010, 216

66 Ayto 2002, 14; Atkinson and Oswald 1969, 5

67 Walker and Henderson 2010, 219

68 Henderson et al 2013, 293–4

69 Walker and Henderson 2010, 218

70 Roberts and Manchester 2012, 260–1

71 Walker 2012, 275–7; Moore and Buckberry 2016

72 *Brit Med J* 1903, 388

73 Hart and North 1998, 9–12; Boydell 2004, 141

74 Wiener 1896; Moore and Buckberry 2016

75 McRae 1999, 181

76 Walker 2012, 176–7; Picard 2003, 114

77 Houston 1996, 134; Porter 1991, 150; Earle 1994, 99–101

78 Houston 1996, 124; Roberts and Cox 2003, 303–4

79 Cox 2000, 75

80 Rogers 2000, 163; Roberts and Manchester 2012, 132–3

81 Rogers and Waldron 1995, 25

82 Roberts and Manchester 2012, 140–1; Rogers 2000, 169

83 Rogers and Waldron 1995, 32; Roberts and Manchester 2012, 138

84 Rogers and Waldron 1995, 75

85 Ibid, 40; Resnick 2002, 2087

86 Aufderheide and Rodríguez-Martín 1998, 95; Resnick 2002, 1779

87 Aufderheide and Rodríguez-Martín 1998, 97; Resnick 2002, 1477

88 Brickley and Ives 2008, 218; Aufderheide and Rodríguez-Martín 1998, 413–14; Resnick 2002, 1947; Ortner 2003, 435

89 Resnick 2002, 1954–5

90 Roberts and Manchester 2012, 240; Resnick 2002, 1763; Connell et al 2012, 239

91 Aufderheide and Rodriguez-Martín 1998, 419

92 Connell et al 2012, 241; Henderson et al 2013, 209

93 Aufderheide and Rodríguez-Martín 1998, 72; Sekiya et al 1997, 148; Cummings and Rega 2008; Resnick 2002, 4608, 4479

CHAPTER 13

THE URBAN DEVELOPMENT OF THE NEW CHURCHYARD (1739 TO THE PRESENT DAY)

The New Churchyard was never used for burial again after 1739, but the entire ground, including the freehold of the keeper's house-cum-shop (Chapter 3.4, 3.5), remained part of the City of London's estates. This chapter traces the later history of the site, its urban development and changing character between 1739 and the 20th century, beginning with the keeper's house, before moving on to discuss how the burial ground became lost beneath London's streets and buildings.

13.1 'Three Crowns and Dove': no. 1 Brokers Row

Documentary sources

Brokers Row

No. 1 Brokers Row was one shop in a cluster located along a street famous for its manufacturers and dealers in furniture, furnishings and household goods, variously described as 'brokers' (middlemen/salesmen) and 'upholders' (upholsterers). *A general description of all trades*, published in 1747, described brokers as those who 'buy and sell all sorts of household-goods that have been used' and upholders as 'tradesmen for decently or sumptuously furnishing an house ... many of them are great shop-keepers, who have abundance of ready-made goods for sale always by them ... and several of them are undertakers too'. The business of brokers and upholders commonly involved 'appraising', when they would be 'employed in cases of death, executions brought in upon goods, or of stock to be turned over from one person to another'.[1]

A description of Brokers Row can be found in the children's book *A peep into London, for good children*, published in 1809:

> Broker-Row, Moorfields, is a long range of open warehouses, where all kinds of furniture, new and second-hand, may be met with. The brokers are rather celebrated for their importunity to passengers; and those who have no intention to make purchases, may sometimes find it rather troublesome.[2]

A later description of Brokers Row at the beginning of the 19th century can be found in Harvey's *London scenes and London people*:

> … shops without fronts, occupied chiefly by dealers in old furniture … these stores afforded an endless choice of decayed upholstery to poorer purchasers: a broken-down four-poster or a rickety tent bedstead might be secured at almost any price, 'No reasonable offer was refused.' …; and if you did but pause for an instant, you must expect to be dragged into some hideous Babel of frowsy chattels, and made a purchaser in spite of yourself.[3]

The dogged salesmanship of the shopkeepers of Brokers Row appears to have been a long-standing source of amusement for Londoners and inspired numerous jokes and anecdotes.[4]

No. 1 Brokers Row

Between the death of Benjamin Clitherow IV in 1740 and its demolition in *c* 1823, the keeper's house/shop was let to a series of individuals or business partners who traded in furniture, furnishings and household goods – 'brokers' and 'upholders' (above).[5] The property fronted on to what is now Blomfield Street (Fig 2), which from the 17th to the late 18th century was known as 'Moorfields Quarters' or 'Moorfields East'. During this time the property was described relative to its location, for example 'at the Corner of Old Bethlem gate, next Morefield' and 'at the corner of Old Bethlem, Moorfields'. The shop was known by the sign of 'The Dove' (*c* 1740–60) and of the 'Three Crowns and Dove' (1760s to '70s) (below). From 1779 to 1824 'Moorfields East' was named 'Brokers Row' (or 'Broker' or 'Broker's'). Most properties in London were not numbered until the late 18th century and the house/shop was not described as '1' until 1767 or '1, Broker-Row' until 1779.[6] By 1831 the entire street had been renamed 'Blomfield Street' after Charles James Blomfield, Bishop of London 1828–57.[7]

No. 1 can be seen on Horwood's map of 1799 on the north side of the junction of 'Broker Row' and 'Broad Street Place' ('Old Bethlem' on John Rocque's map of 1746: Fig 24).[8] More detailed plans dated 1761, 1767, 1773 and 1793 show that the property was modified and extended several times in the 18th century.[9] The original house covered an area *c* 35m². By *c* 1790, the house was almost six times larger and covered an area of 200m² (6% of the former burial ground). The whole property in *c* 1790, including 'herbage'/yard, covered an area of *c* 700m² (21% of the former burial ground).

Lessees of no. 1 Brokers Row 1740–1824

JONATHAN FARR

Jonathan Farr, an 'upholder' of Brokers Row, Moorfields, began renting the north half of the keeper's house from Benjamin Clitherow IV in 1732. He leased the entire property from the City following Clitherow's death in 1740.[10] He lived at and ran his own business there until his death at the age of 52 in December 1760. Apprentice records indicate Farr's business, an upholder's shop under 'the sign of the Dove', was a thriving one, successful enough for him to take at least four apprentices during these years.[11] He died an 'eminent broker' worth £20,000 (c £3,600,000 today, adjusted for inflation).[12]

SARAH FARR (LATER ABBOT, THEN BENTHAM) (tenant 1761 to c 1776)

Sarah Farr, the only surviving child of Jonathan Farr and his wife Mary, inherited the leasehold of no. 1 Brokers Row in 1761 following the death of her father, and appears to have owned it until at least the mid 1770s. Sarah Farr died on 27 September 1809, aged 76. She married Revd Dr John Abbot, rector of All Saints Colchester (Essex), on 23 March 1755. They had two children: John Farr Abbot (1756–94), who became a barrister, and Charles Abbot (1757–1829), the politician who became 1st Baron Colchester of Colchester in 1817. On 14 October 1766, following the death of Dr John Abbot, Sarah Farr married the attorney and widower Jeremy Bentham, father of Jeremy Bentham, the well-known philosopher, and of Sir Samuel Bentham, the naval architect. The couple lived for a short time at no. 20 Broad Street Buildings while subletting no. 1 Brokers Row.[13]

HENRY HALL

On 25 March 1761, the upholder Henry Hall became Sarah Farr's subtenant at no. 1 Brokers Row.[14] Henry Hall was a former apprentice of Jonathan Farr[15] and after moving to no. 1 Brokers Row combined his shop sign, the 'Three Crowns', with his former master's, the 'Dove'. Surviving advertisements list his sign as the 'Three Crowns and Dove', as does the later of his two surviving trading cards (Fig 168).[16]

Henry Hall's move to no. 1 Brokers Row was successful and his upholder/broker business is well documented by newspaper advertisements dated 1767–72.[17] In 1770 he was appointed the Principal Clerk of the Commissioners of Pavements (later Sewers, Lamps and Pavements), a position which came with a salary of £100 per annum. This appears to have prompted him to cease trading as an upholder in favour of public office following his departure from no. 1 Brokers Row in c 1776.[18]

MARK DAWS AND JAMES BOLTER (sub-subtenants c 1771 to 1778)

Mark Daws (or Dawes) was apprenticed to Henry Hall in 1766 at the age of 14 and became a freeman of the Company of Upholders in 1773.[19] His partner, James Bolter, became a freeman of the Company of Upholders in 1760.[20] In 1771, they began sub-subletting the south half of no. 1 Brokers Row from Henry Hall and trading as 'upholders, cabinet-makers, undertakers and auctioneers'.[21] When Henry Hall left no. 1 Brokers Row in c 1776, Daws and Bolter took over the tenancy of no. 1 and thereafter traded under the sign of the 'Three Crowns and Dove,

Fig 168 The trade card of Henry Hall, upholder, at the 'Three Crowns and Dove'

(Trustees of the British Museum, Banks 28.71)

Moorfields'. Their partnership lasted until 16 March 1778 when it was 'by mutual Consent dissolved, each Partner continuing in the same Business'. James Bolter moved to no. 45 Bishopsgate Street while Mark Daws continued to live and trade at no. 1 Brokers Row.[22]

MARK DAWS/MARK DAWS AND BENJAMIN WILSON (tenants 1778 to c 1790)

Mark Daws traded alone until c 1783 but the following year formed a partnership with Benjamin Wilson.[23] Their partnership was one of five firms located in Brokers Row during the 1780s which exported furniture to the American colonies.[24] In 1787 Daws and Wilson were granted the tenancy of three adjoining gardens/yards, two previously owned by Henry Hall and one tenanted by James Bolter. The partnership ended in c 1790; Mark Daws established himself as an 'upholder and undertaker' at no. 86 Little Tower Hill, while Benjamin Wilson continued at no. 1 Brokers Row.[25] Their separation was probably amicable: following Mark Daws's bankruptcy in 1796, his stock in trade, household furniture and the lease of no. 86 Little Tower Hill were all sold at auction at 'Wilson's furniture-warehouse, Moorfields'.[26]

BENJAMIN AND JOHN WILSON (lessees c 1790 to c 1823)

Benjamin Wilson had transferred the business to his son John Wilson by the time no. 1 Brokers Row was demolished in c 1823. John Wilson continued to trade at nos 2–3 Brokers Row (later nos 1–2 Blomfield Street) after 1824.[27]

Archaeological evidence

The east part of no. 1 Brokers Row was modified in c 1762–7 and the property was largely rebuilt in c 1787–93. The latter included the construction of an extension over the north-east yard and the expansion of the shop frontage across the entire west side of the building (Figs 169, 170).

Fig 169 Structural remains associated with no. 1 Brokers Row revealed during excavation, looking north

THE NEW CHURCHYARD

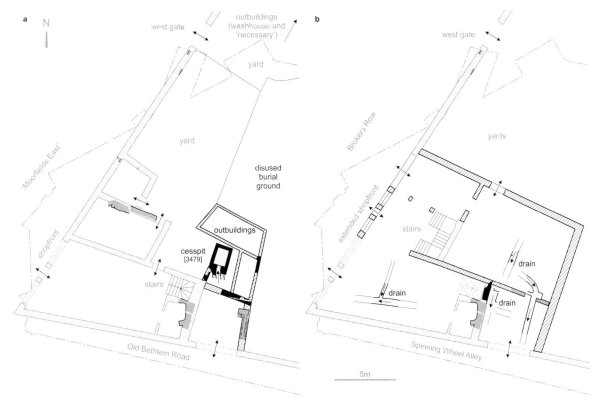

a N

west gate

outbuildings
(washhouse and
'necessary')

yard

b

west gate

Moorfields East'

yard

Brokers Row

disused
burial
ground

yards

shopfront

extended shopfront

outbuildings

stairs

cesspit
[3479]

stairs

drain

stairs

drain

drain

Old Bethlem Road

Spinning Wheel Alley

5m

Fig 170 Phased plan showing the development of no. 1 Brokers Row (formerly the keeper's house), 1762 to 1824: a – modified, *c* 1762–7 (after LMA, COL/CCS/PL/02/142; /089; /177/C); b – rebuilt, *c* 1787–93 (after LMA, COL/CCS/PL/02/270; Fig 176) (scale 1:300)

Brokers Row cesspit assemblages

Two brick-built cesspits, [4765] and [3479] (without brick bases), were found in the south-west corner of the site (Fig 170). Both were built and used in the 18th century and belonged to the keeper's house/no. 1 Brokers Row.

The construction of cesspit [4765] incorporated two reused gravestones: while ledger slab <3053> (Fig 47) is inscribed '1653', undated gravestone <2543> may relate to the burial of Ann/Anne Cock in 1677 or 1712 (Chapter 6.1); the later possible date for <2543> would suggest that this cesspit was not part of the original keeper's house (built *c* 1666–76). This cesspit may have been built by Benjamin Clitherow IV for his own use after he began letting the north half of the property in 1718 (Chapter 3.4), or was perhaps added to the property when it was converted into a shop sometime after 1707 (Chapter 3.5). Cesspit [4765] would have been used by Clitherow while his tenants probably used a 'necessary' and wash house located in the north-west corner of the burial ground. Henry Hall used the 'necessary' and wash house but lost the use of those facilities in 1771 following a dispute with his neighbours/landlords, Jeremy and Sarah Bentham (née Farr). These circumstances almost certainly forced him to build a cesspit, [3479], for his own use in the north-east yard of no. 1 Brokers Row (Figs 170, 171). By 1771 Henry Hall had begun letting the south half of no. 1 Brokers Row to Mark Daws and James Bolter, but continued to live in the north half of the building.[28]

The need for two cesspits would have ended in *c* 1776 when Henry Hall left the property and Daws and Bolter became the sole tenants. Cesspit [4765] appears to have been infilled at this time, and pottery provides a *terminus post quem* (TPQ) of *c* 1775 for this event. The finds recovered from cesspit [3479] show that it continued to be used during the 1780s. The infilling of cesspit [3479] was possibly associated with the construction of the north-east extension of the property, but the precise date of the extension is not known; construction probably occurred after Mark Daws formed his partnership with Benjamin Wilson and the pair became official tenants of the grounds surrounding no. 1 Brokers Row, that is, sometime between 1787 and 1793.[29]

The fills of both cesspits yielded rich assemblages of artefacts and environmental evidence, which are of considerable value as they represent a coherent and evocative collection of rubbish discarded by the known inhabitants of no. 1 Brokers Row. Both well-preserved assemblages represent model 'clearance groups'[30] discarded as part of the abandonment and infilling of both pits. Most items illustrate the everyday life of the inhabitants.

Dating evidence for cesspit [4765] is provided by a small collection of clay pipes (25 bowls, seven stems and three mouthpieces) recovered from fill [4764]; these date mostly to *c* 1730–80, with the latest type made *c* 1740–*c* 1800.[31] In all, 21 pipe bowls recovered from the cesspit are marked with the makers' initials moulded in relief on the heel/spur. Only two have been tentatively identified:

Fig 171 Brokers Row cesspit [3479], looking south

THE NEW CHURCHYARD

'WD', possibly William Delap, recorded in 1730, and 'FS', possibly Francis Stray (Stace, Staw), recorded in 1732 and 1749 in St John Wapping.[32]

Cesspit [4765] also yielded a large quantity of glass (147 fragments, from a minimum of 136 vessels (MNV), total weight 6346g; Fig 172). This consists chiefly of fragments from at least 29 green glass wine bottles (one complete), 17 pharmaceutical phials and 16 table glasses, including wine glasses, a near-

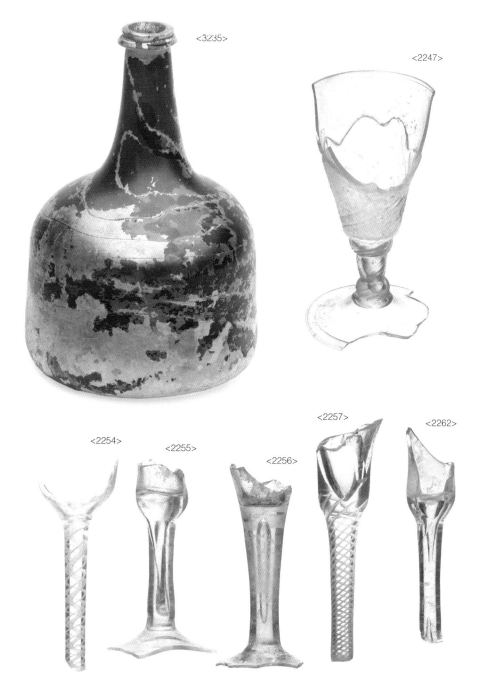

<3235>

<2247>

Fig 172 Selected glassware from Brokers Row cesspit [4765]: complete mallet bottle <3235>; dwarf ale glass <2247>; five wine glass stems <2254>–<2257> and <2262> (scale *c* 1:2)

<2254>

<2255>

<2256>

<2257>

<2262>

complete dwarf or short ale glass and the complete base of a colourless glass tumbler, as well as the base of a jelly glass. All come from fill [4764] and date to *c* 1770–80 at the latest based on the presence of three cylindrical wine bottles with bipartite or double string rims.[33]

In contrast, most of the clay pipes found in cesspit [3479] (six clay pipe bowls, 18 stem fragments and three mouthpieces) can be dated to *c* 1780–*c* 1820.[34] The later types have been marked with their maker's initials, 'II', moulded in relief on the sides of the heel. These initials probably stand for John Jarman, recorded in Bishopsgate 1805–47;[35] if correct, this could place their deposition after 1805. The large collection of glass (257 fragments, 118 MNV, 16,419g) found in cesspit [3479] can be dated to *c* 1770–90 (Fig 173). Green glass wine bottles are the most common form, with at least 65 examples

Fig 173 Selected glassware from Brokers Row cesspit [3479]: six whole cylindrical bottles (left to right) <3210>–<3212>, <3215>, <3218>, <3219> (scale *c* 1:4); three complete 18th-century phials (left to right) <3209>, <3220>, <3221> (scale *c* 1:2)

recorded. There is one squat cylindrical bottle, and all remaining identifiable forms are true cylindrical bottles (eight complete). The cylindrical form developed from the squat cylindrical bottle in the mid 1730s, and continued in production into the 19th century.[36] Fragments of six wine glasses were also recorded, including a form with an opaque twist stem,[37] datable to the 1770s.[38] The complete base of a tumbler and part of a decanter base has also survived. Fragments from at least 21 colourless glass phials were also recorded (20 cylindrical and one hexagonal form), and all typical of the 18th century, as well as 31 fragments of green window glass.

The pottery in both pits is characterised by large numbers of fragments of Chinese porcelain vessels decorated in a number of different styles (fabric codes CHPO BW, CHPO IMARI, CHPO ROSE and CHPO VERTE), with drinking vessels such as tea bowls, saucers, punch and slop/rounded bowls common. Porcelain dishes and plates for serving food and dining are more prevalent in the later cesspit, [3479]. Also present in the fills of both cesspits are English porcelain (ENPO) tea bowls and saucers with patterns and makers' marks that can be attributed to known factories in Worcester (Worcestershire) and in Lowestoft (Suffolk). Creamware (CREA), London-made tin-glazed wares (TGW) and white salt-glazed stonewares (SWSG) are numerous in both cesspits in a similar range of forms, ranging from dinner plates, tea bowls, tankards and coffee cans to ointment and chamber pots, and a rare woman's coach pot (Fig 174).

Finds which might well derive from the commercial activities on the property were identified in later cesspit [3479], which included two copper-alloy furniture handles, one an ornate example with a shell grip (Fig 175). A gold 400 *réis* piece of King João (John) V of Portugal, dated 1721 and minted in

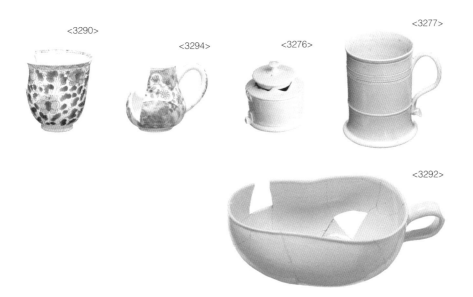

<3290>

<3294>

<3276>

<3277>

<3292>

Fig 174 Selection of ceramics from cesspit [4765]: Chinese porcelain cups <3290> and <3294>; white salt-glazed stoneware mustard pot <3276>, tankard <3277> and coach pot <3292> (scale *c* 1:4)

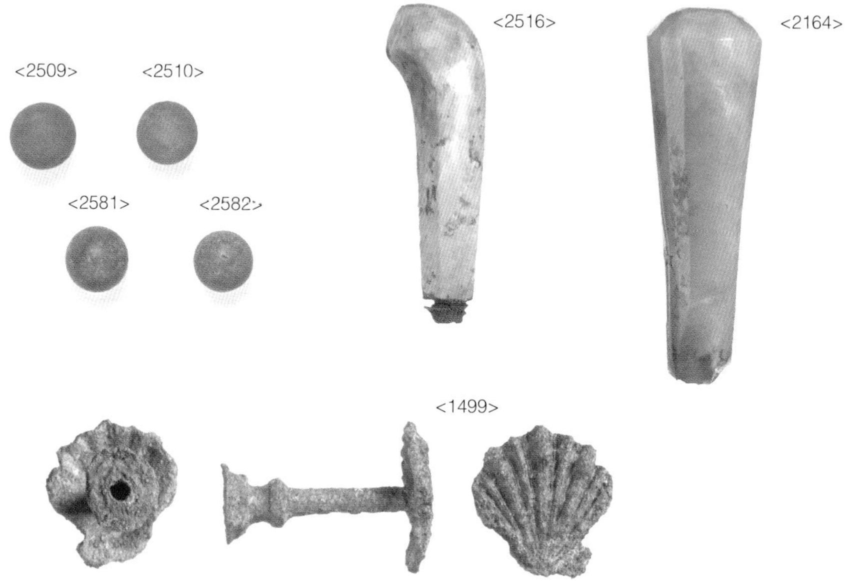

Fig 175 Selection of finds from Brokers Row cesspit [3479]: four stone marbles <2509>, <2510>, <2581>, <2582>; cutlery handles made of shell <2516> and agate <2164>; copper-alloy furniture handle shaped like a shell <1499> (scale *c* 1:2)

Lisbon, could have circulated in early 18th-century London but as a coin not after the 1770s; however, it could have been kept for its gold content.[39]

Notable within this cesspit was a group of 11 cutlery handles, including seven matching 'pistol grip'-shaped handles, all of ivory except for one example in 'mother of pearl' or shell. A large agate handle, a tapering cylinder with a facetted butt, is best paralleled by a carving-knife handle dated to the 17th century.[40] A household's table cutlery could express wealth and social standing, and these may represent discard of unfashionable items by tenants who were moving on; at 19th-century Spitalfields, households took the opportunity to discard in their cesspits anything they did not want to take with them.[41] Other items, such as a group of children's stone marbles and dress accessories like a bone bead and a bone button, are likely to represent accidental loss (Fig 175). Finds from cesspit [4765] tell a similar story albeit on a much smaller scale. This pit produced a knife with an ivory handle, along with an 18th-century copper-alloy shoe buckle, a slate pencil and 38 spherical beads in opaque pale turquoise glass, 30 of them very small (1mm diameter) and doubtless from the same item – a necklace or bracelet, possibly belonging to a child.

As to food remains, cesspit [3479] included the bones of sheep/goat (*Ovis aries/Capra hircus*), cattle (*Bos taurus*), pig (*Sus scrofa*), poultry, game, fish, as well as lobster (*Homarus gammarus*) exoskeleton; a group which represents a diet of generally good quality but does not include 'luxury' items or indicate great affluence. Kitten bones (*Felis catus*) could indicate pets were kept at the property. The two cesspits contained broadly similar evidence of food plant remains as well as a low number of wild plants that may have been growing close by in the disused burial ground which, from 1772, was gardens (below, 13.2). These included common plants of more marginal or waste ground such as dock (*Rumex* spp) and white horehound (*Marrubium vulgare*), but also several wetland plants. Grape (*Vitis vinifera*), fig (*Ficus carica*) and blackberry/raspberry (*Rubus fruticosus/idaeus*) were the dominant food plants; other food remains include cherries (*Prunus avium/cerasus*), blackcurrants/redcurrants/gooseberries (*Ribes* sp), strawberries (*Fragaria vesca*), plums/bullace (*Prunus domestica*), hops (*Humulus lupulus*), hazelnut (*Corylus avellana*), walnut (*Juglans regia*) and mulberries (*Morus nigra*). Also recorded was a seed of medlar (*Mespilus germanica*), quite a rare find archaeologically.[42]

The limited suite of remains recovered from these cesspits may be a result of taphonomic factors, although the possibility of limited access to food plants by their users should also be considered. Fruit remains in general are more likely to survive archaeologically as their seeds are present in the fruit when consumed, while in the case of plants such as vegetables, only the softer leaves and shoots are usually consumed, leading to a common bias in archaeological food plant assemblages towards those plants whose identifiable and hardy parts, such as fruits, and to some degree spices, are utilised in cooking or consumption (all of these cesspit taxa have very hardy seed coats). Many of the food remains present in these samples represent imported foods. Grapes and figs in particular are likely to have been imported from the Continent, probably as dried fruits or in preserves such as jams. The pepper (*Piper nigrum*) from cesspit [4765] is also evidence of importation, in this case from India. Pepper remained a common spice into the 18th and 19th centuries, though the choice of spices available was increasing, with new spices from the New World, such as allspice (*Pimenta dioica*) and chilli (*Capsicum* sp), becoming more popular. Other spices in the assemblage, coriander (*Coriandrum sativum*) and the possible mustard (*Brassica/Sinapis* sp type), could have been grown in the garden (herbage) of the property or in the former burial ground, which are also where the hops in cesspit [4765] may have come from, as well as many of the fruits present in the samples and the garden mignonette (*Reseda odorata*).[43]

13.2 From the New Churchyard to the gardens of Broad Street Buildings (1739–1817)

Documentary sources

The City of London continued the keepership of the New Churchyard after 1739 in order to prevent any 'nuisances, irregularities or indecencies' (Chapter 14.1).[44] For the first few decades following the burial ground's closure, it is clear the City were quick to deal with problems, such as wall repairs and encroachments.[45] After the death of Jonathan Farr in 1760 (above, 13.1), it was discovered that he had made various unauthorised encroachments, including building a stable, a chaise house and an extension to the keeper's house.[46] As a consequence of these modifications, his daughter, Sarah, was forced to accept a new and more expensive lease for the property. Furthermore, at her own expense, she was ordered to demolish all yard structures, level the whole ground, sow grass seed (to be grazed or mowed regularly) and keep the ground in general good order.[47] Sarah Farr evidently did not comply fully or swiftly enough: in 1761, the City threatened to sue her and during 1765–6 she was forced to defend herself to retain the keepership.[48] A plan of all encroachments within the burial ground was ordered in 1767 and Sarah Farr was replaced as keeper in 1768.[49] This action was unjust, since most of these encroachments, if not all, had already been attributed by the City to 'Benjamin Clitherow' in 1739 (Chapter 3.4), something neither she nor the current Common Council seems to have been aware of in the 1760s.[50]

The City was more lenient when there was potential for financial gain. In January 1762, they ordered that all monuments and tombstones should be taken down and laid flat. The following March they agreed to lease three plots of land on the west side of the ground for building, so long as the contractor, at his own expense, 'dig a grave in some convenient part of the burying ground and deposit therein all such bones and leaden and other coffins as should be found in a decent manner under the directions of a person to be appointed by the Committee'.[51] The owners and residents of Broad Street Buildings petitioned against the sale, chiefly because it would spoil their views of Moorfields and devalue their leases. Their petition was unsuccessful and by December the sale had been completed.[52] However, before building work could begin, Henry Hall, newly resident at no. 1 Brokers Row, raised concerns it would disturb the burial ground. He enlisted the support of the church of St Botolph Bishopsgate and objected according to the terms of the original grants of the City, which strictly forbade the use of the land for any other 'use or purpose whatsoever', and together they insisted that 'any manner destructive of it [the burial ground] is illegal and unjustifiable'. This time the City felt they had no alternative but to cancel the building lease.[53]

During the 1760s, the residents of Broad Street Buildings began gaining access to the burial ground by unauthorised doorways and ladders placed against windows, and were accused of 'hanging their linen to dry and permitting their children to commit damage to the trees'.[54] These activities were at first unsanctioned but subsequent petitions for yards or gardens revealed to the City an alternative opportunity for revenue. The City authorised the conversion of the burial ground into gardens in May 1771, so long as 'proper restrictions be inserted to prevent any nuisances or annoyances being committed and adequate and reasonable rents in proportion to their respective quantitys to be granted be reserved and made payable to the City'. The first gardens were demarcated by oak fences in March 1772. Garden plots

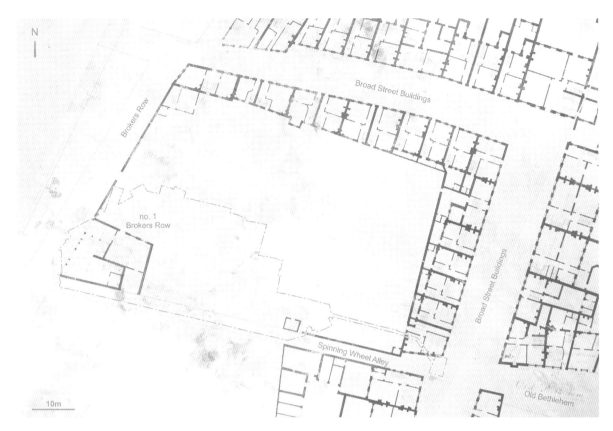

Fig 176 Plan of the City of London's estate in Broad Street Buildings, 1793, with the areas of archaeological investigation superimposed (outlined in grey) (scale 1:850) (LMA, COL/CCS/PL/02/270)

can be seen marked on plans and maps of the 1770s–90s (Fig 176).[55] During these years Broad Street Buildings was inhabited by many notable residents. Ephraim d'Aguilar, second Baron d'Aguilar and son of the Court Jew to Empress Maria Theresa of Austria, lived in luxurious style with 24 servants at no. 29 during the 1770s. He was succeeded at the address by Dennis De Berdt Jr, a merchant and former colonial agent for New Jersey (USA). David Ricardo, the famous political economist, was born at no. 36 on 18 April 1772. Benjamin D'Israeli, the Italian-born merchant and financier (and grandfather of Benjamin Disraeli, the Prime Minister), leased no. 26 from 1791. D'Israeli's house was described as 'a genteel dwelling house, desirably situate … with two rooms on each floor, with suitable offices, a large garden area, and arched cellaring'.[56]

Archaeological evidence

Levelling and landscaping was associated with the establishment of the gardens of Broad Street Buildings in the 1770s. This was represented archaeologically by a horizon of disturbance and deposits found truncating and sealing the burial ground; this was dated after *c* 1750 by pottery. As with finds from the burial ground soils, the building materials, glass and other finds from these post-burial ground deposits are rather mixed in date and many were residual. For example, a number of clay pipes were found (49 bowls), all coming from contexts dating to the early to mid 18th century. Almost half the pipes (23 bowls) were made *c* 1730–60, and date from the latest use and closure of the burial ground; the remainder date back as far as the 1640s, although most were made after *c* 1680. These are ordinary London-made pipes without any kind of decoration, and only three have been marked by their makers, none of whom can be identified.

13.3 Liverpool Street (1817 to the present day)

Documentary evidence

A new road between Bishopsgate and Moorfields was proposed to the City by the Governors of Bethlem Hospital in 1817, widening the existing roads in both their respective estates: Spinning Wheel Alley and (the road) Old Bethlem. At Spinning Wheel Alley the new road would cover approximately the south third of the gardens of Broad Street Buildings (and the burial ground below) and require the demolition of the garden's south boundary wall, as well as no. 1 Brokers Row and no. 36 Broad Street Buildings. Since the scheme was advantageous to trade, the shop owners of Spinning Wheel Alley supported it. However, the residents of Broad Street Buildings petitioned against the works because it was 'inconvenient'. Moreover, they believed it would devalue their properties and that the new road would become a route for cattle out of Smithfield market. A directory of 1817 recorded Broad Street Buildings as a street '93 and a half yards long with 45 houses', inhabited by merchants, a tea dealer, a grocer, a corn factor, two surgeons, three solicitors, and the Prussian consulate and vice-consulate. Notably, no objections were raised by residents that it would disturb the burial ground. The City concluded the scheme could be 'executed without a Faculty' (diocesan permission) because of the 'great benefit to the public' and, since it was 'nearly a Century since interments were made', it would 'not offend public decorum or give umbrage to the feelings of relatives of the deceased'.[57]

The scheme was approved in July 1823.[58] The construction of a new sewer and south boundary wall the following year unearthed the 'mouldering bones of several hundred human bodies' which were 'scattered about in the most indecent manner' before being 'partly re-interred in one pit … and partly carted away'.[59] The new road, Liverpool Street, named after Lord Liverpool, the Prime Minister, can be seen on maps dated 1824–62 (eg Fig 177).[60] Liverpool Street and the new garden boundary wall are shown incidentally in an early 19th-century engraving of St Mary Roman Catholic church.[61]

Fig 177 Liverpool Street and garden boundary wall [1642]/[1648] built in 1824, with wall [1632]: left – the wall overlain on a redrawing of Secondary's plan, Bishopsgate Without, dated March 1858 (LMA, COL/ WD/03/007) (scale 1:1000); right – the garden boundary wall can be seen running diagonally across the centre of the excavation area, cutting burial vault [58] (Fig 48), looking west

The majority of the former burial ground still lay beneath the gardens of Broad Street Buildings. Charles Roach Smith (1807–90), the antiquarian who lived at no. 5 Liverpool Street (c 1843–55),[62] made the following observation:

> on the other side of the street was a long dead wall, which separated the street from a long piece of garden-ground which faced some high houses standing, probably, on the site of Bedlam [burial ground] …When my man buried in it a deceased favourite cat, he said he came upon the remains of human skeletons.[63]

There were other reminders of the site's former use; for example, the Whit Sunday tradition of giving bread to the poor was continued, distributed each year from a table set up in the gardens of no. 20 Broad Street Buildings, and in 1844 the commemorative inscription stone was replaced.[64] However, by the mid 19th century the burial ground was mostly forgotten by Londoners; the gravestones were no longer visible, the gate had been bricked up and the boundary walls were hidden beneath billposters.[65] In the early 1840s further unauthorised encroachments included the construction of several sheds, a plumber's shop and a china shop.[66]

In 1863 Broad Street Buildings and its gardens were sold by the City to the North London Railway (NLR) Company for £25,400, together with several properties in Rose and Crown Court and Liverpool Street.[67] These houses were among 643 properties thought to have been demolished to make way for the new railway.[68] The site was 'invaded by the Railway companies' in 1863 for the construction of Broad Street Station, the main terminus of the new NLR line, and an 'immense quantity of human bones were disinterred'.[69] The bones filled 72 crates and were buried by the NLR in the City of London Cemetery, Manor Park, on 21 November 1865.[70] The remains were 'collected with the greatest of care and are guarded with most jealous vigilance; dozens of boxes have been made for their reinterment. Some of the workmen suspected of tampering with them have been summarily dismissed.'[71] However, the railway company attracted many complaints about their treatment of the burials: 'How vain in these railroad days are dedications of land to special purposes. Church and churchyard alike vanish before the pickaxe and shovel of the navvy';[72] and 'Of all of the outrages committed by the railway companies, nothing, I think, has surpassed the breaking up of this ground.'[73] Contemporary accounts also confirm that the excavations were not 'examined by London antiquaries'.[74] Archaeological excavations in both 1985–6 and 2011–15 revealed that large amounts of disarticulated human bone had been reinterred in the foundations of Broad Street Station.

Nevertheless, Broad Street Station opened with great acclaim on 8 November 1865,[75] and accommodated suburban services until it was closed in 1986 following decades of diminishing use. The burial ground was repeatedly disturbed by further works associated with the station, including the excavation of the Queen Victoria Tunnel as part of the extension of the Metropolitan Railway in 1873–4; the replacing of the original entrance

Fig 178 (left) View looking east down Liverpool Street towards the station, with the facade of Broad Street Station left, *c* 1890–*c* 1900, and (right) the area on the OS 1873 map with the areas of archaeological investigation superimposed (outlined in grey) (scale 1:1250)
(Historic England Archive, CC97/00742)

THE NEW CHURCHYARD

canopy with a new south wall and two stairways in 1890–1 (Fig 178); and the construction of a new entrance building and the Central London Railway ticket hall in 1911–12.[76] It was noted that, during works in 1890, one passenger was approached by a newspaper boy who pointed to a large heap of earth and bones and asked him if he wanted a 'skeleton's head'.[77]

The unexpected discovery of dense human remains during the construction of a subterranean public toilet at the west end of Liverpool Street was reported in the *London Daily News* in July 1903:

> For days human bones were broken by the pick and human skulls thrown out by the spade before the significance of the matter was properly realised. There are now lying in the night-watchman's hut, amid the whirl and traffic of Liverpool Street, thirty-six bags of human bones ... 'The earth,' said one of the workmen, 'is a soft as indiarubber; it is full of bones.'[78]

The works were paused before being allowed to continue under the supervision of the Medical Officer of Health and a licence issued by the Home Secretary. However, the remains were already 'collected into heaps' before any osteological or archaeological observations could be made *in situ*. The total remains disinterred were reportedly 'ten cases of bones, representing the remains of ... 200 to 300 bodies'.[79]

Archaeological excavations have shown the burial ground was further truncated by the installation of 20th-century utilities (pipes and cables). One of the most unusual 20th-century causes of disturbance was from a bomb crater, made during a Zeppelin bombing raid in September 1915.[80]

Archaeological evidence

The south boundary wall of the gardens of Broad Street Buildings, built in 1824, survived as a truncated 0.6m wide corbelled brick footing with piers, [1642]/[1648], which was traced for a distance of 33.7m. As described in contemporary accounts, the wall had cut a swathe through the top of the burial ground and had also partially robbed out vault [58] (Fig 48) which lay along its path. Wall [1642]/[1648] was associated with another wall, [1632] (Fig 177), which historic maps suggest was part of a contemporary outbuilding or small mews house located in the gardens of Broad Street Buildings.

An east–west aligned, egg-shaped brick culvert or sewer was found at the site. It was part of a larger network (built 1824, renewed *c* 1843) and was truncated by the construction of the Queen Victoria Tunnel in 1874–5.[81] This sewer was replaced by another built *c* 1900 which remained active until 2014. Both sewers had been constructed with a combination of tunnelling and intermittent shafts, each of which truncated the entire archaeological sequence.

The footprint of Broad Street Station covered *c* 1200m² or 36% of the New Churchyard and its construction in the 1860s is likely to have disinterred *c* 9000 burials. The front wall of the station's approach road (left on Fig 178) was found to the north of the site and consisted of the foundations of a brick wall built with arches and corbelled piers of brick and concrete.

The construction cut of the underground public toilet built in 1903 truncated *c* 74m² of the burial ground and is likely to have disinterred *c* 500 burials. The structure's construction footprint truncated all archaeology down to the early Roman deposits, 5m below modern ground level. The Zeppelin bomb crater of 1915 was evidenced by an area in the south-west corner of the site characterised by redeposited soil and extensive truncation of burial ground deposits.

Notes to Chapter 13

1 Waller 1747, 14–15, 40–1, 214–15

2 Taylor and Taylor 1809, 11–12

3 Harvey 1863, 35–6

4 *Leicester Chron*, 1 Sept 1815, 3 col B – anecdote about a 20 guineas wager between two gentlemen about walking the length of the street without being harassed by shop keepers; *MLAI* 1826, 112 – a joke called 'Quick and the Broker' about a man being was 'seized upon by a barker, who pulled him into the shop'

5 Summarised here, detailed in Hartle et al in prep

6 Heal 1988, xi; GL, *Kent's* 1767; 1779

7 Elmes 1831, 68

8 Rocque 1746; Horwood 1813

9 LMA, COL/CCS/PL/02/177/C; /142; COL/PL/01/076/D/006; COL/CCS/PL/02/270

10 GRO, Births and Christenings, 1705 and 1708, FHL film no. 1279476; LMA, COL/CHD/FR/02/0518-0519; TNA, IR 1/10, 15; LMA, CLC/525/MS11316/072, 14; *Daily Post*, 23 Apr 1729, 2 col A; *ROLLCO*; LMA, COL/CC/CLC/01/023 (J 31), 25v–6v and 37v–8

11 TNA, IR 1/13, 119; LMA, COL/CHD/FR/02/0614-0619; TNA, IR 1/15, 74; IR 1/16, 3; LMA, COL/CHD/FR/02/0708-0-713; TNA, IR 1/17, 224; LMA, COL/CHD/FR/02/0786-0-793

12 TNA, PROB 11/863/414; *LEPBC*, 29 Dec 1760, 7 col A; *Bank of England*

13 TNA, PROB 11/863/414; LMA, P69/BOT4/A/003/MS04517/001; Pine 1972, 80; TNA, PROB 11/1503/325; *Read's*, 29 Mar 1755, 3 col A; Skaife 1870, 313; Schofield 2006, 136; LMA, COL/CC/CLC/01/052 (J 60), 90–2, 178–80; COL/PL/01/076/D/006; Pine 1972, 80

14 LMA, COL/CC/CLC/01/055 (J 63), 187–8

15 TNA, IR 1/17, 224; LMA, COL/CHD/FR/02/0786-0-793

16 *GNDA*, 15 Apr 1765, 4 col C; 10 Sept 1765, 4 col C; 5 Apr 1766, 3 col B; 14 July 1766, 3 col B; BM, Banks 28.71

17 *GNDA*, 6 May 1767, 3 col B; GL, *Kent's* 1767; *London directory* 1772

18 *LEP*, 16 Nov 1770, 3 col A; LMA, COL/CC/CLC/01/055 (J 63), 187; Chamberlain 1770, 409; *Gentlemen's Mag* 1809

19 LMA, P93/DUN/004; TNA, IR 1/17, 224; Walton 1973, 57

20 Walton 1973, 53

21 *GNDA*, 29 Feb 1776, 4 col A; LMA, CLC/525/MS11316/216, 17; COL/CC/CLC/01/055 (J 63), 187b

22 *London Gazette*, 21–24 Mar 1778, 2 col B; *Daily Advertiser*, 5 Oct 1778, 4 col B; *Public Advertiser*, 4 July 1781, 4 col C; *Daily Advertiser*, 14 July 1778, 3 col A

23 *GNDA*, 14 Mar 1781, 4 col D; LMA, COL/CHD/FR/02/1094-110; CLC/525/MS11316/252, 19; GL, *Bailey's* 1784

24 Fleming 1997

25 GL, *Universal* 1791; *Kent's* 1794; LMA, CLC/B/192/F/001/MS1936/369/571502; GL, *Kent's* 1792; 1794; LMA, CLC/B/192/F/001/MS11936/398/618541; COL/CCS/PL/02/270; GL, *Post Office* 1814; *Johnstone's* 1817

26 *Daily Advertiser*, 4 Mar 1796, 4 col B

27 LMA, CLC/525/MS11316/333, 16; /375, 17; /378, 17

28 LMA, COL/CC/CLC/01/054 (J 62), 73–7, 126–7; /055 (J 63), 50–2; 187–8; COL/CCS/PL/02/089; COL/PL/01/076/D/006

29 LMA, COL/CC/CLC/01/071 (J 79), 4v, 58v, 191v, including a plan dated 1793 showing the built extension

30 Pearce 2000, 145

31 The majority are type 12 in Oswald's (1975) simplified general typology (*c* 1730–80); two bowls of type 11 (*c* 1730–60); one of type 10 (*c* 1700–30). There are three examples of type 26 in Atkinson and Oswald's (1969) London typology (*c* 1740–*c* 1800).

32 Oswald 1975, 135, 145; Hammond 2004, 22

33 Dumbrell 1992, 92

34 The five pipes are type 28 in Atkinson and Oswald's London typology (1969), and the earlier pipe is Oswald's (1975) type 12.

35 Oswald 1975, 139

36 Dumbrell 1992, 100

37 Cf Bickerton 1971, nos 816–17, 824

38 Ibid, nos 444, 470–1

39 Kent 2005, 73–5

40 Brown 2001, 38

41 Harward et al 2015, 262

42 Stewart 2016

43 Ibid

44 LMA, COL/CC/CLC/
01/054 (J 62), 73–7

45 LMA, COL/CC/CLC/
01/025 (J 33), 41v and
88–v; /050 (J 58), 210

46 LMA, COL/CCS/PL/
02/177/C

47 LMA, COL/CC/CLC/
01/045 (J 53), 37v–8v;
/046 (J 54), 11v–12r;
/050 (J 58), 3–5v, 73–7

48 LMA, COL/CC/CLC/
01/045 (J 53), 146; /049
(J 57), 185v–6v; /050 (J
58), 3–5v

49 LMA, COL/CC/CLC/
01/051 (J 59), 250–1;
/052 (J 60), 90–2v and
178–80;
COL/CCS/PL/02/142

50 LMA, COL/CC/CLC/
01/023 (J 31), 25v–6v,
37v–8

51 LMA, COL/CC/CLC/
01/046 (J 54), 11v–12,
24v, 26v–7v, 155–6,
197, 201–v, 207;
COL/CCS/PL/02/149

52 LMA, COL/CC/CLC/
01/046 (J 54), 36–v, 98–
100, 155–6, 213–16v

53 LMA, COL/CC/CLC/
01/046 (J 54), 213–16v;
/047 (J 55), 247, 265v–
6v; P69/BOT4/B/001/
MS04526/004, 7 Dec
1762; COL/CA/01/01/

018 (Rep 16), 492

54 LMA, COL/CCS/PL/
02/142; COL/CC/
CLC/01/025 (J 33), 88–
v; /052 (J 60), 90–2v;
/051 (J 59), 39v

55 Horwood's (1813) map
of London, 1799; LMA,
COL/CC/CLC/01/055
(J 63), 32–3 and 64–5v;
/056 (J 64), 12v–13;
COL/PL/01/076/D/006;
COL/CCS/PL/02/270

56 GL, Kent's 1794; LMA,
CLC/525/MS11316/219,
21; Picciotto 1875, 97–
8; Chesnutt and Laurens
2003, 200; LMA, COL/
CC/CLC/01/069 (J 77),
128–v; Weatherall 1976,
7; OPA, 13 Mar 1797, 4
col D

57 LMA, COL/CC/CLC/
01/106 (J 114), 91v–2,
111v–12, 122v–3, 131,
150v–1, 193–v, 198v–
200v, 239–42v; /107 (J
115), 38v–40; GL,
Johnstone's guide 1817

58 LMA, COL/CC/CLC/
01/107 (J 115), 65v–6,
111v–12, 117v–18

59 Brayley 1828, 9; Urban
1830, 15; LMA, CLA/
006/PL/01/013, 26, 42;
COL/CC/CLC/01/107
(J 115), 141

60 Greenwood and
Greenwood 1827; LMA,

COL/WD/03/007,
Secondary's plan,
Bishopsgate Without,
dated Mar 1858;
COL/SVD/PL/05/0288
/A; Stanford 1862;
Hibbert et al 2008, 490

61 Engraving by Thomas
Hosmer, 1827, with
the garden wall right
forground: LMA,
COLLAGE cat no.
q8020108

62 LMA, CLC/525/
MS11316/426, 6; /445, 8

63 Tuke 1882, 50

64 Malcolm 1802, 348;
GBC 1822, 73; LMA,
COL/CC/CLC/01/132
(J 136), 276

65 J 1863

66 Greenwood and
Greenwood 1827; LMA,
COL/WD/03/007,
ward map 1855–8;
COL/SVD/PL/05/
0288/A; COL/CC/
CLC/01/128 (J 132),
308, 416–17, 437; /130
(J 134), 588, 661, 784,
810; /131 (J 135), 12v–
14, 72v, 96–v, 119v–20,
148v–9, 205, 245–v,
296v

67 PA, HL/PO/PB/1/1861/
24&25V1n240; LMA,
COL/CC/CLC/ 01/154
(J 155)

68 Davies and Grant 1983,
39–40; Thorne 1978,

16–19; Timbs 1868;
Hunting et al 1991, 48–
9; Thorne 1978, 18–19

69 Engineer, 8 Sept 1865,
148; Quisquis 1863, 85

70 Hunting et al 1991, 11

71 Engineer, 8 Sept 1865,
148

72 J 1863, 85

73 Jaydee 1890, 234

74 Sleet 1890, 335;
Engineer, 8 Sept 1865,
148

75 Shown in eg engraving
of Broad Street Station,
1865: LMA, COLLAGE
cat no. q2322771;
Thorne 1978, 18;
Hunting et al 1991, 50–1

76 Builder, 31 Jan 1874, 86;
TNA, RAIL 410/1098;
Sleet 1890, 335;
O'Donoghue 1914, 142

77 Sleet 1890, 335

78 LDN, 27 July 1903, 3
col G

79 Wellcome Library 1904;
Macdonell 1904; 1906

80 LMA, COLLAGE
record nos 37011 and
37021

81 LMA, CLA/006/PL/01/
013, 26, 42; COL/CC/
CLC/01/107 (J 115),
141; CLA/006/AD/10/
022, 142–4

CHAPTER 14

BIOGRAPHICAL APPENDICES

14.1 Keepers of the New Churchyard 1569–1771

Name	Dates	Circumstances of appointment
Thomas Randall, mercer[1]	29 July 1569 to Aug 1585	appointed by his father-in-law, Sir Thomas Rowe (Lord Mayor 1568-9)
Mary Randall[2]	29 July 1569 to c Aug 1585	wife of Thomas Randall, appointed by her father, Sir Thomas Rowe
John Martyn, grocer[3]	c Aug 1585 to 21 Oct 1585	unknown: the keepership appears to have been transferred to him unofficially, possibly by Mary Randall after the death of Thomas Randall in Aug 1585
John Savage, servant to the Swordbearer[4]	21 Oct 1585 to ?1633	appointed by the Court of Aldermen to replace John Martyn
Alexander Wimbish[5] of St Mary Abchurch	26 Sept 1633 to 14 Mar 1635/6	appointed by the Court of Aldermen in unknown circumstances
Benjamin Clitherow I, vintner[6]	29 Mar 1636 to c Feb 1651/2	appointed by the Court of Aldermen at the request of his kinsman (probably cousin), Sir Christopher Clitherow (Lord Mayor 1635-6), following the death of Alexander Wimbish
Benjamin Clitherow II, vintner and draper[7]	12 Feb 1651/2 to c 1664-5	appointed by the Court of Aldermen following the death of his father, Benjamin Clitherow I
Benjamin Clitherow III, draper (turner)[8]	c 1664-5 to c Mar 1705/6	appointed by the Court of Aldermen in unknown circumstances during the mayoralty of Sir John Lawrence (Oct 1664-Oct 1665). The keepership appears to have been transferred from his father, Benjamin Clitherow II, who lived until 1678. Benjamin Clitherow III built the keeper's house (later no. 1 Brokers Row)
Benjamin Clitherow IV, draper (turner)[9]	14 Mar 1705/6 to Nov 1740	appointed by the Court of Aldermen following the death of his father, Benjamin Clitherow III, with the agreement to pay £161 to the Lord Mayor for his admittance. He became the leaseholder of the keeper's house and its herbage
Jonathan Farr, draper (broker and upholder)[10]	14 Jan 1740/1 to Dec 1760	appointed by the Court of Aldermen upon the recommendation of Sir Humphrey Parsons (Lord Mayor 1740) following the death of Benjamin Clitherow IV, with the agreement to pay £140 to the Lord Mayor for his admittance. He became the leaseholder of the keeper's house and herbage
Sarah Abbot (née Farr, and later Bentham)[11]	Jan 1761 to 16 Nov 1768	seemingly inherited the keepership following the death of her father, Jonathan Farr. She became the primary leaseholder of the keeper's house and herbage by inheritance

Name	Dates	Circumstances of appointment
Henry Hall, draper (broker and upholder)[12]	16 Nov 1768 to May 1771	between 1761 and *c* 1776 he sublet the keeper's house and herbage (then no. 1 Brokers Row) from Sarah Bentham (née Farr). He was appointed keeper by the Court of Aldermen after they dismissed from the position Sarah Bentham. The keepership was ended by the City in 1771 because it was considered unnecessary following the conversion of the remaining grounds to gardens/yards

[1] TNA, PROB 11/68/494; LMA, COL/CA/01/01/018 (Rep 16), 492, 494v
[2] TNA, PROB 11/95/133; LMA, COL/CA/01/01/018 (Rep 16), 492
[3] TNA, PROB 11/78/248; LMA, P69/MGT4/A/001/MS05287, item 1; COL/CA/01/01/023 (Rep 21), 228
[4] LMA, COL/CA/01/01/023 (Rep 21), 228
[5] LMA, COL/CA/01/01/051 (Rep 47), 381; P69/MRY1/A/001/MS07666, 62, 63v, 64v, 66, 67v, 68, 139; Dale 1931, 105-6
[6] LMA, COL/CA/01/01/ 054 (Rep 50), 168v; Dale 1931, 225-9
[7] LMA, COL/CA/01/01/065 (Rep 61), 61
[8] LMA, COL/CC/CLC/01/002 (J 10), 72v; COL/CA/01/01/114 (Rep 110), 102v-3
[9] LMA, COL/CA/01/01/114 (Rep 110), 102v-3
[10] LMA, COL/CA/01/01/149 (Rep 145), 43-4, 48, 74-6; COL/CC/CLC/01/025 (J 33), 41v, 88-v
[11] LMA, COL/CC/CLC/01/049 (J 57), 185v-6v; /050 (J 58), 3-5v
[12] LMA, COL/CC/CLC/01/052 (J 60), 178-80

14.2 Gravestones linked to documentary sources

Context/acc no.	Inscription	Documentary sources	Location	Stone type	Form
[494]/<198> and <201>	HE(RE) LIETH Y^e Bod(y) ... Mrs ELIZABETH BRO ... Late (wife) (o)f M^r (Robe)[rt] BROW(NE) D(YED) Y^e ... 27th OF JULY ...	the parish register of the parish of St Bride's Fleet Street records the death of Elizabeth Browne on 27 July 1726: 'Elizabeth Browne Milk Yard [address] Fever [cause of death]'¹ The same parish registers record the christening of Mary Browne, daughter of Robert and Elizabeth Browne of Court Shoe Lane, on 21 Feb 1695/6²	reused in brick structure [494]	Purbeck limestone	headstone
[894]/<3052>	IOHN BA ... BAIL FA(C) ... (AG)ED 23 WEEKS DYED Y^e 13th OF APRILL 1664	the burial register of the parish of St Bride's Fleet Street records the death of John Barden on 13 Apr 1664: 'John Barden a young child in whitefryors [address]'³	reused in structure [494]	?Corallian limestone	?family grave marker
[1135]/<522>	SARAH LONG WIFE OF S(E)ETO^N LONG WHO (D)YED [M]AY TH(E) 2 ... 1672 AIG(I)[ED] ... ... WITH ...	the burial register of the parish of St Giles Cripplegate records her death on 2 June 1672: 'Sarah, wife of Sefton Long stopped stomach [cause of death] Bethlem [burial location]' Her daughter, Sarah, was buried at the ground on 27 Dec 1660: 'Sara daughter of Sefton Long founder feaver [cause of death] Bethlem [burial location]'⁴	reused in brick and masonry wall [1115]/ [1135]	Portland stone	headstone
[1645]/<664>	MARY (G)ODFREE [D](Y)ED THE 2TH [D](A)Y OF SEPT 1665	the burial register of the parish of St Giles Cripplegate records her death on 2 Sept 1665: 'Mary dau[ghter] of [blank] Godfrey, deceased plague [cause of death] Above [burial location]'⁵	reused at the base of wall [1639]	?Corallian limestone	headstone
[+]/<2267>	HERE LYe THY BODY OF JANe ATTeRBVRY WIFe OF WILLIAM ATTeRBVRY WHO DYeD Y 21 OF MAY 1686 IN Y 36 YEARE (O)F...	the burial register of the parish of St Giles Cripplegate records the death of Jane Atterbury on 21 May 1686: 'L [address: the Lordship part of the parish] Jane w[ife] of William Smith Brewer [occupation(s)] Feaver [cause of death] Below [burial location: ground surrounding the church]'⁶ The possible grandson of William and Jane Atterbury was a labourer in the parish of St James Liberty, Westminster. He was tried for theft in 1732, convicted and deported to America in 1733⁷	residual within modern rubble	Purbeck limestone	headstone

Context/acc no.	Inscription	Documentary sources	Location	Stone type	Form
		Jane Atterbury's husband, William, lived until 1730 and his death is recorded in the parish register for St Giles Cripplegate, on 30 Aug of that year: 'L [address] William Atterbery Smith [occupation] Age [cause of death]'[8]			
[4765]/<2543>	H(ere) … interred th(e) … Ann Cock … (in the) …	the burial register of the parish of St Stephen Coleman Street records her death 14 Oct 1677: 'Anne Cock buried in Bedlam'[9] Or Ann Cock of Walmer, Kent, who was admitted to Bethlem Hospital on 7 June 1712 and died there on 24 Dec 1712.[10] She was buried two days later and, although the location was not recorded,[11] Bethlem Hospital used the New Churchyard extensively in this period, and as a non-Londoner she is perhaps more likely to have been sent there rather than a parish ground	reused within 18th-century cesspit [4765]	Portland stone	headstone
[4765]/<3053>	… (b)ands … are … WYKES WAS … STONE THE 7th … (ANN)O D(OMI)NI 1653	the burial register for the parish of St Anne Blackfriars records her death on 7 Jan 1653/4: 'Katherin Wikes Lodger at Mr Louler'[12]	reused in cesspit [4765]	Blue Lias	ledger slab

Inscription: round brackets denote legible, but partially missing or damaged, characters, square brackets conjectured characters, an ellipsis an unknown number of missing character(s)/word(s)/numeral(s)

1   LMA, P69/BRI/A/014/MS06550
2   LMA, P69/BRI/A/006/MS06548
3   LMA, P69/BRI/A/005/MS06540, item 1
4   LMA, P69/GIS/A/002/MS06419, items 6, 7
5   LMA, P69/GIS/A/002/MS06419, item 6
6   LMA, P69/GIS/A/002/MS06419, item 10
7   *Old Bailey Proc*, Feb 1732/3, William Atterbury (t17330221-41); LMA, MJ/SP/T/02/058; Winter and Mitchell 1984
8   LMA, P69/GIS/A/002/MS06419, item 16
9   LMA, P69/STE1/A/002/MS04449/002
10 BRH, ARA-03, 217
11 LMA, P69/STE1/A/008/MS04451/001; P69/STE1/A/009/MS04455
12 LMA, P69/ANN/A/008/MS04510, item 1

14.3 Bodysnatching in early 18th-century London

Date	Involved	Place	Circumstances	Fee	Punishment
1 May 1717[1]	Joseph Bowen, grave-digger, and John Kersey, surgeon of Oxford	'Bethlem churchyard' New Churchyard, St Botolph Bishopsgate	the body of William Childers was removed after interment and carried, concealed in and disguised as a hamper of wine, to the Rose Inn, Smithfield. The body was to be sold to John Kersey, a surgeon, and transported to Oxford for dissection. The crime was discovered after suspicions were raised at the Rose Inn	one guinea to be paid to Joseph Bowen by John Kersey	Joseph Bowen was fined 40s and whipped, or 'severely lashed', from Newgate to Smithfield Bars. There is no record that John Kersey was ever prosecuted
Feb 1717/18[2]	William Dod, grave-digger, and an unnamed soldier	'St Saviours, Southwark'	the body of a woman was removed after interment and taken in a hamper to a house in St Thomas's parish to be sold to a surgeon. Further investigation and exhumations revealed that 25 children and 13 adults were missing from their graves in the churchyard	30s for a child under the age of two and a guinea for each adult. The soldier was paid 5s 'porteridge' for helping carry the body	William Dod was fined 6 nobles (£2) and sentenced to two years imprisonment. The soldier gave 'evidence of the king'
Oct 1719[3]	unnamed 'parish nurse', from Newteners Lane	'Newteners Lane, St Giles'	the body of a 'nurse child' (adopted or fostered child) was sold to a surgeon for dissection. The body was replaced in the coffin with sand before burial. The theft was discovered when the coffin was carried to the church but opened due to the suspicious weight	unknown	the unnamed 'parish nurse' was committed to New Prison (Clerkenwell)
3 Feb 1722/3[4]	Samuel Buxton, grave-digger	'St Giles-in-the-Fields'	a body of an infant child was taken from a pauper's grave to sell to a surgeon. The crime was discovered when the body was being transported hidden in a basket. The vestry of the parish offered a reward of £10 for the discovery of his accomplice or accomplices. After the arrest, a 'prodigious mob' gathered in the churchyard to enquire 'if their deceased relatives were still in their graves'. The 'Justice was obliged to read the Proclamation against Riots to disperse them'	unknown	Samuel Buxton was fined 6s 8d and sentenced to six months hard labour in Clerkenwell Bridewell prison. He died under imprisonment on 19 Mar 1722/3, and had requested his burial be 20 foot deep (c 6m), for fear of reprisals
28 May 1725[5]	unknown	'Pancras churchyard' St Pancras old church	the body of the notorious criminal Jonathan Wild was exhumed after his burial, following his execution at Tyburn. The empty coffin was found later near Kentish Town	unknown	no prosecution

Date	Involved	Place	Circumstances	Fee	Punishment
9 Apr 1736[6]	Thomas Jenkins, grave-digger, and John Brown, servant to Caesar Hawkins (1711–86), surgeon to St George's Hospital	'Stepney parish churchyard' St Dunstan and All Saints, Stepney	the bodies of three women and one man were removed from their coffins. The crime was discovered when one body, hidden in a basket, was taken to John Brown, the servant to a surgeon in Pall Mall Court in the parish of St James, Westminster	unknown	Thomas Jenkins was whipped three times round Stepney churchyard. There is no record that either John Brown or Caesar Hawkins were ever prosecuted

[1]   *Evening Post*, 7 May 1717, 3 col B; *Weekly Packet*, 4–11 May 1717, 3 col A; *WJSP*, 1 June 1717, 3 col A; *Old Bailey Proc*, May 1717, Joseph Bowen (t17170501-35)

[2]   *OWJ*, 8–15 Feb 1717/18, 5 col A; 15–22 Feb 1717/18, 4 col A; 29 Mar–5 Apr 1718, 4 col A

[3]   *WJSP*, 10 Oct 1719, 4 col B

[4]   *Evening Post*, 5–7 Feb 1722/3, 2 col A; *Daily Post*, 8 Feb 1722/3, 1 col B; *WJSP*, 9 Feb 1722/3, 4 col A; *Compleat*, 9 Mar 1722/3, 5 col A; *WJSP*, 23 Mar 1722/3, 4 col A; *London lives [Samuel Buxton]*

[5]   *Daily Post*, 31 May 1725, 1 col A; Bailey 1991, 27–8; Emery and Wooldridge 2011, 153

[6]   *LDPGA*, 12 Apr 1736, 1 col C; LMA, MJ/SP/1736/06/58

BIBLIOGRAPHY

Manuscript sources

Bethlem Royal Hospital Archives, Bethlem Museum of the Mind, London (BRH)

ARA   General admissions registers 1683–1973, available online @ http://archives.museumofthemind.org.uk/ARA.htm

BCB   Minutes of the Court of Governors 1559–1971 (gaps), available online @ http://archives.museumofthemind.org.uk/BCB.htm

Bodleian Libraries, Oxford

JOHN JOHNSON COLLECTION OF PRINTED EPHEMERA

Trade card 28   'Willm. Boyce. Coffinsmaker. At Ye Whight Hart & Coffin', *c* 1680

British Library, London (BL)

E.166.(10)   title page of *London's lamentation; or, a fit admonishment for city and countrey…*, 1641

CRACE COLLECTION OF MAPS OF LONDON

1.31   *The cittie of London*, attributed to Augustine Ryther, engraving, 1633

1.34   *The newest & exactest mapp of the most famous cities London and Westminster with their suburbs; and the manner of their street …* by Thomas Porter, engraving, 1654

British Museum, London (BM)

DEPARTMENT OF PRINTS AND DRAWINGS

Banks 28.71   trade card of Henry Hall, cabinet-maker

Heal 124.38   trade card for William Grinly, undertaker, *c* 1730

Heal 124.6   trade card for William Boyce, undertaker, *c* 1680

General Register Office, London (GRO)

Births and Christenings, England   Select Births and Christenings, Provo, Utah, USA, available online @ www.ancestry.co.uk as England, Select Births and Christenings, 1538–1975

Guildhall Library, City of London (GL)

TRADE DIRECTORIES

Bailey's   *Bailey's Brit directory* 1784, 1 edn

Johnstone's guide   *Johnstone's London commercial guide and street directory* 1817

Johnstone's   Johnstone's London directory 1817

Kent's   Kent's directory 1740, 7 edn; 1767, 34 edn; 1779, 47 edn; 1792, 60 edn; 1794, 62 edn

London directory   London directory (Lowndes) 1772, 3 edn

Post Office   Post Office annu directory (Critchett and Wood) 1814, 15 edn

Universal   Universal Brit directory (London) 1791, 1 edn, 3 issue

Harvard College Library, Map Collection, Cambridge, MA

Hollis ID 010209490   'London surveyed, or, a new map of the cities of London and Westminster and the borough of Southwark', by John Bowles, 1742

Historic England, National Monuments Records (formerly English Heritage) (HE, NMR)

CC97/00742   stereo exterior view of Broad Street Station, listed as *c* 1870–1900 but probably *c* 1890–*c* 1900

London Metropolitan Archives (formerly Greater London Record Office) (LMA)

ARCHDEACONRY COURT OF LONDON (FORMERLY HELD BY GUILDHALL LIBRARY, MANUSCRIPTS SECTION): WILLS

MS 9052/5/50   James Tassard, 1618

CITY OF LONDON COMMISSIONERS OF SEWERS

CLA/006/AD/10/022   City sewers record book, 1840

CLA/006/PL/01/013   plan book, *c* 1770s–1840s

CHAMBERLAIN'S DEPARTMENT: ACCOUNTS

COL/CHD/CT/01   /001, 1633–5; /002, 1636–8; /003, 1639–40; /004, 1641–3; /005, 1644–6; /006, 1647–9; /007, 1650–1; /008, 1652–5; /009, 1656–8; /010, 1659–61

CLAYTON AND MORRIS (SCRIVENERS, MERCHANT BANKERS AND ESTATE AGENTS)

CLC/B/050/A/003/MS01993   lease by George Villiers, Duke of Buckingham, Mary, Duchess of Buckingham, Thomas Sprat, Bishop of Rochester, and Robert Clayton to Francis Jenks, Citizen and Fishmonger, of a piece of ground called Buckingham Court, Westminster, adjoining Wallingford House

COLLAGE (CITY OF LONDON LIBRARY AND ART GALLERY ELECTRONIC; PART OF THE FORMER GUILDHALL LIBRARY'S PRINT ROOM COLLECTION):

Main Print Collection

q2322771   North London Railway's City terminus, Broad Street Station, Liverpool Street, 1865

q8019625   side view of St Mary Roman Catholic church and adjacent buildings, *c* 1825 q8020108   view of St Mary Roman Catholic church, Moorfields and surrounding area, with figures, 1827

Miles and Kaye Collection

37011   view of 6–12 Broad Street Place, Blomfield Street, 1915

37021   bomb damage at the corner of Liverpool Street and Blomfield Street, 1915

COMPTROLLER AND CITY SOLICITOR

COL/CCS/SO/01/04/016   Jenks, Francis and Sarah v Halford, Richard and Anne

COURT OF ALDERMEN: REPERTORIES

COL/CA/01/01   /008 (Rep 8), 1528–33; /018 (Rep 16), 1566–70; /019 (Rep 17), 1570–3; /022 (Rep 20), 1579–83; /023 (Rep 21), 1583–8; /029 (Rep 26/2), 1604–5; /030 (Rep 27), 1605–7; /031 (Rep 28), 1607–9; /032 (Rep 29), 1609–10; /033 (Rep 30), 1610–12; /036 (Rep 32), 1614–16; /037 (Rep 33), 1616–18; /038 (Rep 34), 1618–20; /043 (Rep 39), 1624–5; /044 (Rep 40), 1625–6; /051 (Rep 47), 1632–3; /054 (Rep 50), 1635–6; /057 (Rep 53), 1638–9; /064 (Rep 60), 1649–50; /065 (Rep 61), 1650–1; /066 (Rep 62), 1651–3; /067 (Rep 63), 1653–5; /068 (Rep 64), 1655–6; /069 (Rep 65), 1656–7; /073 (Rep 69), 1662–4; /074 (Rep 70), 1664–5; /078 (Rep 74), 1668–9; /096 (Rep 92), 1686–7; /103 (Rep 99), 1694–5; /111 (Rep 107), 1702–3; /112 (Rep 108), 1703–4; /114 (Rep 110), 1705–6; /118 (Rep 114), 1709–10; /129 (Rep 125), 1720–1; /147 (Rep 143), 1738–9; /149 (Rep 145), 1740–1

COURT OF COMMON COUNCIL: JOURNALS

COL/CC/01/01   /019 (JORS/19), 1567–72

COL/CC/CLC/01   /002 (J 10), 1702–4; /003 (J 11), 1705–8; /023 (J 31), 1739; /025 (J 33), 1741–2; /045 (J 53), 1761; /046 (J 54), 1762; /047 (J 55), 1763; /049 (J 57), 1765; /050 (J 58), 1766; /051 (J 59), 1767; /052 (J 60), 1768; /054 (J 62), 1770; /055 (J 63), 1771; /056 (J 64), 1772; /069 (J 77), 1785–6; /071 (J 79), 1787–8; /076 (J 84), 1792–3; /106 (J 114), 1822–3; /107 (J 115), 1823–4; /128 (J 132), 1840; /130 (J 134), 1842; /131 (J 135), 1843; /132 (J 136), 1844–5; /154 (J 155), 1863

COURT OF ORPHANS

CLA/002/01/004   common serjeant's book vol 4, 1678–93

CLA/002/02/01/2153   orphans' inventories, Jenkes, Francis, citizen and fishmonger, 4 February 1686/7

FREEDOM ADMISSION PAPERS

COL/CHD/FR/02   1681–1925 (gaps)

LAND TAX COMMISSIONERS ASSESSMENT BOOKS

CLC/525/MS11316/001–378   1692–1825 (gaps)

LETTER BOOKS OF THE CITY OF LONDON

COL/AD/01/009 (I)   1400–22

COL/AD/01/020 (V)   1566–70

MAPS AND PLANS

COL/CCS/PL/02/089   Bethlehem burying ground 'Mr Hall's Plan', c 1771

COL/CCS/PL/02/142   Bethlem burying ground: 'A Plan of Old Bethlem Burying Ground', 1767

COL/CCS/PL/02/149   Moorfields: plan for letting three lots east of Moorfields behind a gated wall and north of the ground and building late belonging to Mr Farr and west of the churchyard, 1762

COL/CCS/PL/02/177/C   Moorfields: 'A Plan of Mr Jonathan Farr's house in Moorfields [east of Moorfields] and of the new tenements adjoining thereto which new tenements are erected upon ground not contained in his lease, 1761'

COL/CCS/PL/02/270   'Plan of the City's Estate in Broad Street Buildings', Old Bethlem, New Broad Street, Spinning Wheel Alley and the Brokers Row, c 1793

COL/PL/01/076/D/006   plan of Bethlem burial ground, 1773

COL/SVD/PL/05/0288/A   'Property to the north of Liverpool Street between Blomfield Street and (Sun Street Passage) Showing also property in Rose and Crown Court', c 1841

COL/WD/03/007   large-scale ward plans by S Angall and M Meredith, 1855–8

SC/GL/STP/006/004/016   Platte Grondt der Verbrande Stadt London (map of burnt London), by Marcus Willemsz Doornick, 1666

MIDDLESEX SESSIONS OF THE PEACE

MJ/SP/1736/06/58   Thomas Jenkins, gravedigger, confession, 1736

MJ/SP/T/02/058   transportation of 51 people to America for seven years, 1733

PARISH RECORDS

P69/ALH2/A/002/MS05032   All Hallows Bread Street, City of London, register general, 1618–54

P69/ALH3/A/001/MS05022   All Hallows Honey Lane, City of London, register general, 1538–1697

P69/ALH7/A/002/MS05161   All Hallows the Great, City of London, composite register, 1720–65

P69/AND1/A/009/MS04507   St Andrew by the Wardrobe, City of London, register of burials, 1558–1812

P69/ANN/A/008/MS04510   St Ann Blackfriars, City of London, register of burials, 1566–1849

P69/AUG/A/001/MS08872   St Augustine Watling Street, City of London, register of baptisms, marriages and burials, 1559–1750

P69/BAT1/A/001/MS04374   St Bartholomew by the Exchange, City of London, register of baptisms, marriages and burials, 1558–1737

P69/BAT3/A/010/MS06780   St Bartholomew the Great, City of London, register of burials, 1678–1716, and Nonconformist births, 1695–1710

P69/BOT2/A/015/MS09222   St Botolph Aldgate, City of London, register of burials, 1558–1665

P69/BOT4/A/001   St Botolph Bishopsgate, City of London, composite registers, 1558–1734

P69/BOT4/A/002/MS04516   St Botolph Bishopsgate, City of London, composite registers, 1677/8–1717

P69/BOT4/A/003/MS04517　St Botolph Bishopsgate, City of London, composite registers, 1717–79

P69/BOT4/B/001/MS04526/004　St Botolph Bishopsgate, City of London, vestry minute books, 1754–87

P69/BRI/A/005/MS06540　St Bride Fleet Street, City of London, register of baptisms, marriages and burials, 1653–1736

P69/BRI/A/006/MS06548　St Bride Fleet Street, City of London, draft register of baptisms, marriages and burials, 1695–1706

P69/BRI/A/014/MS06550　St Bride Fleet Street, City of London, draft register of burials, 1709–26

P69/DIO/A/001/MS017602　St Dionis Backchurch, City of London, register of burials, 1538–1737

P69/DUN2/A/018/MS10350　St Dunstan in the West, City of London, register of burials, 1709–39

P69/GIS/A/002/MS06419　St Giles Cripplegate, City of London, register general, 1561–1763

P69/GIS/B/001/MS06048/001　St Giles Cripplegate, City of London, vestry minute books, 1659–1808

P69/JS2/A/002/MS09140　St James Garlickhithe, City of London, register general, 1535–1693

P69/JS2/A/003/MS09139　St James Garlickhithe, City of London, register general, 1622–66

P69/KAT2/A/001/MS07889/001　St Katherine Cree, City of London, register of baptisms, marriages and burials, 1663–93

P69/LAW1/A/002/MS06975　St Lawrence Jewry, City of London, register of baptisms, marriages and burials, 1538–1715

P69/MGT4/A/001/MS05287　St Margaret Pattens, City of London, registers of baptisms 1559–1812, marriages 1559–1754, banns 1653–7 and burials 1558–1812

P69/MIC1/A/003/MS06988　St Michael Bassishaw, City of London, register of baptisms, marriages and burials, 1661/2–1812

P69/MIC2/A/003/MS04063　St Michael Cornhill, City of London, registers of baptisms, marriages and burials, 1653–1783

P69/MIC5/A/003/MS05144　St Michael Paternoster Royal, City of London, composite register, 1675–1743

P69/MIC6/A/001/MS09147　St Michael Queenhithe, City of London, register general, 1653–1710

P69/MIL2/A/001/MS04429　St Mildred Poultry, City of London, composite registers, 1538–1812

P69/MRY1/A/001/MS07666　St Mary Abchurch, City of London, register of baptisms, marriages and burials, 1558–1736

P69/NIC1/A/001/MS17621　St Nicholas Acon, City of London, registers of baptisms, marriages and burials, 1539–1812

P69/NIC2/A/002/MS05686   St Nicholas Cole Abbey, City of London, register of baptisms, marriages and burials, 1650/1–95 (joint with St Nicholas Olave from *c* 1670)

P69/PET1/A/001/MS08820   St Peter Cornhill, City of London, register of baptisms and marriages, 1538–1774, and burials 1539–1774

P69/PET3/A/001/MS05721   St Peter Paul's Wharf, City of London, registers of baptisms, marriages and burials, 1607–77

P69/SEP/B/001/MS03149/002   St Sepulchre Holborn, City of London, vestry minute books, 1662–83

P69/STE1/A/002/MS04449   St Stephen Coleman Street, City of London, register of baptisms, marriages and burials, 1558–1717

P69/STE1/A/008/MS04451   St Stephen Coleman Street, City of London, register of burials, 1689–1812

P69/STE1/A/009/MS04455   St Stephen Coleman Street, City of London, rough register of deaths, 1711–23

P76/LUK/001   St Luke Finsbury Old Street, composite register, 1733–42

P82/AND/A/010/MS06673   St Andrew Holborn, Holborn Circus, City of London, register of burials, 1556–1755

P82/GEO1/056   St George Bloomsbury, Camden, register of burials, 1730–61

P91/LEN/A/001/MS07493   St Leonard Shoreditch, Hackney, register of baptisms and marriages, 1558–1653

P91/LEN/A/002/MS07494   St Leonard Shoreditch, Hackney, register of baptisms, marriages and burials, 1653–77

P91/LEN/A/003/MS07495   St Leonard Shoreditch, Hackney, register of baptisms, 1676–94, and marriages, 1677–98

P91/LEN/A/008/MS07498   St Leonard Shoreditch, Hackney, register of marriages, 1698–1822

P91/LEN/A/012/MS07499   St Leonard Shoreditch, Hackney, register of burials, 1674–1858

P92/GEO/141   St George the Martyr Borough High Street, Southwark, composite register, 1665–85

P92/GEO/142   St George the Martyr Borough High Street, Southwark, composite register, 1685–1714

P93/DUN/004   St Dunstan and All Saints, Tower Hamlets, register of baptisms, 1745/6–70

P93/PAU3/033   St Paul Shadwell, Tower Hamlets, register of burials, 1680–1707

ROYAL AND SUN ALLIANCE INSURANCE GROUP

CLC/B/192/Γ/001   policy registers, 1710–1863

Museum of London (MOL)

LIBRARY

Image id 138416/acc no. A6855   wool, silk and linen corset, 17th century

Image no. 2120/acc no. 42.39/142   plague broadsheet comprising nine scenes relating to the 1665 plague, by John Dunstall, 1666

Image no. 3262   'The anatomist overtaken by the watch in carry'ng off Miss W—ts in a hamper', by William Austin, 1773

SOCIAL HISTORY COLLECTION

Object no. 7192   limestone sign with thick paint layers, Broad Street Buildings, 1737

National Portrait Gallery, London (NPG)

1847   Lodwicke Muggleton, by unknown artist, plaster cast of death mask, 1697

4939   Lodowicke Muggleton, by or after William Wood, oil on canvas, c 1674

D26853   Henry Jessey (Jacie), after unknown artist, line engraving, c 1664

D30093   William Walwyn, by Robert White, line engraving, late 17th century

Parliamentary Archives, UK (PA)

HL/PO/PB/1/1861/24&25V1n240   North London Railway Company (City Branch) Act, 1861

The National Archives, London (TNA)

APPRENTICES AND MASTERS

IR 1   apprenticeship books, 1710–1811

CHANCERY

C 3/449/55   Six Clerks Office: pleadings, series II, Elizabeth I to Interregnum – Jenkes v Clarke

C 7/182/68   Six Clerks Office: pleadings before 1714 – Jenkes v Halford

C 11/20/12   Six Clerks Office: pleadings 1714–58 – Greystock v Bickley

C 142/718/144   inquisitions post mortem, series II, and other inquisitions, Henry VII to Charles I: Jenks, Herbert (lunatic), Worcester, 1660–1

COMMISSION AND INQUISITION OF LUNACY

C 211/13/J1   Herbert Jenks, of Worcestershire: commission and inquisition of lunacy, into his state of mind and his property, 1660

LONDON AND NORTH WESTERN RAILWAY COMPANY

RAIL 410/1098   alterations to Broad Street Station, 1891

PREROGATIVE COURT OF CANTERBURY: WILLS

(date is date proved)

PROB 11/30/502   Henry Clythero, 8 Aug 1545

PROB 11/52/418   Sir Thomas Rowe, 31 Oct 1570

PROB 11/65/13   Dame Mary Rowe, 18 Jan 1582/3

PROB 11/68/494   Thomas Randall, 16 Aug 1585

PROB 11/71/136   Peter Simmonds, 9 Sept 1587

PROB 11/78/248   John Martyn, 5 Nov 1591

PROB 11/95/24   Thomas Eaton, 25 Jan 1599/1600

PROB 11/95/133   Mary Randall, 28 Feb 1599/1600

PROB 11/109/212   John Bradshawe, 6 Mar 1606/7

PROB 11/111/163   Henry Cletherowe, 22 Feb 1607/8

PROB 11/152/739   Lawrence Anthony, 27 Nov 1627

PROB 11/187/398   Sir Christopher Clythero, 22 Nov 1641

PROB 11/240/148   Katherine Wykes, 4 Feb 1653/4

PROB 11/260/370   John Quince, 5 Dec 1656

PROB 11/301/450   Joane Clarke, 10 Sept 1660

PROB 11/357/197   Benjamin Clitheroe, 5 July 1678

PROB 11/359/132   Robert Overton, 29 Jan 1678/9

PROB 11/365/71   William Walwyn, 14 Jan 1680/1

PROB 11/365/319   Christopher Thomlinson, 26 Feb 1680/1

PROB 11/369/460   Richard Halford, 8 Apr 1682

PROB 11/381/636   Alexander Delamaine, 30 Dec 1685

PROB 11/393/401   Anne Delamaine, 22 Dec 1688

PROB 11/423/122   Elizabeth Jenkes, 10 Nov 1694

PROB 11/447/393   Sarah Jenkes, 5 Oct 1698

PROB 11/506/349   Sarah Williams, 21 Feb 1708/9

PROB 11/541/129   Frances Williams, 19 July 1714

PROB 11/570/451   Jacob Hubbard, 22 Oct 1719

PROB 11/588/159   Roger Williams, 19 Nov 1722

PROB 11/863/414   Jonathan Farr, 17 Mar 1761

PROB 11/1503/325   Sarah Bentham, 9 Oct 1809

Victoria and Albert Museum, Department of Design, Prints and Drawings, London (V&A)

E997 to E1011–1903 (M 63e) 1783   trade catalogue of Tuesby and Cooper of Southwark

Wellcome Library, London (WL)

Bills of Mortality   1657–1859

L0014659/ICV no. 10723   'Two men placing the shrouded corpse which they have just disinterred into a sack while Death, as a nightwatchman holding a lantern, grabs one of the grave-robbers from behind', by Thomas Rowlandson, watercolour, 1775

Printed and other secondary works

14CHRONO   14CHRONO marine reservoir database, http://calib.org/marine/ (last accessed 11 April 2017)

Achinstein, S, 2003   *Literature and dissent in Milton's England*, Cambridge

Achtman, M, Zurth, K, Morelli, G, Torrea, G, Guiyoule, A, and Carniel, E, 1999   *Yersinia pestis*, the cause of plague, is a recently emerged clone of *Yersinia pseudotuberculosis*, *Proc Nat Acad Sci United States America* 96, 14043–8

Acosta, F L, Quinones-Hinojosa, A, Schmidt, M H, and Weinstein, P R, 2003   Diagnosis and management of sacral Tarlov cysts, *Neurosurg Focus* 15, 1–7

Adams, R, 1971   *The parish clerks of London*, London

Agas, R, *c* 1562   'Civitas Londinum', reproduced in Margary 1981

Allen, C, 1687   *Curious observations in that difficult part of chirurgery relating to the teeth: shewing, how to preserve the teeth and gums from all accidents they are subject to*, London

Allgaier, R L, Vallabh, K, and Lahri, S, 2012   Scurvy: a difficult diagnosis with a simple cure, *African J Emergency Med* 2, 20–3

Anderson, C A, Curzon, M E J, Van Loveren, C, Tatsi, C, and Duggal, M S, 2009   Sucrose and dental caries: a review of the evidence, *Obesity Rev* 10 (suppl 1), 41–54

Anderson, T, 1991   Human bone studies, in *Canterbury's archaeology: 15th annual report 1990–1*, 56–61, Canterbury (consulted at https://issuu.com/alfalfa2/docs/canterburys_archaeology_1990_1991, last accessed 16 January 2017)

Anderson, T, 2004   Dental treatment in medieval England, *Brit Dent J* 197, 419–25

Andrews, J, Briggs, A, Porter, R, Tucker, P, and Waddington, K, 1997   *The history of Bethlem*, London

Anselment, R, 2009   Freke, John (1652–1717), in *Oxford dictionary of national biography* (consulted at http://www.oxforddnb.com/view/article/67401, last accessed 12 July 2016)

Arneborg, J, Heinemeier, J, Lynnerup, N, Nielsen, H L, Rud, N, and Sveinbjörnsdóttir, Á E, 1999   Change of diet of the Greenland Vikings determined from stable carbon isotope analysis and 14C dating of their bones, *Radiocarbon* 41(2), 157–68

Arnold, C, 2007   *Necropolis: London and its dead*, London

Arrizabalaga, J, Henderson, J, and French, R, 1997   *The great pox: the French disease in renaissance Europe*, New Haven, CT

Atkinson, D R, and Oswald, A, 1969   London clay tobacco pipes, reprinted from *J Brit Archaeol Ass* 3 ser 32, 1–67, London (consulted at http://www.reenactor.ru/ARH PDF/Atkinson_Oswald_London_pipes.pdf, last accessed 16 January 2017)

Aufderheide, A C, and Rodríguez-Martín, C, 1998   *The Cambridge encyclopaedia of human palaeopathology*, Cambridge

Austen, R A, and Smith, W D, 1990   Private tooth decay as public economic virtue: the slave-sugar triangle, consumerism and European industrialisation, *Social Sci Hist* 14, 95–115

Ayto, E G, 2002 (1987)   *Clay tobacco pipes*, 3 edn, Princes Risborough

Baddeley, J, 1888   *An account of the church and parish of St Giles: Without Cripplegate, in the*

City of London. Compiled from various old authorities, including the churchwardens' accounts, and the vestry minute books of the parish, London

Baggs, A, Baugh, G, Cox, D, McFall, J, and Stamper, P, 1998   Eaton-under-Heywood, in *A history of the county of Shropshire: Vol 10* (ed C Currie), 320–33, London (consulted at http://www.british-history.ac.uk/vch/salop/vol10/pp320-333, last accessed 13 July 2016)

Bailey, B, 1991   *The resurrection men*, London

Balmford, J, 1603   *A short dialogue concerning the plagues infection*, London

Bank of England   Bank of England: inflation calculator [£20,000 in the year 1760], http://www.bankofengland.co.uk/education/Pages/resources/inflationtools/calculator/default.aspx (last accessed 16 January 2017)

Bannerman, W B (ed), 1912   *The registers of St Mildred, Bread Street, and of St Margaret Moses, Friday Street, London*, Harleian Soc 42, London

Bannerman, W B (ed), 1913   *The registers of All Hallows Bread Street and of St John the Evangelist, Friday Street, London*, Harleian Soc 43, London

Bannerman, W B (ed), 1914   *The registers of St Mary le Bowe, Cheapside, All Hallows, Honey Lane, and of St Pancras, Soper Lane, London*, Harleian Soc 44, London

Bannister, A, 1923   *Diocese of Hereford, institutions, 1539–1900*, Hereford

Barnes, E, 1994   *Developmental defects of the axial skeleton in palaeopathology*, Niwot

Baron, J H, 2009   Sailors' scurvy before and after James Lind: a reassessment, *Nutr Rev* 67, 315–32

Barron, C M, and Davies, M (eds), 2007   *The religious houses of London and Middlesex*, London

Bashford, L, and Pollard, T, 1998   'In the burying place' – the excavation of a Quaker burial ground, in Cox (ed) 1998, 154–66

Bayliss, A, Shepherd Popescu, E, Beavan-Atherfield, N, Bronk Ramsey, C, Cook, G T, and Locker, A, 2004   The potential significance of dietary offsets for the interpretation of radiocarbon dates: an archaeologically significant example from medieval Norwich, *J Archaeol Sci* 431, 563–75

Beier, A L, and Finlay, R (eds), 1986   *London 1500–1700: the making of a metropolis*, London

Bell, G W, Joshi, B B, and Macleod, R I, 2011   Maxillary sinus disease: diagnosis and treatment, *Brit Dent J* 210, 113–18

Benjamin, B, and Graunt, J, 1964   John Graunt's 'observations', *J Inst Actuaries* 90, 1–61

Betts, I M, and Weinstein, R I, 2010   *Tin-glazed tiles from London*, London

Bevan, M, and Baker, P, 2008   Brooke, Humphrey (bap 1618, d 1693), in *Oxford dictionary of national biography* (consulted at http://www.oxforddnb.com/view/article/3548, last accessed 12 July 2016)

Bickerton, L M, 1971   *An illustrated guide to 18th-century English drinking glasses*, London

Blatt, S, Redmond, B G, Cassman, V, and Sciulli, P, 2011   Dirty teeth and ancient trade: evidence of cotton fibres in human dental calculus from Late Woodland, Ohio, *Int J Osteoarchaeol* 21, 669–78

Blondiaux, J, and Charlier, P, 2008   Palaeocytology in skeletal remains: microscopic examination of putrefaction fluid deposits and dental calculus of skeletal remains from French archaeological sites, *Int J Osteoarchaeol* 18, 1–10

Boldsen, J L, Milner, G R, Konigsberg, L W, and Wood, J W, 2002 Transition analysis: a new method for estimating age from skeletons, in *Palaeodemography: age distributions from skeletal samples* (eds R D Hoppa and J W Vaupel), 73–106, Cambridge

Bos, K I, Schuenemann, V J, Golding, G B, Burbano, H A, Waglechner, N, Coombes, B K, McPhee, J B, DeWitte, S N, Myer, M, Schmedes, S, Wood, J, Earn, D J D, Herring, D A, Bauer, P, Poinar, H N, and Krause, J, 2011 A draft genome of *Yersinia pestis* from victims of the Black Death, *Nature* 478, 506–10

Boston, C, 2008 Rycote chapel: coffins in the crypt, Thame, Oxfordshire: archaeological watching brief report, Oxford Archaeol, http://archaeologydataservice.ac.uk/archiveDS/archiveDownload?t=arch-841-1/dissemination/pdf/oxfordar1-51599_1.pdf (last accessed 8 January 2017)

Boucher, A, Craddock-Bennett, L, and Daly, T, 2015 *Death in the close: a medieval mystery*, Edinburgh

Boulton, J, 2014 Traffic in corpses: interment, burial fees and vital registration in Georgian London, *Continuity Change* 29, 181–208

Boulton, J, and Schwarz, L, 2010 Yet another inquiry into the trustworthiness of the 18th-century London's Bills of Mortality, *Local Popul Stud* 85, 28–45

Boyd, P, 1934 *Roll of the Drapers' Company of London*, Croydon

Boydell, C, 2004 Fashioning identities: gender, class and the self, *J Contempor Hist* 39, 137–46

Brain, C, and Pearce, J, in prep 17th-century glass-working waste from Liverpool Street, London

Braun and Hogenberg, 1572 'A map of London, Westminster and Southwark', reproduced in Margary 1981

Bray, W, [1901] *The diary of John Evelyn Esq FRS*, London

Brayley, E, 1828 *Londiniana: or, reminiscences of the British metropolis: Vol 3*, London

Brears, P, 1985 *Food and cooking in 17th-century Britain: history and recipes*, London

Brewer, B J, Wubben, R C, and Carrera, G F, 1986 Excessive retroversion of the glenoid cavity: a cause of non-traumatic posterior instability of the shoulder, *J Bone Joint Surg American* 68, 724–31

Brickley, M, and Ives, R, 2008 *The bioarchaeology of metabolic disease*, Oxford

Brickley, M, Buteux, S, Adams, J, and Cherrington, R, 2006 *St Martin's uncovered: investigations in the churchyard of St Martin's-in-the-Bull Ring, Birmingham 2001*, Oxford

Brickley, M, Mays, S, and Ives, R, 2010 Evaluation and interpretation of residual rickets deformities in adults, *Int J Osteoarchaeol* 20, 54–66

Brimblecombe, P, 1987 *The big smoke: a history of air pollution in London since medieval times*, London

Brit Med J, 1903 The evil effects of the corset, *Brit Med J* 1, 388

Bronk Ramsey, C, 1995 Radiocarbon calibration and analysis of stratigraphy: the OxCal program, *Radiocarbon* 36, 425–30

Bronk Ramsey, C, 1998 Probability and dating, *Radiocarbon* 40, 461–74

Bronk Ramsey, C, 2001 Development of the radiocarbon calibration program OxCal,

Radiocarbon 43, 355–63

Bronk Ramsey, C, 2009a   Bayesian analysis of radiocarbon dates, *Radiocarbon* 51, 37–60

Bronk Ramsey, C, 2009b   Dealing with outliers and offsets in radiocarbon dating, *Radiocarbon* 51, 1023–45

Brown, P (ed), 2001   *British cutlery: an illustrated history of design, evolution and use*, London

Browne, A, Cary, H, and Hackman, A, 1843   *Catalogus Librorum Impressorum Bibliothecae Bodleianae in Academia Oxoniensi*, Oxford

Bucholz, R O, and Ward, P J, 2012   *London: a social and cultural history 1550–1750*, Cambridge

Buck, C E, Cavanagh, W G, and Litton, C D, 1996   *Bayesian approach to interpreting archaeological data*, Chichester

Buckley, F, 1915   *Old London glasshouses*, London

Buikstra, J E, and Ubelaker, D H (eds), 1994   *Standards for data collection from human skeletal remains: proceedings of a seminar at the Field Museum of Natural History*, Arkansas Archaeol Survey Res Ser 44, Fayetteville

Builder, 1874   [building works associated with Broad Street Station], *Builder*, 31 January, 86

Burrage, C, 1912   *The early English Dissenters: Vol 1*, Cambridge

Burt, N M, Semple, D, Waterhouse, K, and Lovell, N C, 2013   *Identification and interpretation of joint disease in palaeopathology and forensic anthropology*, Springfield

Caffey, J, 1952   On some late skeletal changes in chronic infantile cortical hyperostosis, *Radiol* 59, 5

Cal E Mayor R   *Calendar of early mayor's Court rolls of then City of London 1298–1307* (ed A H Thomas), 2015, reprint of original 1924 edn, Cambridge

Cal L Book   *Calendar of letter books (A, E–I) of the City of London* (ed R R Sharpe), 1899, 1903–5, 1907, 1909, London

Cal Plea and Mem R   *Calendar of plea and memoranda rolls preserved among the archives of the Corporation of the City of London, 1364–81* (ed A H Thomas), 1929, Cambridge

Cal S P Dom 1635–6   *Calendar of state papers domestic: Charles I, 1635–6* (ed J Bruce), 1866, London (consulted at http://www.british-history.ac.uk/cal-state-papers/domestic/chas1/1635-6/pp521-549, last accessed 14 March 2017)

Cal S P Dom 1638   *Calendar of state papers domestic: Charles I, 1638* (eds J Bruce and W Hamilton), 1871, London (consulted at http://www.british-history.ac.uk/cal-state-papers/domestic/chas1/1638-9, last accessed 21 March 2017)

Cal S P Dom 1639   *Calendar of state papers domestic: Charles I, 1639* (ed W D Hamilton), 1873, London (consulted at http://www.british-history.ac.uk/cal-state-papers/domestic/chas1/1639, last accessed 27 March 2017)

Cambridge alumni   A Cambridge alumni database, http://venn.lib.cam.ac.uk/acad/intro.html (last accessed 27 March 2017)

Carlyle, E I, 1900   *Dictionary of national biography, 1885–1900: Vol 61*, London

Carpenter, G R (ed), 1896   *Daniel Defoe's journal of the plague year*, New York

Carty, N, Hill, J, Henderson, M, Knox, E L, and Walker, D, 2016   Broadgate ticket hall: human osteology post-excavation assessment report and updated project design, unpub MOLA rep

Carver, J, 2012   London Crossrail: the New Churchyard AD 1569 to AD 1714, archaeology investigation and dealing with mass exhumation, in *CHNT 17 (Proceedings of 17th international conference on Cultural Heritage and New Technologies)*, 10–18, Vienna

Chamberlain, H, 1770   *The new and compleat history and survey of the cities of London and Westminster*, London

Champion, J, 1993   Epidemics and the built environment in 1665, in J A I Champion (ed) 1993, 35–52

Champion, J A I (ed), 1993   *Epidemic disease in London*, Centre Metropolitan Hist Working Pap Ser 1, London

Cherryson, A, Crossland, Z, and Tarlow, S, 2012   *A fine and private place, the archaeology of death and burial in post-medieval Britain and Ireland*, Leicester Archaeol Monogr 22, Leicester

Chesnutt, D R, and Laurens, H, 2003   *The papers of Henry Laurens*, Columbia, SC

Chisholm, B S, Nelson, D E, and Schwarcz, H P, 1982   Stable carbon isotope ratios as a measure of marine versus terrestrial protein in ancient diets, *Sci* 216, 1131–2

Christen, J A, 1994   Summarising a set of radiocarbon determinations: a robust approach, *Applied Statist* 43, 489–503

Clapp, R W, Jacobs, M M, and Loechler, E L, 2008   Environmental and occupational causes of cancer: new evidence, 2005–7, *Rev Envir Health* 23, 1–37

Clark, P, 1979   Migration in England during the late 17th and early 18th centuries, *Past Present* 83, 57–90

Clark, P, and Souden, D C (eds), 1987   *Migration and society in early modern England*, London

Clark, W C, 2015   London: a multi-century struggle for sustainable development in an urban environment, HKS Res Working Pap Ser RWP15–047, Cambridge, MA (consulted at http://nrs.harvard.edu/urn-3:HUL.InstRepos:22356529, last accessed 30 January 2017)

Clowes, W A, 1596   *A profitable and necessary book of observations*, London

Colclough, D, 2005   *Freedom of speech in early Stuart England*, Cambridge

Collection   *A collection of the yearly Bills of Mortality from 1657 to 1758 inclusive*, 1759, [pages not numbered], London (consulted at https://archive.org/details/collectionyearl00hebegoog, last accessed 27 March 2017)

Collins Cook, D, and Lucas Powell, M, 2012   Treponematosis: past, present and future, in Grauer (ed) 2012, 472–92

Collinson, P, 1983   *Godly people: essays on English Protestantism and puritanism*, London

Common Sense, 1738   *Common Sense Englishman's J* [selected issue] (consulted at British Library, Burney Newspapers Collect)

Compleat, 1723   [Samuel Buxton], *Compleat Set St James's J* no. 66 (9 March), 5 col A

Connell, B, and Miles, A, 2010   *The City Bunhill burial ground, Golden Lane, London: excavations at south Islington schools, 2006*, MOLA Archaeol Stud Ser 21, London

Connell, B, and Rauxloh, P, 2007 (2003)   A rapid method for recording human skeletal data (ed N Powers), 2 edn, unpub MOL rep

Connell, B, Gray Jones, A, Redfern, R, and Walker, D, 2012   *A bioarchaeological study of medieval burials on the site of St Mary Spital: excavations at Spitalfields Market, London E1, 1991–2007*, MOLA Monogr Ser 60, London

Cook, G T, Ascough, P L, Bonsall, C, Hamilton, D, Russell, N, Sayle, K L, Scott, M, and Bownes, J, 2015   Best practice methodology for 14C calibration of marine and mixed terrestrial/marine samples, *Quat Geochronol* 27, 164–71

Cowie, R, Bekvalac, J, and Kausmally, T, 2008   *Late 17th- to 19th-century burial and earlier occupation at All Saints, Chelsea Old Church, Royal Borough of Kensington and Chelsea*, MoLAS Archaeol Stud Ser 18, London

Cox, M, 1993   Epidemics and skeletal populations: problems and limitations, in J A I Champion (ed) 1993, 71–9

Cox, M, 1996   *Life and death in Spitalfields 1700 to 1850*, CBA Occas Pap 21, York

Cox, M (ed), 1998   *Grave concerns: death and burial in England 1700–1850*, CBA Res Rep 113, York

Cox, M, 2000   Aging adults from the skeleton, in Cox and Mays (eds) 2000, 61–81

Cox, M, and Mays, S (eds), 2000   *Human osteology in archaeology and forensic science*, London

Craddock-Bennett, L, 2013   Providence chapel and burial ground, Sandwell, West Bromwich, *Post-Medieval Archaeol* 47, 382–6

Craig, S, 2000   *London in the 1690s: a social atlas*, London

Creighton, C, 1891   *A history of epidemics in Britain from AD 664 to the extinction of the plague*, Cambridge

Crossrail, 2014   C502 Liverpool Street Station SS-WSI addendum for detailed archaeological excavation at Liverpool Street Station Broadgate ticket hall C502-XRL-T1-RST-CR101_50002 revision 1.0, http://learninglegacy.crossrail.co.uk/wp-content/uploads/2016/06/C502-XRL-T1-RST-C101-50002-BTH-SS-WSI-Addendum-Rev-2.0-17.07.14.pdf (last accessed 5 January 2017)

Cubitt, R S, Hartle, R, and Marshall, M, in prep a   The Clitherow workshop 'at the Corner of Old Bethlem gate, next Morefield': evidence for late 17th- and early 18th-century bone and ivory working from the New Churchyard

Cubitt, R S, Hartle, R, Marshall, M, and Richardson, B, in prep b   An important 16th-century finds assemblage from Moorfields, London

Culpeper, N, 1814 (1653)   *Culpeper's complete herbal and English physician*, enlarged edn, London

Cummings, C, and Rega, E, 2008   A case of dyschondrosteosis in an Anglo-Saxon skeleton, *Int J Osteoarchaeol* 18, 431–7

Cummins, N, Morgan, K, and Ó Gráda, C, 2013   *Living standards and plague in London, 1560–1665*, Dublin

Daily Advertiser, 1778–96   [selected issues] (consulted at British Library, Burney Newspapers Collect)

Daily Post, 1723–9   [selected issues] (consulted at British Library, Burney Newspapers Collect)

Dale, T, 1931   *The inhabitants of London in 1638*, London (consulted at @www.british-history.ac.uk, last accessed 15 February 2016)

D'Ambrosio, N, Soohoo, S, Warshall, C, Johnson, A, and Karimi, S, 2008 Craniofacial and intracranial manifestations of Langerhans cell histiocytosis: report of findings in 100 patients, *American J Roentgentol* 191, 589–97

Dandy, D J, and Edwards, D J, 1998   *Essential orthopaedics and trauma*, Edinburgh

Davenport, R, Boulton, J, and Schwartz, L, 2010   Infant and young adult mortality in London's West End, 1750–1824, Working Pap Newcastle Univ: the Pauper Lives project

Davies, R, and Grant, M D, 1983   *London and its railways*, London

Davis, S, Henderson, M, and Ritchie, S, 2010   Marshall Street baths and Dufours Place cleansing depot, London W1, City of Westminster: a post-excavation assessment and updated project design, unpub MOL rep

Defoe, D, 1986 (1722)   *A journal of the plague year*, reprint, Harmondsworth

Dekker, T, 1603   *The wonderfull yeare. 1603. Wherein is shewed the picture of London, lying sicke of the plague …*, London

Dekker, T, 1625   *A rod for run-awayes …*, London

De Krey, G S, 2008   Jenks, Francis (bap 1640, d 1686), in *Oxford dictionary of national biography* (consulted at http://www.oxforddnb.com/view/article/67254, last accessed 27 June 2016)

De Laune, T, 1681   *The present state of London*, London

DeNiro, M J, 1985   Post-mortem preservation and alteration of *in vivo* bone collagen isotope ratios in relation to palaeodietary reconstruction, *Nature* 317, 806–9

DeWitte, S N, 2010   Age patterns of mortality during the Black Death in London, 1349–50, *J Archaeol Sci* 37, 3394–400

DeWitte, S N, 2014a   The anthropology of plague: insights from bioarchaeological analyses of epidemic cemeteries, in *Pandemic disease in the medieval world: rethinking the Black Death* (ed M H Green), Medieval Globe 1, 97–124, Bradford

DeWitte, S N, 2014b   Health in post-Black Death London (1350–1538): age patterns of periosteal new bone formation in a post-epidemic population, *American J Phys Anthropol* 155, 260–7

DeWitte, S N, 2014c   Mortality risk and survival in the aftermath of the medieval Black Death, *PLoS ONE* 9, e96513, doi:10.137/journal.pone.0096513

DeWitte, S N, 2016   Medieval and early modern trends in survivorship: assessment of demographic trends using the transition analysis method of adult age estimation, archive rep

DeWitte, S N, and Slavin, P, 2013   Between famine and death. Physiological stress and dairy deficiency in England on the eve of the Black Death (1315–50): new evidence from palaeoepidemiology and manorial accounts, *J Interdisciplin Hist* 44, 37–61

DeWitte, S N, Hughes-Morey, G, Bekvalac, J, and Karsten, J, 2016   Wealth, health and frailty in industrial-era London, *Annu Human Biol* 43, 241–54

Dickenson, J, 1598   *Greene in conceipt …*, London

Dittmar, J M, and Mitchell, P D, 2015   The afterlife of Laurence Sterne (1713–68): body snatching, dissection and the role of Cambridge anatomist Charles Collignon, *J Med*

Biogr 24, 559–65 (consulted at http://journals.sagepub.com/doi/abs/10.1177/0967772015601584?rss=1&, last accessed 5 January 2017)

Dockery, D W, Pope, C A, Xu, X, Spengler, J D, Ware, J H, Fay, M E, Ferris, B G, Jr, and Speizer, F E, 1993   An association between air pollution and mortality in six US cities, *New England J Med* 329, 1753–9

Dodsley, R, and Dodsley, J, 1761   *London and its environs described: Vol II*, London

Drummond, J C, and Wilbraham, A, 1991   *The Englishman's food: five centuries of English diet*, with new introduction by T Jaine, London

Duckworth, T, 1995 (1984)   *Orthopaedics and fractures*, 3 edn, Lecture Notes Ser, Oxford

Dumbrell, R, 1992   *Understanding antique wine bottles*, Woodbridge

Dunbar, E, Cook, G T, Naysmith, P, Tripney, B G, Xu, S, 2016   AMS 14C dating at the Scottish Universities Environmental Research Centre (SUERC) radiocarbon dating laboratory, *Radiocarbon* 58, 9–23

Earle, P, 1994   *A city full of people: men and women of London 1650–1750*, London

EB   Encyclopaedia Britannica: John Biddle, English theologian, https://www.britannica.com/biography/John-Biddle (last accessed 24 October 2016)

Egan, G, 2005   *Material culture in London in an age of transition*, MoLAS Monogr Ser 19, London

Elmes, J, 1831   *A topographical dictionary of London and its environs*, London

Emery, P A, and Wooldridge, K, 2011   *St Pancras burial ground: excavations for St Pancras International, the London terminus of High Speed 1, 2002–3*, Gifford Monogr, London

Engineer, 1865   [Broad Street Station], *Engineer*, 8 September, 148

Evans, G (ed), 1988   *Elizabethan-Jacobean drama: the theatre in its time*, New York

Evans, J, 1811 (1808)   *A sketch of the denominations of the Christian world*, 12 edn, London

Evening Post, 1709–23   [selected issues] (consulted at British Library, Burney Newspapers Collect)

Faithorne and Newcourt, 1658   'An exact delineation of the Cities of London and Westminster and the suburbs thereof together with the Borough of Southwark', reproduced in Margary 1981

Farthing, M J G, 2013   Nicholas Culpeper (1616–54): London's first general practitioner?, *J Med Biogr* 23, 152–8

Fauchard, P, 1728   *Le Chirurgien dentiste*, Paris

Finlay, R, 1981   *Population and metropolis: the demography of London, 1580–1640*, Cambridge

Fiorato, V, Boylston, A, and Knüsel, C (eds), 2000   *Blood red roses: the archaeology of a mass grave from the battle of Towton AD 1461*, Oxford

Firth, C H, 1899   *Dictionary of national biography, 1885–1900: Vol 59*, London

Firth, C H, and Rait, R S, 1911   *Acts and ordinances of the Interregnum, 1642–60*, London

Fleming, E A, 1997   Staples for genteel living: the importation of London household furnishings into Charleston during the 1780s, *American Furniture* (consulted at http://www.chipstone.org/html/publications/1997AF/Fleming/Flemingindex97.html, last accessed 1 March 2015)

Flying Post, 1702   [selected issue] (consulted at British Library, Burney Newspapers Collect)

Fowler, L, and Powers, N, 2012   *Doctors, dissection and resurrection men: excavations in the 19th-century burial ground of the London hospital*, MOLA Monogr Ser 62, London

Fuller, T, 1626   *A sermon intended for Paul's crosse, but preached in the church of St Paul's, London, the III of December, M.DC.XXV*, London

Galloway, A (ed), 1999   *Broken bones: anthropological analysis of blunt force trauma*, Springfield

GBC   Great Britain Commissioners for Inquiry into Charities, 1822 *The report of the commissioners for enquiring concerning charities in England and Wales: Vol. 4*, London

Gentlemen's Mag, 1809   [Henry Hall], *Gentlemen's Mag* 79(2), 686

Gentles, I J, 2004   Lockyer, Robert (1625/6–1649), in *Oxford dictionary of national biography* (consulted at http://www.oxforddnb.com/view/article/47102, last accessed 1 July 2016)

Gilchrist, R, 2008   Magic for the dead? The archaeology of magic in later medieval burials, *Medieval Archaeol* 52, 119–59

Glass, D V, 1950   Graunt's life table, *J Inst Actuaries* 76, 60–4

Glouberman, S, 2009   Knowledge transfer and the complex story of scurvy, *J Evalu Clin Practice* 553–7

GNDA   *Gazetteer and New Daily Advertiser*, 1765–81 [selected issues] (consulted at British Library, Burney Newspapers Collect)

Goodman, A H, and Armelagos, G J, 1988   Childhood stress and decreased longevity in a prehistoric population, *American Anthropol* 90, 936–44

Goodman, A H, Martin, D L, Armelagos, G J, and Clarke, G A, 1984   Indications of stress from bones and teeth, in *Palaeopathology at the origins of agriculture* (eds M Cohen and G J Armelagos), 13–49, New York

Goodman, J, 1993   *Tobacco in history: the cultures of dependence*, London

Gordon, A, 1888   *Dictionary of national biography, 1885–1900: Vol 14*, London

Gordon, A, 1892   *Dictionary of national biography, 1885–1900: Vol 29*, London

Gowland, R L, and Chamberlain, A T, 2005   Detecting plague: palaeodemographic characterisation of a catastrophic death assemblage, *Antiquity* 79, 146–57

Grainger, I, and Phillpotts, C, 2011   *The Cistercian abbey of St Mary Graces, East Smithfield, London*, MOLA Monogr Ser 44, London

Grainger, I, Hawkins, D, Cowal, L, and Mikulski, R, 2008   *The Black Death cemetery, East Smithfield, London*, MoLAS Monogr Ser 43, London

Grauer, A L (ed), 2012   *A companion to palaeopathology*, Chichester

Grauer, A L, and Roberts, C A, 1996   Palaeoepidemiology, healing, and possible treatment of trauma in the medieval cemetery population of St Helen's-in-the-Walls, York, England, *American J Phys Anthropol* 100, 531–44

Graunt, J, 1662   *Natural and political observations, mentioned in a following index and made upon the Bills of Mortality*, London (consulted at http://www.neonatology.org/pdf/graunt.pdf, last accessed 27 March 2017)

Green, M, 1888a   *Calendar of the proceedings of the committee for the advance of money 1642–56: Part 2*, London

Green, M, 1888b   *Calendar of the proceedings of the committee for the advance of money 1642–56: Part 3*, London

Greenwood, C, and Greenwood, J, 1827   'Map of London from an Actual Survey', reproduced in Margary 1982, *'Map of London from an Actual Survey' by C and J Greenwood, 1827*, Margary in assoc Guildhall Library, Kent

Gregg, P, 1981   *King Charles I*, London

Hacking, P, 2006   Human bone, in Oxford Castle: post-excavation analysis and research design (ed A Norton), 116–18, unpub Oxford Archaeol rep

Hall, A R, 1992   The last teasel factory in Britain and some observations on teasel (*Dipsacus fullonum* L and *D sativus* (L) Honckeny) remains from archaeological deposits, *Circaea J Ass Envir Archaeol* 9, 9–15

Hammond, P, 2004   Tobacco pipe-makers in the PCC wills indexes, *Soc Clay Pipe Res Newsl* 66, 15–23

Hanawalt, B A, 1993   *Growing up in medieval London: the experience of childhood in history*, New York

Harding, V, 1989   'And one more may be laid there': the location of burials in early modern London, *London J* 14, 112–29

Harding, V, 1990   The population of London, 1550–1700: a review of the published evidence, *London J* 15, 111–28

Harding, V, 1993   Burial of the plague dead in early modern London, in J A I Champion (ed) 1993, 53–64

Harding, V, 2002   *The dead and the living in Paris and London: 1500–1670*, Cambridge

Harding, V, 2011   Housing and health in early modern London, in *Environment, health and history* (eds V Berridge and M Gorsky), 23–44, Basingstoke

Hardy, A, 1993   The medical response to epidemic disease during the long 18th century, in J A I Champion (ed) 1993, 65–70

Hart, A, and North, S, 1998   *Historical fashion in detail: the 17th and 18th centuries*, London

Hartle, R, Jeffries, N, and Pearce, J, in prep   Household goods discarded by Moorfields brokers: material culture in 18th-century London

Harvey, W, 1863   *London scenes and London people*, London

Harward, C, Holder, N, and Jeffries, N, 2015   *The Spitalfields suburb 1539–c 1880: excavations at Spitalfields Market, London E1, 1991–2007*, MOLA Monogr Ser 61, London

Harward, C, Holder, N, Phillpotts, C, and Thomas, C, in prep   *The medieval priory and hospital of St Mary Spital and the Bishopsgate suburb: excavations at Spitalfields Market, London E1, 1991–2007*, MOLA Monogr Ser 59, London

Heal, A, 1988   *London furniture makers 1660–1840*, London

Hegarty, A, 2011   *Biographical register of St John's College, Oxford, 1555–1660*, Woodbridge

Hempel, S, 2007   *The medical detective, John Snow, cholera and the mystery of the Broad Street pump*, London

Henderson, M, Miles, A, and Walker, D, with Connell, B, and Wroe-Brown, R, 2013 *'He being dead yet speaketh': excavations at three post-medieval burial grounds in Tower Hamlets, east London, 2004–10*, MOLA Monogr Ser 64, London

Henderson, M, Miles, A, and Walker, D, 2015 *St Marylebone's Paddington Street north burial ground, excavations at Paddington Street, London W1, 2012–13*, MOLA Archaeol Stud Ser 34, London

Hendy, J, Charlton, S, and Radini, A, 2013 Ancient human dental calculus: an unexpected journey into the past, *Post Hole* 29 (consulted at http://www.theposthole.org/read/article/205, last accessed 5 January 2017)

Hibbert, C, Keay, J, Keay, J, and Weinreb, B, 2008 (1993) *The London encyclopaedia*, 3 edn, London

Higgins, D A, and Davey, P, 1994 Appendix 4: draft guidelines for using the clay tobacco pipe record sheets, in White, S D, *The dynamics of regionalisation and trade: Yorkshire clay tobacco pipes c 1600–1800*, BAR Brit Ser 374, 487–90, Oxford

Hill, T, 2010 *Pageantry and power: a cultural history of the early modern Lord Mayor's show, 1585–1639*, Manchester

Hillson, S, 2000 Dental pathology, in *Biological anthropology of the human skeleton* (eds M A Katzenburg and S R Saunders), 249–86, New York

Hillson, S, 2005 (1986) *Cambridge manuals in archaeology: teeth*, 2 edn, Cambridge

Hillson, S, 2014 *Tooth development in human evolution and bioarchaeology*, Cambridge

Hillson, S W, 1979 Diet and dental disease, *World Archaeol* 11, 147–62

Hogarth, W, 1733 *A harlot's progress*, London

Hogarth, W, 1751 *The four stages of cruelty*, London

Horne, J, 1989 *English tin-glazed tiles*, London

Horwood, R, 1813 [Horwood's map, compiled 1792–9] Plan of the Cities of London and Westminster, the borough of Southwark, 3 edn, reproduced in Margary, H, 1985 *The A–Z of Regency London*, Margary in assoc Guildhall Library, Kent

Houston, R A, 1996 The population of Britain and Ireland 1500–1750, in *British population history from the Black Death to the present day* (ed M Anderson), 99–190, Cambridge

Huizenga, L S, 1937 The royal touch, *Int J Leprosy* 5, 175–8

Humphrey, L, 2000 Growth studies of past populations: an overview and an example, in Cox and Mays (eds) 2000, 23–38

Hunting, P, Malt, D, Bennet, J, and Gray, C, 1991 *Broadgate and Liverpool Street Station*, London

Hurley, J A, Anderson, T E, Dear, W, Andrish, J T, Bergfeld, J A, and Weiker, G G, 1992 Posterior shoulder instability: surgical versus conservative results with evaluation of glenoid version, *American J Sports Med* 20, 396–400

Ivimey, J, 1814 *A history of the English Baptists: Vol 2*, London

J, 1863 Old Bedlam, *Notes Queries* 3 ser 4(83), 1 August, 85

Jaydee, 1890 Bell Alley: Defoe, *Notes Queries* 7 ser 10(183), 20 September, 234

Judd, M A, 2002   Ancient injury recidivism: an example from the Kerma period of ancient Nubia, *Int J Osteoarchaeol* 12, 89–106

Judd, M A, and Roberts, C A, 1998   Fracture patterns at the medieval leper hospital in Chichester, *American J Phys Anthropol* 105, 43–55

Judd, M A, and Roberts, C A, 1999   Fracture trauma in a medieval British farming village, *American J Phys Anthropol* 109, 229–43

Kaufmann, H J, Mahboubi, S, and Mandell, G A, 1977   Case report 39: monosteal infantile cortical hyperostosis, *Skeletal Radiol* 2, 109

Kausmally, T, 2015   William Hewson (1739–74) and the Craven Street anatomy school: anatomical teaching in the 18th century, unpub PhD thesis, Univ College London

Keene, D, Earle, P, Spence, C, and Barnes, J, 1992   City of London, Bishopsgate Ward (Within and Without), Bishopsgate Without, the first division, Moorfields to the right hand, in *Four shillings in the pound aid 1693/4 the City of London, the City of Westminster, Middlesex*, London (consulted at http://www.british-history.ac.uk/no-series/london-4s-pound/1693-4/bishopsgate-moorfields-to-the-right-hand, last accessed 21 April 2016)

Kent, J P C, 2005   *Coinage and currency in London, from the London and Middlesex records and other sources: from Roman times to the Victorians*, London

Khung, S, Budzik, J F, Amzallag-Bellenger, A, Lambilliote, A, Ares, G S, Cotten, A, and Boutry, N, 2013   Skeletal involvement in Langerhans cell histiocytosis, *Insights Imaging* 4, 569–79

Kirkup, J, 1978   *The surgeon's mate by John Woodall, 1617*, Bath

Kirkup, J, 2007   *A history of limb amputation*, London

Knüsel, C, 2000   Bone adaptation and its relationship to physical activity in the past, in Cox and Mays (eds) 2000, 381–401

Knüsel, C, and Göggel, S, 1993   A cripple from the medieval hospital of Saints James and Mary Magdalen, Chichester, *Int J Osteoarchaeol* 3, 155–65

Kolonel, L N, Altshuler, D, and Henderson, B E, 2004   The multi-ethnic cohort study: exploring genes, lifestyle and cancer risk, *Nature Rev Cancer* 4, 519–27

König, K G, 2000   Diet and oral health, *Int Dent J* 50, 162–74

Lambert, F, 1921   Some recent excavations in London, *Archaeologia* 71, 55–112

Lamont, W, 2004   Delamaine, Alexander (bap 1631, d 1685), in *Oxford dictionary of national biography* (consulted at http://www.oxforddnb.com/view/article /7429, last accessed 24 October 2016)

Landers, J, 1993   *Death and the metropolis: studies in the demographic history of London 1670–1830*, Oxford

Lane, J, 2001 *A social history of medicine: health, healing and disease in England, 1750–1950*, London

Lanfranco, L P, and Eggers, S, 2012   Caries through time: an anthropological overview, in *Contemporary approach to dental caries* (ed Ming-Yu Li), 3–34, Rijeka

Lang, R G, 1993   *Two Tudor subsidy assessment rolls for the City of London 1541 and 1582*, London

Lanting, J N, and van der Plicht, J, 1998   Reservoir effects and apparent 14C ages, *J Irish Archaeol* 9, 151–65

Larsen, C S, 1997   *Bioarchaeology: interpreting behaviour from the human skeleton*, Cambridge

Laumbach, R J, and Kippen, H M, 2012   Respiratory health effects of air pollution: update on biomass smoke and traffic pollution, *J Allergy Clin Immunol* 129, 3–11

LDN   *London Daily News*, 1903 [selected issue] (consulted at British Library)

LDPGA   *London Daily Post and General Advertiser*, 1736 [selected issue] (consulted at British Library, Burney Newspapers Collect)

Leicester Chron, 1815   [selected issue] (consulted at British Library)

LEP   *Lloyds Evening Post*, 1770 [selected issue] (consulted at British Library, Burney Newspapers Collect)

LEPBC   *Lloyds Evening Post Brit Chron*, 1760 [selected issue] (consulted at British Library, Burney Newspapers Collect)

Levy, E, 1990   Moorfields, Finsbury and the City of London in the 16th century, *London Topogr Rec* 26, 78–96

Lewis, M, 2016   Work and the adolescent in medieval England (AD 900–1550): the osteological evidence, *Medieval Archaeol* 60, 138–71

Lewis, M E, 2004   Endocranial lesions in non-adult skeletons: understanding their aetiology, *Int J Osteoarchaeol* 14, 82–97

Lewis, M E, 2007   *The bioarchaeology of children*, Cambridge

LHT   London hearth tax: City of London, 1662, http://www.british-history.ac.uk/london-hearth-tax/london/1662 (last accessed 18 February 2016)

Lichtenstein, P, Holm, N V, Verkasalo, P K, Iliadou, A, Kaprio, J, Koskenvuo, M, Pukkala, E, Skytthe, A, and Hemminki, K, 2000   Environmental and heritable factors in the causation of cancer: analyses of cohorts of twins from Sweden, Denmark and Finland, *New England J Med* 343, 78–85

Lilly, J, 1771   *A collection of modern entries: or, select pleadings in the courts of King's Bench, Common Pleas and Exchequer*, London

Lilly, W, 1651   *Monarch or no monarchy in England*, London

Litten, J, 1998   The English funeral 1700–1850, in Cox (ed) 1998, 3–16

Litten, J, 2002   *The English way of death: the common funeral since 1450*, London

Littledale, W (eds), 1903   *The registers of St Vedast, Foster's Lane and of St Michael Le Quern, London: Vol 2, Marriages and burials*, Harleian Soc 30, London

London Gazette, 1778   [selected issue] (consulted at British Library, Burney Newspapers Collect)

London lives [Samuel Buxton]   London lives 1690 to 1800: Middlesex sessions: sessions papers, justices' working documents, February 1723, https://www.londonlives.org/browse.jsp?foo=bar&path=SM_PS/LMSMPS50209.xml&div=LMSMPS50209PS502090060 (last accessed 4 January 2017)

Lorenz, A J, 1954   The conquest of scurvy, *J American Diet Ass* 30, 665–70

Loudon, I, 1986   Obstetric care, social class and maternal mortality, *Brit Med J* 6, 606–8

Lovell, N C, 1997   Trauma analysis in palaeopathology, *Yearb Phys Anthropol* 40, 139–70

Maat, G J R, and Mastwijk, R W, 2000   Avulsion injuries of vertebral endplates, *Int J Osteoarchaeol* 10, 142–52

Macdonell, W R, 1904   A study of the variation and correlation of the human skull with special reference to English crania, *Biometrika* 3, 191–244

Macdonell, W R, 1906   A second study of the English skull, with special reference to Moorfields crania, *Biometrika* 5, 86–104

McKinley, J, 2008   *The 18th-century Baptist church and burial ground at West Butts Street, Poole, Dorset*, Salisbury

McRae, R, 1999   *Pocketbook of orthopaedics and fractures*, Edinburgh

Magiorkinis, E, Beloukas, A, and Diamantis, A, 2011   Scurvy: past, present and future, *European J Intern Med* 22, 147–52

Maitland, W, 1739   *The history of London, from its foundation by the Romans to the present time: Vol 2*, London

Malcolm, J P, 1802   *Londinium redivivum or an antient history and modern description of London*, London

Manchester, K L, 1998   An orange a day keeps the scurvy away, *Trends Pharmacol Sci* 19, 167–70

Mann, W R, and Hunt, D R, 2005 (1990)   *Photographic regional atlas of bone disease, a guide to pathologic and normal variation in the human skeleton*, 2 edn, Springfield

Margary, H, 1981   *A collection of early maps of London 1553–1667*, Margary in assoc Guildhall Library, Kent

Margerison, B J, and Knüsel, C J, 2002   Palaeodemographic comparison of a catastrophic and an attritional death assemblage, *American J Phys Anthropol* 119, 134–43

Masters, B R (ed), 1984   *Chamber accounts of the 16th century*, London Rec Soc 20, London

Masters, P M, 1987   Preferential preservation of non-collagenous protein during bone diagenesis: implications for chronometric and stable isotope measurements, *Geochimica et Cosmochimica Acta* 51, 3209–14

Mays, S, 1999   The study of human skeletal remains from English post-medieval sites, in *Old and New Worlds* (eds G Egan and R L Michael), 331–41, Oxford

Mays, S, 2003   The rise and fall of rickets in England, in *The environmental archaeology of industry* (eds P Murphy and P Wiltshire), 144–53, Oxford

Mays, S, 2014   The palaeopathology of scurvy in Europe, *Int J Palaeopathol* 5, 55–62

Merbs, C F, 1983   *Patterns of activity induced pathology in a Canadian Inuit population*, Archaeol Survey Canada Pap 119, Ottawa

Mercurius Pragmaticus, 1649   [selected issue] (consulted at British Library, Burney Newspapers Collect)

Merry, M, and Baker, P, 2009   'For the house herself and one servant': family and household in late 17th-century London, *London J* 34, 205–32

Milbourn, T, 1872   *History of St Mildred the Virgin church*, London

Miles, A, with Connell, B, 2012   *New Bunhill Fields burial ground, Southwark: excavations at Globe Academy, 2008*, MOLA Archaeol Stud Ser 24, London

Miles, A, and Bekvalac, J, 2014   Excavations at Royal Mint Square, *London Archaeol* 14, 31–6

Miles, A, and White, W, 2008   *Burial at the site of the parish church of St Benet Sherehog before and after the Great Fire: excavations at 1 Poultry, City of London*, MoLAS Monogr Ser 39, London

Miles, A, Powers, N, and Wroe-Brown, R, with Walker, D, 2008   *St Marylebone church and burial ground in the 18th to 19th centuries: excavations at St Marylebone school, 1992 and 2004–6*, MoLAS Monogr Ser 46, London

MLAI   Mirror of literature, amusement and instruction: Vol 8, 1826, London

Molleson, T, and Cox, M, 1993   *The Spitalfields project: Vol 2, The anthropology: the middling sort*, CBA Res Rep 86, York

Mon Angl   Dugdale, W, *Monasticon Anglicanum* 6(2), 1846 (eds J Caley, H Ellis and B Bandinel), London

Montgomery, J, Morley, R, Lisic, N, Beaumont, J, Nowell, G, Ottley, C, and Peterkin, J, 2016   A report on the combined isotope and trace element data for 20 individuals from the New Churchyard, archive rep

Moore, J, and Buckberry, J, 2016   The use of the corsetry to treat Pott's disease of the spine from 19th-century Wolverhampton, England, *Int J Palaeopathol* 14, 74–80

Moorrees, C F A, Fanning, E A, and Hunt, E E, Jr, 1963a   Age variation of formation stages for ten permanent teeth, *J Dent Res* 42, 1490–502

Moorrees, C F A, Fanning, E A, and Hunt, E E, Jr, 1963b   Formation and resorption of three deciduous teeth in children, *American J Phys Anthropol* 21, 205–13

Morning Chron, 1806   [selected issue] (consulted at British Library)

Morrissey, M, 2011   *Politics and the Paul's cross sermons, 1558–1642*, Oxford

Morton, R, 1720 (1689)   *Phthisiologia: or, a treatise of consumptions …*, 2 edn, London

Mushrif, V, 2000–1   Porotic hyperostosis: a bio-cultural perspective on iron deficiency anemia, *Bull Deccan College Res Inst* 60 (diamond jubilee vol), 367–72

Mytum, H, 2004   *Mortuary monuments and burial grounds of the historic period*, New York

Neal, D, 1837   *The history of the puritans or Protestant Nonconformists: Vol 2*, London

Newbrun, E, 1982   Sugar and dental caries: a review of human studies, *Sci* ns 217, 418–23

Newman, L F, 1946   Some notes on food and dietetics in the 16th and 17th centuries, *J Roy Anthropol Inst Great Britain Ireland* 76, 39–49

Newton, G, 2011   Infant mortality variations, feeding practices and social status in London between 1550 and 1750, *Social Hist Med* 24, 260–80

Noël Hume, I, 1974   *All the best rubbish*, London

Norden, J, 1593   *Norden's maps of London and Westminster, engraved by Pieter van den Keere 1593*, reproduced in London Topogr Soc Publ 7 for 1899

Norman, P, and Reader, F, 1906   Recent discoveries in connexion with Roman London, *Archaeologia* 60, 169–250

Novak, S A, 2000   Battle-related trauma, in Fiorato et al (eds) 2000, 90–102

Nyffeler, R W, Sheikh, R, Atkinson, T S, and Gerber, C, 2006   Effects of glenoid component version on humeral head displacement and joint reaction forces: an experimental study, *J Shoulder Elbow Surg* 15, 625–9

O'Donoghue, G, 1914   *The story of Bethlehem Hospital from its foundation in 1247*, London

Ogilby, J, and Morgan, W, 1676   'Large and Accurate Map of the City of London', reproduced in Margary, H, 1976 *'Large and Accurate Map of the City of London' by John Ogilby and William Morgan, 1676*, Margary in assoc Guildhall Library, Kent

Old Bailey Proc   *Old Bailey proceedings online*, www.oldbaileyonline.org, version 7.2 30 September 2016

OPA   *Oracle and Public Advertiser*, 1797 [selected issues] (consulted at British Library, Burney Newspapers Collect)

Ortner, D J, 2003   *Identification of pathological conditions in human skeletal remains*, London

Ortner, D J, and Putshar, W G J, 1981   *Identification of pathological conditions in human skeletal remains*, Smithsonian Contrib Anthropol 28, Washington, DC

Oswald, A, 1960   *English clay tobacco pipes*, J Brit Archaeol Ass 23, 40–102

Oswald, A, 1975   *Clay pipes for the archaeologist*, BAR 14, Oxford

OWJ   *Original Weekly J*, 1718 [selected issues] (consulted at British Library, Burney Newspapers Collect)

Payne, D E, 2008   Children of the poor in London 1700–80, unpub PhD thesis, Univ Hertfordshire

Peacock, E, 1851   John Lilburne, *Notes Queries* 1 ser 4(95), 23 August, 134

Pearce, J, 2015   Smoking, in Harward et al 2015, 286–97

Pearce, J E, 2000   A late 18th-century inn clearance assemblage from Uxbridge, Middlesex, *Post-Medieval Archaeol* 34, 144–86

Pearson, K, and Morant, G M, 1935   *The portraiture of Oliver Cromwell with special reference to the Wilkinson head*, Biometrika 26, London

Pelling, M, 1986   Barber-Surgeons, the body, and disease, in Beier and Finlay (eds) 1986, 82–112

Pelling, M, and Webster, C, 1979   Medical practitioners, in *Health, medicine and mortality in the 16th century* (ed C Webster), 164–235, Cambridge

Pepys diary   *The diary of Samuel Pepys: daily entries from the 17th-century London diary*, http://www.pepysdiary.com/diary/ (last accessed 4 January 2017)

Pfizenmaier, S, 2016   *Charterhouse Square: Black Death cemetery and Carthusian monastery, meat market and suburb*, Crossrail Archaeol Ser 7, London

Picard, L, 2003 (1997)   *Restoration London: everyday life in London 1660–70*, repub in pbk, London

Picard, L, 2004   *Elizabeth's London: everyday life in Elizabethan London*, London

Picciotto, J, 1875   *Sketches of Anglo-Jewish history*, London

Pike, G H, 1770   *Ancient meeting-houses, or, memorial pictures of nonconformity in old London*, London

Pincus, S, 1995   Coffee politicians does create: coffee houses and restoration political culture, *J Modern Hist* 67, 807–34

Pine, L G, 1972   *The new extinct peerage 1884–1971: containing extinct, abeyant, dormant and suspended peerages with genealogies and arms*, London

Porter, R, 1991   *English society in the 18th century*, London

Porter, R, 1997   *The greatest benefit to mankind: a medical history of humanity from antiquity to the present*, London

Porter, S, 2011   *Shakespeare's London: everyday life in London 1580–1616*, Stroud

Porter, S, 2012a   *The great plague of London*, Stroud

Portcr, S, 2012b   *Pepys's London: everyday life in London 1650–1703*, Stroud

Powell, H J, 2014 (1923)   *Glassmaking in England*, reprinted in pbk, Cambridge

Power, R C, Salazar-García, D C, Straus, L G, González Morales, M R, and Henry, A G, 2015   Micro-remains from El Mirón cave human dental calculus suggest a mixed plant-animal subsistence economy during the Magdalenian in northern Iberia, *J Archaeol Sci* 60, 39–46

Powers, N, 2005   Cranial trauma and treatment: a case study from the medieval cemetery of St Mary Spital, London, *Int J Osteoarchaeol* 15, 1–14

Powers, N (ed), 2008   Human osteology method statement, http://archive.museumoflondon.org.uk/NR/rdonlyres/2D513AFA-EB45-43C2-AEAC-30B256245FD6/0/MicrosoftWordOsteologyMethodStatementMarch 2008.pdf (last accessed 4 January 2017)

Poynter, F N L, 1962   Nicholas Culpeper and his books, *J Hist Med Allied Sci* 17, 155

Prison, [?1725]   *The present state of the prison of Ludgate*, London

Public Advertiser, 1781   [selected issue] (consulted at British Library, Burney Newspapers Collect)

Quisquis, 1863   Plague pit, *Notes Queries* 3 ser 4(83), 1 August, 85

Radini, A, Nikita, E, and Shillito, L-M, 2016   Human dental calculus in a medieval urban environment, in *Everyday life in medieval Europe: environmental and artefactual approaches to dwelling in town and country* (eds B Jervis, L Broderick and I Grau), 297–313, Turnhout

Raithby, J (ed), 1819   *Statutes of the realm: Vol 5, 1628–80*, London (consulted at http://www.british-history.ac.uk/statutes-realm/vol5, last accessed 18 June 2016)

Ranieri, S, and Telfer, A, with Walker, D, and Yendell, V, 2017   *Liverpool Street: suburban Roman road and burials in the Walbrook valley*

Rappaport, S, 1989   *Worlds within worlds: structures of life in 16th-century London*, Cambridge

Rasmussen, S, Allentoft, M E, Nielsen, K, Orlando, L, Sikora, M, Sjögren, K-G, Pedersen, A G, Schubert, M, Van Dam, A, Kapel, C M O, Nielsen, H B, Brunak, S, Avetisyan, P, Epimakhov, A, Khalyapin, M V, Gnuni, A, Kriiska, A, Lasak, I, Metspalu, M, Moiseyev, V, Gromov, A, Pokutta, D, Saag, L, Varul, L, Yepiskoposyan, L, Sicheritz-Pontén, T, Foley, R A, Lahr, M M, Nielsen, R, Kristiansen, K, and Willerslev, E, 2015   Early divergent strains of *Yersinia pestis* in Eurasia 5000 years ago, *Cell* 163, 571–82

Rawcliffe, C, 2013   *Urban bodies: communal health in late medieval English towns and cities*, Woodbridge

Razzell, P, 2000   Evaluating the same-name technique as a way of measuring burial register reliability in England, *Local Popul Stud* 64, 8–22

Razzell, P, 2011   Infant mortality in London, 1538–1850: a methodological study, *Local Popul Stud* 87, 45–64

Razzell, P, and Spence, C, 2007   The history of infant, child and adult mortality in London, 1550–1850, *London J* 32, 271–92

Read's   *Read's Weekly J or Brit Gazetteer*, 1755 [selected issues] (consulted at British Library, Burney Newspapers Collect)

Redfern, R, 2002   Sex and the city: a biocultural investigation into female health in Roman Britain, in *Proceedings of the 12th annual theoretical Roman archaeology conference* (eds G Carr, E Swift and J Weekes), 147–70, Oxford

Reeve, J, and Adams, M, 1993   *The Spitalfields project: Vol 1, The archaeology: across the Styx*, CBA Res Rep 85, London

Reimer, P J, Bard, E, Bayliss, A, Beck, J W, Blackwell, P, Bronk Ramsey, C, Buck, C E, Cheng, H, Edwards, R L, Friedrich, M, Grootes, P M, Guilderson, T P, Haflidason, H, Hajdas, I, Hatté, C, Heaton, T J, Hoffmann, D L, Hogg, A G, Hughen, K A, Kaiser, K F, Kromer, B, Manning, S W, Niu, M, Reimer, R W, Richards, D A, Scott, E M, Southon, J R, Staff, R A, Turney, C S M, and van der Plicht, J, 2013   IntCal13 and Marine13 radiocarbon age calibration curves 0–50,000 years cal BP, *Radiocarbon* 55, 1869–87

Reimer, P J, Hoper, S, McDonald, J, Reimer, R, Svyatko, S, and Thompson, M, 2015   *The Queen's University, Belfast: laboratory protocols used for AMS radiocarbon dating at the 14CHRONO centre*, Swindon

Reiter, P, 2000   From Shakespeare to Defoe: malaria in England in the Little Ice Age, *Emerging Infectious Disease* 6, 1–11

Resnick, D, 2002   *Diagnosis of bone and joint disorders*, Philadelphia

Richardson, B, 2014   Plates and other vessels from early modern and recent graves, in *The chiming of crack'd bells: recent approaches to the study of artefacts in archaeology* (eds P Blinkhorn and C Cumberpatch), 65–71, Oxford

Richardson, R, 1988   *Death, dissection and the destitute*, London

Richardson, R, 2001 (1988)   *Death, dissection and the destitute*, 2 edn, London

Riley, H, 1868   *Memorials of London and London life in the 13th, 14th and 15th centuries*, London (consulted at www.british-history.ac.uk/no-series/memorials-london-life/pp601-624, last accessed 13 October 2016)

Roberts, C, and Cox, M, 2003   *Health and disease in Britain: from prehistory to the present day*, Stroud

Roberts, C A, 2012   Re-emerging infections: developments in bioarchaeological contributions to understanding tuberculosis today, in Grauer (ed) 2012, 434–58

Roberts, C A, and Manchester, K, 2012 (2005)   *The archaeology of disease*, 3 edn, reprint, Stroud

Roberts, C A, Lucy, D, and Manchester, K, 1994   Inflammatory lesions of ribs: an analysis of the Terry Collection, *American J Phys Anthropol* 95, 169–82

Rocque, J, 1746   'A Plan of the Cities of London Westminster and Southwark with contiguous buildings from an actual survey' by John Rocque, reproduced in Margary, H, 1971 *'A Plan of the Cities of London Westminster and Southwark' by John Rocque in 1746* (ed H Margary), in assoc Guildhall Library, Kent

Rogers, J, 2000   *The palaeopathology of joint disease*, in Cox and Mays (eds) 2000, 163–82

Rogers, J, and Waldron, T, 1995   *A field guide to joint disease in archaeology*, Chichester

ROLLCO   Records of London's livery companies online (consulted at http://www.londonroll.org/, last accessed 1 March 2016)

Rothman, N, Wacholder, S, Caporaso, N E, Garcia-Closas, M, Buetow, K, Fraumeni, J F, Jr, 2001   The use of common genetic polymorphisms to enhance the epidemiologic study of environmental carcinogens, *Biochimica et Biophysica Acta* 1471, 1–10

Rusen, P, 1910   *Church inscriptions of the City of London*, London

Rushworth, J, 1680   *Historical collections: Vol 2*, London

St Benet Sherehog   Museum of London, Wellcome osteological research database: St Benet Sherehog, http://www.museumoflondon.org.uk/collections/other-collection-databases-and-libraries/centre-human-bioarchaeology/osteological-database/medieval-cemeteries/st-benet-sherehog (last accessed 28 March 2017)

St Thomas's Hospital   Museum of London, Wellcome osteological research database: St Thomas's Hospital cemetery summary, https://www.museumoflondon.org.uk/collections/other-collection-databases-and-libraries/centre-human-bioarchaeology/osteological-database/post-medieval-cemeteries/st-thomas-hospital-post-medieval (last accessed 28 March 2017)

Salmon, T, 1735   *A critical review of the state trials*, London

Santos, A L, and Roberts, C A, 2001   A picture of tuberculosis in young Portuguese people in the early 20th century: a multidisciplinary study of the skeletal and historical evidence, *American J Phys Anthropol* 115, 38–49

Santos, A L, and Roberts, C A, 2006   Anatomy of a serial killer: differential diagnosis of tuberculosis based on rib lesions of adult individuals from the Coimbra identified skeletal collection, Portugal, *American J Phys Anthropol* 130, 38–40

Schneider, F, Jr, 1926   Sugar, *Foreign Affairs* 4, 311–20

Schoeninger, M J, DeNiro, M J, and Tauber, H, 1983   Stable nitrogen isotope ratios of bone collagen reflect marine and terrestrial components of prehistoric diets, *Sci* 216, 1381–3

Schofield, J, 1984   *The building of London from the Conquest to the Great Fire*, London

Schofield, J, 2011   *London, 1100–1600: the archaeology of a capital city*, Sheffield

Schofield, P, 2006   *Utility and democracy: the political thought of Jeremy Bentham*, Oxford

Schuenemann, V J, Bos, K, DeWitte, S, Schmedes, S, Jamieson, J, Mittnik, A, Forrest, S, Coombes, B K, Wood, J W, Earn, D J D, White, W, Krause, J, and Poinar, H N, 2011   Targeted enrichment of ancient pathogens yielding the pPCP1 plasmid of *Yersinia pestis* from victims of the Black Death, *Proc Nat Acad Sci United States America* 108, E746–E752

Scott, W, 1812 (1748)   *A collection of scarce and valuable tracts on the most interesting and entertaining subjects: Vol 7*, 2 edn, London

Sekiya, J K, Jebson, J L, and Louis, D S, 1997   Hereditary disorders with maladies of the wrist and elbow, *Iowa Orthopaed J* 17, 147–50

Shakespeare, W, 1992   *The complete works of William Shakespeare* (ed W J Craig), London

Sharp, A, 2006   Lilburne, John (?1615–1657), in *Oxford dictionary of national biography* (consulted at http://www.oxforddnb.com/view/article/16654, last accessed 8 July 2016)

Shoemaker, R, 2004   *The London mob: violence and disorder in 18th-century England*, London

Shrewsbury, J F D, 1970   *A history of the bubonic plague in the British Isles*, Cambridge

Sibly, E, 1802   *Culpeper's English physician and complete herbal*, London

Siena, K P, 1998   Pollution, promiscuity, and the pox: English venereology and the early modern medical discourse on social and sexual danger, *J Hist Sexuality* 8, 553–74

Siena, K P, 2004   *Venereal disease, hospitals and the urban poor: London's 'foul wards', 1600–1800*, Woodbridge

Skaife, R H, 1870   On the register of burials in York Minster, *Yorkshire Archaeol Topogr J* 1, 226–330

Slack, P, 1986   Metropolitan government in crisis: the response to plague, in Beier and Finlay (eds) 1986, 60–81

Sleet, T R, 1890   Bell Alley: Defoe, *Notes Queries* 7 ser 10(252), 25 October, 335

Sloane, B, 2011   *The Black Death in London*, Stroud

Smith, B H, 1991   Standards of human tooth formation and dental age assessment, in *Advances in dental anthropology* (eds M A Kelley and C S Larsen), 143–68, New York

Smith, J, 1867   *A descriptive catalogue of Friends' books: Vol 2*, London

Smith, J T, 1829 (1828)   *Nollekens and his times: Vol 1*, 2 edn, London

Smith, M, 1958   *A short history of dentistry*, London

Song, Y S, Sook Lee, I, Yi, J H, Cho, K H, Kim, D K, and Song, J W, 2011   Radiologic findings of adult pelvis and appendicular skeletal Langerhans cell histiocytosis in nine patients, *Skeletal Radiol* 40, 1421–6

Spence, C, 2016   *Accidents and violent death in early modern London, 1650–1750*, Stud Early Modern Cultural, Political Social Hist 25, Woodbridge

Spraggon, J, 2003   *Puritan iconoclasm during the English Civil War*, Woodbridge

Squire, J, 1621   *A sermon. Appointed for the New-Church-yard, by London, on White-Sunday, 1619*, London

Stanford, E, 1862   'Stanford's Library Map of London', reproduced in Margary, H, 1980 *'Stanford's Library Map of London, 1862'*, Margary in assoc Guildhall Library, Kent

Start, H, and Kirk, L, 1998   The bodies of Friends: the osteological analysis of a Quaker burial ground, in Cox (ed) 1998, 167–77

Stewart, K, 2016   Plant remains from the post-medieval cess pits at Broadgate, Crossrail (XSM10), unpub MOLA rep

Stieber, J R, and Dormans, J P, 2005   Manifestations of hereditary multiple exostoses, *J American Acad Orthopaed Surg* 13, 110–20

Stirland, A J, 2000   *Raising the dead: the crew of King Henry VIII's great ship, the* Mary Rose, Chichester

Stow, J, 1603   *A survey of London* (2 vols), with introduction and notes by C L Kingsford, repr 1908, Oxford

Strype, J (ed), 1720   *A survey of the cities of London and Westminster… brought down from the year 1633 … to the present time* (2 vols), London

Stuart-Macadam, P, 1992   Porotic hyperostosis: a new perspective, *American J Phys Anthropol* 87, 39–47

Stuart-Macadam, P, 2006   Integrative anthropology: a focus on iron-deficiency anemia, *Archaeol Pap American Anthropol Ass* 16, 129–37

Stuart-Macadam, P L, 1991   Anaemia in Roman Britain: Poundbury Camp, in *Health in past societies: biocultural interpretations of human skeletal remains in archaeological contexts* (eds H Bush and M Zvelebil), BAR Brit Ser 567, 101–13, Oxford

Stubblebine, J M, 1981   Psychiatric symptoms of neurosyphilis, *W J Med* 135, 340–1

Stuiver, M, and Kra, R S, 1986   Editorial comment, *Radiocarbon* 28(2B), ii

Stuiver, M, and Polach, H A, 1977   Reporting of 14C data, *Radiocarbon* 19, 355–63

Stuiver, M, and Reimer, P J, 1986   A computer program for radiocarbon age calibration, in Proceedings of the 12th international 14C conference (eds M Stuiver and R S Kra), *Radiocarbon* 28(2B): 1022–30

Swerdloff, B A, Ozonoff, M B, and Gyepes, M T, 1970   Late recurrence of infantile cortical hyperostosis (Caffey's disease), *American J Roentgenol* 108, 461–7

Taft, B, 2008   Walwyn, William (bap 1600, d 1681), in *Oxford dictionary of national biography* (consulted at http://www.oxforddnb.com/view/article/28661, last accessed 30 June 2016)

Tarlov, I M, 1970   Spinal perineurial and meningeal cysts, *J Neurol Neurosurg Psychiatry* 33, 833–43

Taylor, A, and Taylor, J, 1809   *A peep into London, for good children*, London

Taylor, J, 1630   *All the workes of Iohn Taylor the water-poet: beeing sixty and three in number*, London

Te Brake, W H, 1975   Air pollution and fuel crises in pre-industrial London, 1250–1650, *Technol Culture* 16, 337–59

Thorne, R, 1978   *Liverpool Street Station*, London Architect Monogr, London

Timbs, J, 1868   *Curiosities of London*, London

Tindall, G, 2016   *The tunnel through time: a new route for an old London journey*, London

Török, E, Moran, E, and Cooke, F, 2009   *Oxford handbook of infectious diseases and microbiology*, Oxford

Touger-Decker, R, and van Loveren, C, 2003   Sugars and dental caries, *American Soc Clin Nutr* 78, 881S–92S

Tuke, D, 1882   *Chapters in the history of the insane in the British Isles*, London

Tuross, N, Fogel, M L, and Hare, P E, 1988   Variability in the preservation of the isotopic composition of collagen from fossil bone, *Geochimica et Cosmochimica Acta* 52, 929–35

Underwood, T L (eds), 1999   *The acts of the witnesses: the autobiography of Lodowick Muggleton and other early Muggletonian writings*, Oxford

Urban, S, 1830   [account], *Gentleman's Mag Hist Chron* 147, 15

Vincent, T, 1811 (1667)   *God's terrible voice in the city by plague and fire*, Bridgeport, CT

Waldron, T, 1991   Variations in the rates of spondylolysis in early populations, *Int J Osteoarchaeol* 1, 63–5

Waldron, T, 2009   *Palaeopathology*, Cambridge

Walker, D, 2012   *Disease in London, 1st–19th centuries: an illustrated guide to diagnosis*, MOLA Monogr Ser 56, London

Walker, D, and Henderson, M, 2010   Smoking and health in London's East End in the first half of the 19th century, *Post-Medieval Archaeol* 44, 209–22

Waller, J, 2000   Combat techniques, in Fiorato et al (eds) 2000, 130–6

Waller, T, 1747   *A general description of all trades*, London

Walton, K M, 1973   The Worshipful Company of Upholders of the City of London, *Furniture Hist* 9, 41–79

Ward, G K, and Wilson, S R, 1978   Procedures for comparing and combining radiocarbon age determinations: a critique, *Archaeometry* 20, 19–31

Warinner, C, Rodrigues, J F M, Vyas, R, Trachsel, C, Shved, N, Grossmann, J, Radini, A, Hancock, Y, Tito, R Y, Fiddyment, S, Speller, C, Hendy, J, Charlton, S, Luder, H U, Salazar-García, D C, Eppler, E, Seiler, R, Hansen, L H, Castruita, J A S, Barkow-Oesterreicher, S, Teoh, K Y, Kelstrup, C D, Olsen, J V, Nanni, P, Kawai, T, Willerslev, E, von Mering, C, Lewis, C M, Jr, Collins, M J, Gilbert, M T P, Rühli, F, and Cappellini, E, 2014   Pathogens and host immunity in the ancient human oral cavity, *Nature Genet* 46, 336–44

Warinner, C, Speller, C, and Collins, M J, 2015   A new era in palaeomicrobiology: prospects for ancient dental calculus as a long-term record of the human oral microbiome, *Phil Trans Roy Soc B* 370, http://dx.doi.org/10.1098/rstb.2013.0376 (last accessed 5 January 2017)

Weatherall, D, 1976   *David Ricardo: a biography*, The Hague

Webb, C, 2006   *London Livery Company apprenticeship registers: Vol 43, Vintners' Company 1609–1800*, London

Webb, C, 2014   *London Livery Company apprenticeship registers: Vol 45 Turners' Company 1604–1800*, London

Weekly Packet, 1717   [selected issue] (consulted at British Library, Burney Newspapers Collect)

Wellcome Library, 1904   [Report of the medical officer of health for the City of London, 1903], (consulted at http://wellcomelibrary.org/moh/report/b18253271#?asi=0, last accessed 4 January 2017)

Wenham, S J, 1989   Anatomical interpretations of Anglo-Saxon weapon injuries, in *Weapons and warfare in Anglo-Saxon England* (ed S Chadwick Hawkes), Oxford Univ Comm Archaeol Monogr 21, 123–39, Oxford

West, N O, 1997   *The Overtons: 700 years with allied families from England to Virginia, Kentucky and Texas*, Lubbock, TX

Weston, D A, 2012   Non-specific infection in palaeopathology: interpreting periosteal reactions, in Grauer (ed) 2012, 492–513

Wheatley, H B, and Cunningham, P, 1891   *London past and present*, London

Whittaker, D, 2000   *Ageing from the dentition*, in Cox and Mays (eds) 2000, 83–99

Wiener, A C, 1896   The extension corset and its indications, *J American Med Ass* 26, 807–13

Wilbur, A K, Farnbach, A W, Knudson, K J, and Buikstra, J E, 2008   Diet, tuberculosis and the palaeopathological record, *Curr Anthropol* 49, 963–91

Williamson, C M, 1919   *Lodowick Muggleton*, London

Willmott, H, 2002   *Early post-medieval vessel glass in England c 1500–1670*, CBA Res Rep 132, York

Willmott, H, 2005   *A history of English glassmaking AD 43–1800*, Stroud

Wilson, F P, 1925   *The plague pamphlets of Thomas Dekker*, Oxford

Wilson, J D, 1926   *Life in Shakespeare's England: a book of Elizabethan prose*, Cambridge

Winter, V A, and Mitchell, W A, 1984   *Descendants of William Atterbury, 1733 English immigrant*, Oklahoma City

WJ   Westminster J or New Weekly Miscellany, 1746 [selected issue] (consulted at British Library, Burney Newspapers Collect)

WJSP   Weekly Journal or Saturday's Post, 1717–23 [selected issues] (consulted at British Library, Burney Newspapers Collect)

Wood, J W, Milner, G R, Harpending, H C, and Weiss, K M, 1992   The osteological paradox, problems of inferring prehistoric health from skeletal samples, *Curr Anthropol* 33, 343–70

Woolley, H, 1675 (1672)   *The Queen-like closet, or rich cabinet: stored with all manner of rare receipts for preserving, candying and cookery. To which is added, a supplement*, 3 edn, London

Woolley, H, 1682 (1675)   *The gentlewomans companion; or, a guide to the female sex: containing directions of behaviour, in all places; companies, relations and conditions, from their childhood down to old age…: with letters and discourses upon all occasions whereunto is added, a guide for cook-maids*, 3 edn, London

Wright, S M, 2010   London's religious houses: a review of ongoing research, *Church Archaeol* 12, 49–63

Wright, S M, 2014   London's religious houses, in *Lübecker Kolloquium zur Stadtarchäologie im Hanseraum IX: Die Klöster*, 75–89, Lübeck

Wroe-Brown, R, 2001   St Paul's Cathedral choir practice facilities, London EC4, unpub MOL rep